B10/68

Charles Ryavec

1969

OXFORD MATHEMATICAL MONOGRAPHS

———

MEROMORPHIC FUNCTIONS

BY

W. K. HAYMAN, F.R.S.

Professor of Pure Mathematics
Imperial College of Science and Technology
London

OXFORD
AT THE CLARENDON PRESS

Oxford University Press, Ely House, London W. 1

GLASGOW NEW YORK TORONTO MELBOURNE WELLINGTON
CAPE TOWN SALISBURY IBADAN NAIROBI LUSAKA ADDIS ABABA
BOMBAY CALCUTTA MADRAS KARACHI LAHORE DACCA
KUALA LUMPUR HONG KONG TOKYO

FIRST PUBLISHED 1964
REPRINTED LITHOGRAPHICALLY IN GREAT BRITAIN
AT THE UNIVERSITY PRESS, OXFORD
BY VIVIAN RIDLER
PRINTER TO THE UNIVERSITY
1968

ACKNOWLEDGEMENTS

I WOULD like to acknowledge my great debt to previous works on this subject and in particular to books by Nevanlinna [1, 3], Wittich [1] and Valiron [3]. I also owe a great deal to discussions with A. Edrei, W. H. J. Fuchs, J. G. Clunie and A. Wilson, and particularly to J. A. Jenkins who read the last two chapters with great care and suggested a number of corrections and changes which are incorporated in the text. Dr. I. M. James, the editor of this series, encouraged me to write the greatly expanded introduction which will, I hope, make the general aim of this book clearer than it would otherwise have been. I was also greatly helped by J. Krzyz and A. Wilson, and by Miss B. Evans, Miss J. Cresswell, Miss A. Mills, and Mrs. S. MacGarry, who helped to create order out of some very chaotic manuscripts, and by Mr. A. F. Beardon, Mr. K. Lucas and Dr. J. M. Anderson, who read the proofs and prepared the index of this book and corrected many cases of inaccuracy and lack of clarity.

W. K. H.

1962

CONTENTS

CONTENTS

INTRODUCTION

LET $f(z)$ be a function meromorphic (i.e. regular except for poles) and not constant in the complex plane. For any complex a, including ∞, we denote by $n(r, a) = n(r, a, f)$ the number of roots, with due count of multiplicity, of the equation $f(z) = a$ in $|z| \leqslant r$ and by $n(r, \infty)$ the number of poles of $f(z)$ in $|z| \leqslant r$. We write

$$N(r, a) = \int_0^r \frac{[n(t, a) - n(0, a)]\,dt}{t} + n(0, a)\log r.$$

In this book we are concerned with the distribution of the roots of the equation $f(z) = a$ for different values of a and functions $f(z)$ and in particular with the relative rates of growth of $N(r, a)$ as a varies over the complex plane.

The basic result here is the existence of the *characteristic function* $T(r, f)$ such that, for every a,

$$T(r, f) = N(r, a) + m(r, a) + O(1) \tag{0.1}$$

as $r \to \infty$, where $m(r, a) \geqslant 0$. This is the *first fundamental theorem of Nevanlinna* (Theorem 1.2). It provides an upper bound to the number of roots of the equation $f(z) = a$, valid for all r and a.

The first chapter of the book starts from the first fundamental theorem and develops the basic properties of meromorphic functions as related to their characteristic function. It is shown that $T(r, f)$ is an increasing convex function of $\log r$ and consequently tends to infinity with r (Theorem 1.3). A modified form $T_0(r, f)$ of the characteristic function due to Ahlfors and Shimizu is introduced which permits a more elegant formulation of (0.1) in the form of an identity

$$T_0(r, f) = N(r, a) + m_0(r, a)$$

valid for all a. On the whole $T_0(r, f)$ and $T(r, f)$ can be used interchangeably but sometimes one or other has advantages. Their difference remains bounded as $r \to \infty$.

The order ρ of a function $f(z)$ is the lower bound of all positive numbers k such that $\quad T(r, f) = O(r^k), \quad$ as $r \to \infty$.

If no such number k exists, $f(z)$ is said to have infinite order. In Theorems 1.9 and 1.11 it is shown that functions of finite order can be uniquely represented as an infinite product in terms of their zeros and poles apart from a factor of the form $e^{P(z)}$, where $P(z)$ is a polynomial.

The first fundamental theorem (0.1) gave us an upper bound for $N(r, a)$ and so the number of roots of the equation $f(z) = a$. The more difficult question of lower bounds is investigated in Chapter 2. The basic result is *Nevanlinna's second fundamental theorem* 2.1, which asserts that for $q \geqslant 3$ distinct values $a_1, a_2,..., a_q$ we have

$$\sum_{\nu=1}^{q} m(r, a_\nu) \leqslant 2T(r, f) - N_1(r) + S(r, f), \tag{0.2}$$

where $N_1(r)$ is a positive term concerned with multiple roots of the equation $f(z) = a$ and $S(r, f)$ plays in general the role of a rather unimportant error term (Theorem 2.2). However, the main difficulty in the proof of the second fundamental theorem lies in the estimation of $S(r, f)$. We deduce immediately Picard's famous theorem that $f(z)$ must assume all values in the complex plane with at most two exceptions, since if $f(z) \neq a_\nu$ ($\nu = 1, 2, 3$) we should have $N(r, a_\nu) = 0$ and so $m(r, a_\nu) = T(r, f) + O(1)$ ($\nu = 1, 2, 3$). This would contradict (0.2).

However, the second fundamental theorem permits a significant extension of Picard's theorem. It shows that in general the term $m(r, a)$ is small compared with $T(r, f)$ and so $N(r, a)$ comes near to $T(r, f)$, the maximum possible growth allowed by the first fundamental theorem. More precisely, we define the *deficiency*

$$\delta(a, f) = \varliminf_{r \to \infty} \frac{m(r, a)}{T(r, f)} = 1 - \varlimsup_{r \to \infty} \frac{N(r, a)}{T(r, f)}.$$

We may regard $\delta(a, f)$ loosely as the proportion by which the number of roots of the equation $f(z) = a$ is less than the maximum permitted number. With this definition we have as an easy consequence of (0.2) the *deficiency relation* (Theorem 2.4). This states that the set of *deficient values*, i.e. for which $\delta(a) > 0$, is countable and that

$$\sum \delta(a) \leqslant 2, \tag{0.3}$$

where the sum is taken over all deficient values. This result still holds if multiple roots of $f(z) = a$ are counted only once in the definitions of $n(r, a)$, $N(r, a)$ and $\delta(a, f)$.

Chapter 2 closes with some examples on and applications of the second fundamental theorem and the deficiency relation. We show that if $f(z)$ is meromorphic (regular) in the plane, the equation $f(z) = a$ has some simple roots except for at most four (two) values of a. The Weierstrass function $\wp(z)$ with $a = \infty, e_1, e_2, e_3$ and $\cos z$ with $a = \mp 1$ show that four and two cannot be replaced by smaller numbers. It is also shown that if two functions $f_1(z)$, $f_2(z)$ assume 5 distinct values at the same points in the complex plane, then they are identical (Theorem 2.6). The functions e^z, e^{-z}, which have no zeros and poles and take the values ∓ 1 at the same points, show that 5 cannot be replaced by 4. These results are due to R. Nevanlinna, as is most of the preceding theory. We also prove a result of I. N. Baker which shows that if $f(z)$ is an integral function not of the form $az+b$, then for every integer n with at most one exception there exist cycles of n distinct points z_0, z_1, z_2,..., $z_n = z_0$, such that $f(z_p) = z_{p+1}$, $p = 0$ to $n-1$ (Theorem 2.7). The polynomial $f(z) = z^2 - 2z$ has no such cycle for $n = 2$ and so shows that the exceptional integer can actually occur.

Chapters 1 and 2 are concerned with the basic fundamentals of Nevanlinna theory and provide a convenient introduction for those not wishing to carry the subject further. In Chapters 3 and 4 we consider more recent developments.

In Chapter 3 we discuss the problem of the extent to which the equations $f^{(l)}(z) = a$ have roots for different values of a and l. For this problem the first and second fundamental theorems provide very powerful tools. Some basic results are the following.

(i) A derivative $f^{(l)}(z)$ of a meromorphic function $f(z)$ assumes all finite complex values with at most one exception, (Theorem 3.4). On the other hand, $f(z) = \tan z \neq \mp i$, so that $f(z)$ itself may have two exceptional values which are not assumed.

(ii) If $f(z) \neq a$ for some finite a, then $f^{(l)}(z)$ assumes every finite value except possibly zero (Theorem 3.5).

(iii) If $f(z)$ has at most a finite number of poles and $f(z) \neq a$, for some finite a, then for $l \geqslant 2$, $f^{(l)}(z)$ assumes every finite value, except when $f(z) - a = e^{Az+B}$ or $f(z) - a = (Az+B)^{-n}$ for some positive integer n, and constants A, B.

If $f(z) = \exp[\int e^{g(z)} dz]$, where $g(z)$ is any integral function, we have $f(z) \neq 0$, $f'(z) \neq 0$, so that (iii) is false for $l = 1$. On the other hand, it is not known whether the restriction on the poles can be removed in (iii). The above results due to Y. Tumura, J. G. Clunie and the author are based also on earlier work of H. Milloux.

In Chapter 4 we are mainly concerned with the question of whether any more than the deficiency relation (0.3) can be said about the deficiencies of a function $f(z)$ meromorphic in the plane. For integral functions we have $\delta(\infty) = 1$ and so (0.3) gives

$$\sum_{a \neq \infty} \delta(a,f) \leqslant 1.$$

We show by examples that at least for integral functions of infinite order arbitrary deficiencies subject to this relation may occur (Theorem 4.1). The corresponding problem of constructing general meromorphic functions with arbitrary deficiencies subject only to (0.3) remains open except in special cases.

We next show that for meromorphic functions of finite order ρ the deficiencies are subject to inequalities of the form

$$\sum \delta(a,f)^\alpha < A(\alpha,\rho),$$

where α is any number such that $\alpha > \frac{1}{3}$ and $A(\alpha,\rho)$ depends only on α and ρ. We show by examples that $\sum \delta(a,f)^\alpha$ need not converge for any $\alpha < \frac{1}{3}$. The case $\alpha = \frac{1}{3}$ remains open (Theorems 4.2 and 4.4). The above results are due to W. H. J. Fuchs and the author. Following R. Nevanlinna and A. Pfluger we then show that for integral functions of finite order ρ equality is possible in (0.3) only if ρ is a positive integer (Theorem 4.7). Some further refinements are stated without proof. It is not known whether an analogous result holds for meromorphic functions of finite order, except that in this case ρ may certainly be an odd multiple of $\frac{1}{2}$.

We next develop a recent result of A. Edrei and W. H. J. Fuchs giving the complete restrictions on a pair of deficiencies $\delta(a,f)$ and $\delta(b,f)$ when $f(z)$ is a meromorphic function of order ρ, where $0 \leqslant \rho \leqslant 1$ (Theorem 4.10). The method uses essentially a result of A. A. Gol'dberg (Theorem 4.9) which shows that it is enough to consider functions with positive zeros and negative poles. Gol'dberg was also the first to construct meromorphic functions with infinitely many deficient values and his ideas underlie most of the examples quoted above. The rest of Chapter 4 is concerned with applications and refinements of Theorem 4.10. The last result due to Teichmüller and Gol'dberg states that if a meromorphic function $f(z)$ of order $\rho < \frac{1}{2}$ satisfies

$$\delta(a,f) > 1 - \cos \pi\rho$$

for some value a, then there exists a sequence $r_n \to +\infty$, such that

$$f(z) \to a,$$

uniformly as $|z| \to \infty$ through the sequence of circles $|z| = r_n$. It follows in particular that $f(z)$ has no deficient values other than a (Theorem 4.15).

Many, if not most, of the results of Chapters 3 and 4 have been obtained only in the last decade and have not previously appeared in book form. Some are new and others, such as the fundamental results of Gol'dberg, are not easily accessible to the western reader.

The first four chapters of this book are concerned with what is usually called Nevanlinna theory. In Chapter 5 we develop a theory due to Ahlfors which is in many ways parallel to that of Nevanlinna. If $f(z)$ is meromorphic in $|z| \leqslant r$ we denote by

$$\pi S(r) = \pi S(r,f) = r \frac{d}{dr} T_0(r,f)$$

the area, with due count of multiplicity, of the image of $|z| < r$ under the mapping from the z-plane onto the Riemann sphere of unit diameter induced by $w = f(z)$. If D is a fixed domain of the Riemann sphere and $I(r, D)$ denotes the area of that part of the image which lies above D and $I_0(D)$ the area of D, we define $S(r, D) = I(r, D)/I_0(D)$. Then *Ahlfors's first fundamental theorem* states that

$$|S(r) - S(r, D)| < h_1 L(r),   \tag{0.4}$$

where $L(r)$ denotes the length of the image of $|z| = r$ under the map by $w = f(z)$ onto the Riemann sphere (Theorem 5.2). The constant h_1 depends only on the domain D.

Next if Δ is a subdomain of $|z| < r$ which is mapped in a $(p, 1)$ manner by $w = f(z)$ onto D then Δ is said to be an island over D of multiplicity p. Clearly each such island contributes just p to the quantity $S(r, D)$. Let $\bar{n}(r, D)$ be the total number of distinct islands over D (without count of multiplicity). Then *Ahlfors's second fundamental theorem* states that, for q domains D_j, lying on the sphere, which are simply connected and whose closures are disjoint, we have

$$\sum_{j=1}^{q} [S(r) - \bar{n}(r, D_j)] \leqslant 2S(r) + h_2 L(r)   \tag{0.5}$$

(Theorem 5.5). Here h_2 depends only on the domains D_j. The inequalities (0.4), (0.5) become significant if $f(z)$ is meromorphic in a circle $|z| < R$ and if there exists a sequence $r = r_n \to R$, such that

$$\frac{L(r_n)}{S(r_n)} \to 0.$$

This happens if $R = \infty$ and $f(z)$ is not constant or if R is finite and

$$\varlimsup_{r \to R} (R-r)S(r) = +\infty$$

(Theorem 5.4). In this case $L(r)$ plays in (0.4) and (0.5) a similar role to the error term $S(r, f)$ occurring in (0.2). Suppose for instance that in this case $f(z)$ has no islands of multiplicity one over five distinct domains D_j. Then each island over D_j contributes at least two to $S(r, D_j)$ and so it follows from (0.4) that

$$\bar{n}(r, D_j) \leqslant \tfrac{1}{2} S(r, D) < \tfrac{1}{2} S(r) + O\{L(r)\} \quad (0 < r < R).$$

On combining this with (0.5) we obtain

$$\tfrac{1}{2} S(r) < h L(r) \quad (0 < r < R)$$

giving a contradiction. Thus $f(z)$ *possesses an island of multiplicity one over at least one of 5 domains* D_j (Theorem 5.6). This is Ahlfors's famous five-islands Theorem. The number 5 is again best possible as is shown by Weierstrass's function $\wp(z)$. For this function the equations $\wp(z) = e_1, e_2, e_3, \infty$ have no simple roots and so $\wp(z)$ possesses no island of multiplicity one over any domain containing the images of one of these four points on the Riemann sphere. A corresponding three-islands theorem holds for integral functions.

The arguments needed to prove the above theorems are almost entirely of a geometric and topological character and it has been necessary to take for granted some results from the topology of surfaces. The conclusions of Ahlfors's theory are so striking that the reader will be prepared to master the somewhat complicated and lengthy proofs.

Many of the results in the first five chapters apply also to functions $f(z)$ meromorphic in a finite disk $|z| < R$, provided that $T(r, f)$ grows sufficiently rapidly as $r \to R$. In the last chapter of this book we consider results for functions in the unit disk, which either have no analogues or only trivial analogues for functions in the plane. We develop the theory of normal families of functions in the unit disk and show that Ahlfors's results developed in Chapter 5 together with a basic theorem of Dufresnoy (Theorem 6.1) lead to very general sufficient conditions for a family of functions to be normal in $|z| < 1$. Thus the family $\mathscr{F}$ of functions $f(z)$, possessing no simple islands over five assigned domains whose closures are disjoint, is normal. For such functions $f(z)$ there are restrictions on the growth of $T(r, f)$, and if $f(z)$ is regular, on the maximum modulus $M(r, f) = \max_{|z| = r} |f(z)|$, and these are investigated. As special cases we obtain classical theorems of Schottky, Landau, Bloch, and Bohr. In the last part of the chapter we develop Nevanlinna's representation of functions $f(z)$ having bounded characteristic in the unit circle as the ratio of two bounded functions (Theorem 6.11) and deduce the existence almost everywhere on $|z| = 1$ of radial and angular limits of $f(z)$ (Theorem 6.12) and the classical integral representation of $f(z)$ (Theorem 6.13).

1

THE ELEMENTARY THEORY

1.0. Introduction

IT was shown by Weierstrass [1] that every integral function can be expressed as an infinite product in terms of its zeros. Hadamard [1] showed that if the order of the function, as defined by the rate of growth of its maximum modulus, is finite, this expression is 'almost' unique. In discussing meromorphic functions $f(z)$ we can no longer use the maximum modulus as a convenient tool for expressing the rate of growth of the function. Instead we use Nevanlinna's characteristic $T(r,f)$. In the course of the book it is hoped to show the tremendous gain in elegance, clarity, and depth which results from this basic concept, even in the special case of integral functions. In the present chapter we shall introduce the characteristic in the form due to Ahlfors [1] and Shimizu [1] as well as R. Nevanlinna [1, 3]. We shall discuss the fundamental properties of these notions and develop the product expansions of functions meromorphic in the plane.

1.1. The Poisson–Jensen formula

In what follows a big role will be played by the following identity:†

THEOREM 1.1. *Suppose that $f(z)$ is meromorphic in*

$$|z| \leqslant R \quad (0 < R < \infty)$$

and that a_μ ($\mu = 1$ to M) are the zeros and b_ν ($\nu = 1$ to N) the poles of $f(z)$ in $|z| < R$. Then if $z = re^{i\theta}$ ($0 < r < R$) and if $f(z) \neq 0, \infty$, we have

$$\log|f(z)| = \frac{1}{2\pi} \int_0^{2\pi} \log|f(Re^{i\phi})| \frac{R^2 - r^2}{R^2 - 2Rr\cos(\theta-\phi)+r^2} \, d\phi +$$

$$+ \sum_{\mu=1}^{M} \log\left|\frac{R(z-a_\mu)}{R^2 - \bar{a}_\mu z}\right| - \sum_{\nu=1}^{N} \log\left|\frac{R(z-b_\nu)}{R^2 - \bar{b}_\nu z}\right|. \quad (1.1)$$

The case when there are no zeros or poles is usually called Poisson's [1] formula. The case when $z = 0$ is called Jensen's [1] formula.

---

† This and other results of Chapters 1 and 2 are due to R. Nevanlinna [1] in their present form, unless the contrary is explicitly stated.

Proof. Case (i). Suppose first that $f(z)$ has no zeros or poles in $|z| \leqslant R$. Then

$$\log f(z) = \log f(0) + \int_0^z \frac{f'(\zeta)}{f(\zeta)} \, d\zeta$$

is regular in $|z| \leqslant R$. Thus by Cauchy's theorem of residues

$$\log f(0) = \frac{1}{2\pi i} \int_{|z|=R} \log f(z) \frac{dz}{z} = \frac{1}{2\pi} \int_0^{2\pi} \log f(Re^{i\phi}) \, d\phi.$$

Taking real parts we obtain the result when $z = 0$. In the general case we use a map of $|\zeta| \leqslant R$ onto $|w| < 1$ so as to send $\zeta = z$ to $w = 0$. Put

$$w = \frac{R(\zeta - z)}{R^2 - \bar{z}\zeta},$$

so that $|\zeta| = R$ corresponds to $|w| = 1$. Thus on $|\zeta| = R$,

$$d \log w = i d \arg w,$$

so that dw/w is purely imaginary and we have

$$\frac{dw}{w} = \frac{d\zeta}{\zeta - z} + \frac{\bar{z} \, d\zeta}{R^2 - \bar{z}\zeta} = \frac{(R^2 - |z|^2) \, d\zeta}{(R^2 - \bar{z}\zeta)(\zeta - z)}.$$

Since $\log f(z)$ is regular in $|z| \leqslant R$, Cauchy's theorem of residues gives

$$\log f(z) = \frac{1}{2\pi i} \int \log f(\zeta) \frac{(R^2 - |z|^2) \, d\zeta}{(R^2 - \bar{z}\zeta)(\zeta - z)}, \tag{1.2}$$

where the integral is taken around $|\zeta| = R$. Also on $|\zeta| = R$, $\zeta = Re^{i\phi}$, $d\zeta = iRe^{i\phi} \, d\phi$, and

$$(R^2 - \bar{z}\zeta)(\zeta - z) = R(R - re^{i(\phi-\theta)})(Re^{i\phi} - re^{i\theta})$$
$$= Re^{i\phi}\{R^2 - 2Rr\cos(\phi - \theta) + r^2\}.$$

Thus we obtain

$$\log f(z) = \frac{1}{2\pi} \int_0^{2\pi} \log f(Re^{i\phi}) \frac{(R^2 - r^2) \, d\phi}{R^2 - 2Rr\cos(\theta - \phi) + r^2}, \tag{1.3}$$

which gives the result on taking real parts.

Case (ii). Suppose next that $f(\zeta)$ has a finite number of zeros and poles on $|\zeta| = R$, but none in $|\zeta| < R$. In this case we obtain (1.2) if the integral is taken around the boundary $C(\delta)$ of the domain $D(\delta)$ consisting of all points of $|z| < R$ distant more than δ from a pole or zero of $f(\zeta)$. For small δ, $C(\delta)$ consists of arcs of $|\zeta| = R$ together with small circular arcs or indentations of radius δ centred on the zeros and poles of $f(\zeta)$ on $|\zeta| = R$. Since the total length of these indentations is $O(\delta)$ and the integrand is $O(\log 1/\delta)$ uniformly on the indentations, their total contribution to the integral in (1.2) tends to zero with δ, and by making $\delta \to 0$ we obtain (1.3) and hence (1.1) even in this case.

Case (iii). In the general case and with the notation of Theorem 1.1 set

$$\psi(\zeta) = f(\zeta) \prod_{\nu=1}^{N} \left\{ \frac{R(\zeta-b_\nu)}{R^2-\bar{b}_\nu \zeta} \right\} / \prod_{\mu=1}^{M} \left\{ \frac{R(\zeta-a_\mu)}{R^2-\bar{a}_\mu \zeta} \right\}. \tag{1.4}$$

Then $\psi(\zeta) \neq 0, \infty$ in $|\zeta| < R$ and so we may apply Theorem 1.1 to $\psi(\zeta)$. Also if $\zeta = Re^{i\phi}$, $|a| < R$,

$$\left| \frac{R(\zeta-a)}{R^2-\bar{a}\zeta} \right| = \left| \frac{Re^{i\phi}-a}{R-\bar{a}e^{i\phi}} \right| = \left| \frac{R-ae^{-i\phi}}{R-\bar{a}e^{i\phi}} \right| = 1.$$

Thus $|\psi(\zeta)| = |f(\zeta)|$ on $|\zeta| = R$, and the application of (1.1) to $\psi(\zeta)$ instead of $f(\zeta)$ yields

$$\log|\psi(z)| = \frac{1}{2\pi} \int_0^{2\pi} \log|f(Re^{i\phi})| \frac{(R^2-r^2)\,d\phi}{R^2-2Rr\cos(\theta-\phi)+r^2}.$$

Using (1.4) we obtain Theorem 1.1 in the general case.

As an important special case take $z = 0$ in Theorem 1.1. We obtain Jensen's formula

$$\log|f(0)| = \frac{1}{2\pi} \int_0^{2\pi} \log|f(Re^{i\phi})|\,d\phi + \sum_{\mu=1}^{M} \log\frac{|a_\mu|}{R} - \sum_{\nu=1}^{N} \log\frac{|b_\nu|}{R} \tag{1.5}$$

provided that $f(0) \neq 0, \infty$. Suppose next that $f(z)$ has a zero of order λ or a pole of order $-\lambda$ at $z = 0$ so that

$$f(z) = c_\lambda z^\lambda + \dots.$$

Then $\psi(z) = R^\lambda f(z)/z^\lambda$ is regular, non-zero at $z = 0$, and has the same modulus on $|z| = R$ as $f(z)$ and the same zeros and poles except $z = 0$. Also $\psi(0) = R^\lambda c_\lambda$. Hence

$$\log|c_\lambda| = \frac{1}{2\pi} \int_0^{2\pi} \log|f(Re^{i\phi})|\,d\phi + \sum_{\mu=1}^{M} \log\frac{|a_\mu|}{R} - \sum_{\nu=1}^{N} \log\frac{|b_\nu|}{R} - \lambda \log R. \tag{1.5a}$$

This tiresome modification is one of the minor irritations of the theory. In general we shall tacitly assume that our functions behave in such a way that the terms in (1.5) do not become infinite in our use of (1.5), knowing that the exceptional cases can be treated.

1.2. The characteristic function

Following Nevanlinna we proceed to rewrite Jensen's formula. We define:

$$\log^+ x = \log x, \quad \text{if } x \geqslant 1,$$
$$\log^+ x = 0, \qquad \text{if } 0 \leqslant x < 1.$$

Clearly if $x > 0$, $\log x = \log^+ x - \log^+ 1/x$. Thus

$$\frac{1}{2\pi} \int_0^{2\pi} \log|f(Re^{i\phi})|\,d\phi = \frac{1}{2\pi} \int_0^{2\pi} \log^+|f(Re^{i\phi})|\,d\phi - \frac{1}{2\pi} \int_0^{2\pi} \log^+\left|\frac{1}{f(Re^{i\phi})}\right|\,d\phi.$$

We write
$$m(R, f) = \frac{1}{2\pi} \int_0^{2\pi} \log^+|f(Re^{i\phi})|\,d\phi. \tag{1.6}$$

Next let r_1, r_2,..., r_N be the moduli of the poles b_1, b_2,..., b_N of $f(z)$ in $|z| < R$. Then

$$\sum_{\nu=1}^{N} \log\left|\frac{R}{b_\nu}\right| = \sum_{\nu=1}^{N} \log\frac{R}{r_\nu} = \int_0^R \log\frac{R}{t}\,dn(t),$$

where $n(t)$ is number of poles in $|z| < t$. On integrating by parts we obtain

$$\sum_{\nu=1}^{N} \log\left|\frac{R}{b_\nu}\right| = \left\{\log\frac{R}{t}\,n(t)\right\}_0^R - \int_0^R n(t)\,d\log\left(\frac{R}{t}\right) = \int_0^R n(t)\frac{dt}{t}.$$

We write $n(t,f)$ for the number of poles of $f(z)$ in $|z| < t$, poles of order p being counted p times, and

$$N(R, f) = \sum_{\nu=1}^{N} \log\left|\frac{R}{b_\nu}\right| = \int_0^R n(t, f)\frac{dt}{t}, \tag{1.7}$$

$$N\left(R, \frac{1}{f}\right) = \sum_{\mu=1}^{M} \log\left|\frac{R}{a_\mu}\right| = \int_0^R n\left(t, \frac{1}{f}\right)\frac{dt}{t}. \tag{1.8}$$

With this notation (1.5) becomes

$$\log|f(0)| = m(R,f) - m(R, 1/f) + N(R,f) - N(R, 1/f),$$

or
$$m(R,f) + N(R,f) = m(R, 1/f) + N(R, 1/f) + \log|f(0)|.$$

We now write
$$T(R,f) = m(R,f) + N(R,f). \tag{1.9}$$

Then Jensen's formula becomes simply

$$T(R,f) = T(R, 1/f) + \log|f(0)|. \tag{1.10}$$

The term $m(R,f)$ is a sort of averaged magnitude of $\log|f|$ on arcs of $|z| = R$ where $|f|$ is large. The term $N(R,f)$ relates to the poles. The function $T(R,f)$ is called the *characteristic function* of $f(z)$ (R. Nevanlinna [1]). It plays a cardinal role in the whole theory of meromorphic functions.

We proceed to develop some simple properties. We note that if $a_1,...,$ a_p are any complex numbers then

$$\log^+\left|\prod_{\nu=1}^{p} a_\nu\right| \leqslant \sum_{\nu=1}^{p}\log^+|a_\nu|,$$

and $\qquad \log^+\left|\sum_{\nu=1}^{p} a_\nu\right| \leqslant \log^+(p \max_{\nu=1,...,p}|a_\nu|) \leqslant \sum_{\nu=1}^{p}\log^+|a_\nu|+\log p.$

By applying these inequalities to p meromorphic functions $f_1(z),...,f_p(z)$ and using (1.6) we obtain at once

$$m\left\{r,\sum_{\nu=1}^{p}f_\nu(z)\right\} \leqslant \sum_{\nu=1}^{p}m\{r,f_\nu(z)\}+\log p,$$

$$m\left\{r,\prod_{\nu=1}^{p}f_\nu(z)\right\} \leqslant \sum_{\nu=1}^{p}m\{r,f_\nu(z)\}.$$

Evidently if $f(z)$ is the sum or product of the functions $f_\nu(z)$, then the order of a pole of $f(z)$ at a point z_0 is at most equal to the sum of the orders of the poles of the $f_\nu(z)$ at z_0. Thus we deduce

$$N\left\{r,\sum_{\nu=1}^{p}f_\nu(z)\right\} \leqslant \sum_{\nu=1}^{p}N\{r,f_\nu(z)\},$$

$$N\left\{r,\prod_{\nu=1}^{p}f_\nu(z)\right\} \leqslant \sum_{\nu=1}^{p}N\{r,f_\nu(z)\}.$$

Using (1.9) we deduce

$$T\left\{r,\sum_{\nu=1}^{p}f_\nu(z)\right\} \leqslant \sum_{\nu=1}^{p}T\{r,f_\nu(z)\}+\log p,$$

$$T\left\{r,\prod_{\nu=1}^{p}f_\nu(z)\right\} \leqslant \sum_{\nu=1}^{p}T\{r,f_\nu(z)\}.$$

In particular taking $p=2$, $f_1(z)=f(z)$, $f_2(z)=a=$ constant, we deduce $T(r,f+a) \leqslant T(r,f)+\log^+|a|+\log 2$ and since we may replace $f+a,f$ by $f,f-a$ and a by $-a$, we deduce

$$|T(r,f)-T(r,f-a)| \leqslant \log^+|a|+\log 2. \qquad (1.11)$$

1.3. The first fundamental theorem

We can now prove Nevanlinna's first fundamental theorem.

THEOREM 1.2. *If a is any complex number then*

$$m\left(R,\frac{1}{f-a}\right)+N\left(R,\frac{1}{f-a}\right) = T(r,f)-\log|f(0)-a|+\epsilon(a,R),$$

where $\qquad\qquad |\epsilon(a,R)| \leqslant \log^+|a|+\log 2.$

In fact (1.9) and (1.10) yield

$$m\left(R, \frac{1}{f-a}\right) + N\left(R, \frac{1}{f-a}\right) = T\left(R, \frac{1}{f-a}\right) = T(R, f-a) - \log|f(0) - a|.$$

Using (1.11) we obtain our result.

If there is no doubt as to which function $f(z)$ is referred to, it is frequently convenient to write $m(R, a)$, $N(R, a)$, $n(R, a)$, $T(R)$ instead of $m\{R, 1/(f-a)\}$, $N\{R, 1/(f-a)\}$, $n\{R, 1/(f-a)\}$, $T(R, f)$ if a is finite, and $m(R, \infty)$, $N(R, \infty)$, $n(R, \infty)$ instead of $m(R, f)$, $N(R, f)$, $n(R, f)$.

If we allow R to vary, the first fundamental theorem can then be written simply as

$$m(R, a) + N(R, a) = T(R) + O(1)$$

for every a, finite or infinite. The term $m(R, a)$ refers to the average smallness in a certain sense of $f-a$, on the circle $|z| = R$, the term $N(R, a)$ to the number of roots of the equation $f(z) = a$ in $|z| < R$. For any a the sum of these two terms is the same apart from a bounded term. However, we shall see in the next chapter that in general it is the term N which predominates.

Examples. (i) Let

$$f(z) = c\frac{z^p + \dots + a_p}{z^q + \dots + b_q}, \quad \text{where } c \neq 0,$$

be a rational function. Suppose first $p > q$. Then $f(z) \to \infty$ as $z \to \infty$ so that $m(r, a) = 0$ for $r > r_0$, when a is finite. The equation $f(z) = a$ has p roots so that $n(t, a) = p$ $(t > t_0)$, and so

$$N(r, a) = \int_0^r n(t, a)\frac{dt}{t} = p \log r + O(1) \quad \text{as } r \to \infty.$$

Thus as $r \to \infty$, $T(r, f) = p \log r + O(1),$

and

$$N(r, a) = p \log r + O(1), \quad m(r, a) = O(1), \quad \text{for } a \neq \infty.$$

Similarly, if $p < q$,

$$T(r, f) = q \log r + O(1),$$

$$N(r, a) = q \log r + O(1), \quad m(r, a) = O(1), \quad \text{for } a \neq 0.$$

Finally, if $p = q$,

$$T(r, f) = q \log r + O(1),$$

$$N(r, a) = q \log r + O(1), \quad m(r, a) = O(1), \quad \text{for } a \neq c$$

Putting these results together we see that in all cases

$$T(r,f) = d\log r + O(1),$$

$$N(r,a) = d\log r + O(1), \quad m(r,a) = O(1) \quad \text{if } a \neq f(\infty),$$

where $d = \max(p,q)$.

Thus in this case $m(r,a)$ is bounded as $r \to \infty$ except for one value of a, namely $f(\infty)$. If the equation $f(z) = a$ has a root of multiplicity α at ∞ where $0 < \alpha < d$, then

$$m(r,a) = \alpha\log r + O(1), \qquad N(r,a) = (d-\alpha)\log r + O(1).$$

(ii) Let $f(z) = e^z = e^{r\cos\theta + ir\sin\theta}$, for $z = re^{i\theta}$. Then

$$m(r,f) = \frac{1}{2\pi} \int_{-\frac{1}{2}\pi}^{\frac{1}{2}\pi} r\cos\theta \, d\theta = r/\pi, \qquad N(r,f) = 0,$$

so that
$$T(r,f) = m(r,\infty) + N(r,\infty) = r/\pi.$$

In this case
$$m(r,0) = r/\pi, \qquad N(r,0) = 0.$$

If $a \neq 0, \infty$, and z_0 is a root of the equation $e^{z_0} = a$, we see that all other roots are of the form $z_0 + 2k\pi i$, where k is an integer. From this we see that $n(t,a)$, the number of roots of $f(z) = a$ in $|z| < t$, satisfies

$$n(t,a) = (t/\pi) + O(1),$$

so that
$$N(r,a) = (r/\pi) + O(\log r), \qquad m(r,a) = O(\log r) \quad (a \neq 0,\infty).$$

A more delicate analysis will show that if $a \neq 0, \infty$, we have in fact

$$m(r,a) = O(1), \quad \text{so that } N(r,a) = (r/\pi) + O(1).$$

It is an open question whether for an integral function of *finite order* ρ there can be more than a finite number of values of a for which $m(r,a) \to \infty$.[‡] A. A. Goldberg [2, 4] has recently constructed examples of meromorphic functions of finite order for which $m(r,a) \to \infty$ and in fact

$$\lim_{r\to\infty} \frac{m(r,a)}{T(r)} > 0$$

for infinitely many a and in fact any pre-assigned sequence of values a.

(iii) Show that if $P(z) = az^p + \ldots$ is a polynomial and $f(z) = e^{P(z)}$, then

$$T(r,f) \sim \frac{|a|}{\pi} r^p \quad (r \to \infty).$$

(iv) Show that if $f(z) = e^{e^z}$, then[†]

$$T(r,f) \sim \frac{e^r}{(2\pi^3 r)^{\frac{1}{2}}} \quad (r \to \infty).$$

† See Chapter 4, Lemma 4.3.
‡ Examples of this have now been given by Arakeljan[1]

(v) Show that if $f(z)$ is meromorphic in $|z| < R$, and

$$g(z) = \frac{af+b}{cf+d}$$

where a, b, c, d are constants such that $ad-bc \neq 0$, and if $f(0) \neq \infty$, $g(0) \neq \infty$, then

$$T(r,f) = T(r,g)+O(1) \quad (0 < r < R).$$

[Set

$$f_0 = f, \quad f_1 = f_0+d/c, \quad f_2 = cf_1, \quad f_3 = 1/f_2, \quad f_4 = \frac{(bc-ad)f_3}{c},$$

$$g = f_5 = f_4+a/c,$$

if $c \neq 0$ and show that

$$T(r,f_{\nu+1}) = T(r,f_\nu)+O(1) \quad (\nu = 0 \text{ to } 4).]$$

1.4. Cartan's identity and convexity theorems

We proceed to prove an interesting identity due to H. Cartan [1].

THEOREM 1.3. *Suppose that $f(z)$ is meromorphic in $|z| < R$. Then*

$$T(r,f) = \frac{1}{2\pi} \int_0^{2\pi} N(r, e^{i\theta})\, d\theta + \log^+|f(0)| \quad (0 < r < R).$$

COROLLARY 1.† *The Nevanlinna characteristic, $T(r,f)$, is an increasing convex function of $\log r$ for $0 < r < R$.*

COROLLARY 2. *We have in all cases*

$$\frac{1}{2\pi} \int_0^{2\pi} m(r, e^{i\theta})\, d\theta \leqslant \log 2.$$

We note that from Jensen's formula (1.5) applied with $f(z) = a-z$ and $R = 1$

$$\frac{1}{2\pi} \int_0^{2\pi} \log|a-e^{i\theta}|\, d\theta = \log|a| \quad \text{if } |a| \geqslant 1,$$

$$= \log|a|-\log|a| = 0 \quad \text{if } |a| < 1.$$

Thus in all cases

$$\frac{1}{2\pi} \int_0^{2\pi} \log|a-e^{i\theta}|\, d\theta = \log^+|a|. \tag{1.12}$$

Now (1.5) applied to $f(z)-e^{i\theta}$ gives

$$\log|f(0)-e^{i\theta}| = \frac{1}{2\pi} \int_0^{2\pi} \log|f(re^{i\phi})-e^{i\theta}|\, d\phi + N(r,\infty)-N(r, e^{i\theta}).$$

---

† This was originally proved by R. Nevanlinna [1] by another method.

We integrate both sides with respect to θ and change the order of integration in the resulting double integral on the right-hand side. This is permissible since the double integral is absolutely convergent. Using (1.12) we deduce

$$\log^+|f(0)| = \frac{1}{2\pi}\int\limits_0^{2\pi}\log^+|f(re^{i\phi})|\,d\phi + N(r,\infty) - \frac{1}{2\pi}\int\limits_0^{2\pi}N(r,e^{i\theta})\,d\theta$$

and this gives Theorem 1.3. Since $N(r,e^{i\theta})$ is evidently an increasing convex function of $\log r$, we deduce at once that $T(r,f)$ has the same property. In fact we have in general

$$r\frac{d}{dr}T(r,f) = \frac{1}{2\pi}\int\limits_0^{2\pi}n(r,e^{i\theta})\,d\theta.$$

This proves Corollary 1. Next we have from Theorem 1.2 that

$$T(r,f) = m(r,e^{i\theta}) + N(r,e^{i\theta}) + \log|f(0) - e^{i\theta}| + G(\theta),$$

where $|G(\theta)| \leqslant \log 2$. We integrate both sides with respect to θ and use the Theorem 1.3 and (1.12). We obtain

$$T(r,f) = \frac{1}{2\pi}\int\limits_0^{2\pi}m(r,e^{i\theta})\,d\theta + T(r,f) - \log^+|f(0)| + \log^+|f(0)| +$$

$$+ \frac{1}{2\pi}\int\limits_0^{2\pi}G(\theta)\,d\theta.$$

Thus

$$\frac{1}{2\pi}\int\limits_0^{2\pi}m(r,e^{i\theta})\,d\theta = -\frac{1}{2\pi}\int\limits_0^{2\pi}G(\theta)\,d\theta \leqslant \log 2.$$

This proves Corollary 2. The result shows that $m(r,a)$ is bounded in the average on the circle $|a| = 1$ and a corresponding result holds on any other circle.† Thus if $T(r,f)$ is large, $m(r,a)$ is bounded and $N(r,a)$ is nearly equal to $T(r)$ for 'most' a in a certain sense.

It is evident that $N(r,a)$ is a convex increasing function of $\log r$ and so is $T(r,f)$ by Theorem 1.3. On the other hand $m(r,a)$ need be neither increasing nor convex in general. Consider, for example, $f(z) = z/(1-z^2)$. Then $|f(z)| < 1$ for $|z| < \frac{1}{2}$, and $|z| > 2$, so that $m(r,f) = 0$ for $r \leqslant \frac{1}{2}$ or $r \geqslant 2$. On the other hand, $f(\mp 1) = \infty$, so that $m(1,f) > 0$.

---

† Frostman [1] showed that a corresponding result holds when a circle is replaced by any set of positive capacity. Ahlfors [2] showed that $m(r,a) = O\{T(r)\}^{\frac{1}{2}+\epsilon} + O(1)$ outside such a set. See also R. Nevanlinna [3, pp. 260-4].

1.5. The Ahlfors–Shimizu characteristic

We now come to a second formulation of the first fundamental theorem, due to Ahlfors [1] and Shimizu [1]. Before we can do this we need the following identity:†

LEMMA 1.1. *Suppose that D is a bounded domain bounded by a finite system of closed analytic curves γ, that $f(z)$ is regular in D and on γ and that $G(R)$ is twice continuously differentiable on the set of values R assumed by $|f(z)|$ in D and γ. Then*

$$\int_\gamma \frac{\partial G(|f(z)|)}{\partial n}\,ds = \iint_D g(|f(re^{i\theta})|)|f'(re^{i\theta})|^2 r\,dr d\theta;$$

where $g(R) = G''(R)+(1/R)G'(R)$, s denotes arc length along γ and $\partial/\partial n$ differentiation along the normal to γ out of D.

We have by Green's formula‡

$$\int_\gamma \frac{\partial G(|f|)}{\partial n}\,ds = \iint_D \nabla^2 G(|f|) r\,dr d\theta.$$

To evaluate $\nabla^2 G(|f|)$, suppose first that $f(z) \neq 0$ in D. Then $v = \log|f|$ is harmonic in D, and we put

$$|f| = e^v, \qquad G(|f|) = G(e^v).$$

$$\frac{\partial}{\partial x}\,G(e^v) = e^v G'(e^v)\,\frac{\partial v}{\partial x},$$

$$\left(\frac{\partial}{\partial x}\right)^2 G(e^v) = \{e^{2v}G''(e^v)+e^v G'(e^v)\}\left(\frac{\partial v}{\partial x}\right)^2 + e^v G'(e^v)\,\frac{\partial^2 v}{\partial x^2},$$

$$\left(\frac{\partial}{\partial y}\right)^2 G(e^v) = \{e^{2v}G''(e^v)+e^v G'(e^v)\}\left(\frac{\partial v}{\partial y}\right)^2 + e^v G'(e^v)\,\frac{\partial^2 v}{\partial y^2}.$$

Adding, and using the fact that v is harmonic, we obtain

$$\nabla^2 G(e^v) = \{e^{2v}G''(e^v)+e^v G'(e^v)\}\left\{\left(\frac{\partial v}{\partial x}\right)^2+\left(\frac{\partial v}{\partial y}\right)^2\right\}.$$

Writing again $e^v = R = |f(z)|$, and noting that

$$\left(\frac{\partial v}{\partial x}\right)^2+\left(\frac{\partial v}{\partial y}\right)^2 = \left|\frac{d}{dz}\log f\right|^2 = \frac{|f'|^2}{R^2},$$

we deduce that

$$\nabla^2 G(e^v) = \left\{G''(R)+\frac{1}{R}\,G'(R)\right\}|f'(z)|^2.$$

---

† Spencer [1]. The present proof is due to Flett [1].

‡ For a proof of this in the present simple case see, for example, Hayman [4], chapter 4.

The result now follows. If $f(z)$ has zeros in D, we exclude them by small circles, over which the contribution of $\int (\partial G/\partial n)\,ds$ is negligible since by hypothesis $\partial G(R)/\partial R$ is bounded near $R = 0$.

We apply Lemma 1.1 with

$$G(R) = \log \sqrt{(1+R^2)}, \qquad g(R) = \frac{2}{(1+R^2)^2}.$$

Let $f(z)$ be meromorphic in $|z| < r$, and suppose that $f(z)$ has no poles on $|z| = r$. We exclude poles b_ν of multiplicity k_ν in $|z| < r$ by small circles of radius ρ. On such a circle

$$|f(b_\nu+\rho e^{i\phi})| \sim \frac{c_\nu}{\rho^{k_\nu}},$$

$$\log \sqrt{\{1+|f(b_\nu+\rho e^{i\phi})|^2\}} = k_\nu \log\frac{1}{\rho}+O(1),$$

$$\frac{\partial}{\partial n} \log\sqrt{\{1+|f(b_\nu+\rho e^{i\phi})|^2\}} = \frac{k_\nu}{\rho}+O(1).$$

Hence a pole of multiplicity k_ν gives rise to a term $2\pi k_\nu$. Thus we obtain

$$\frac{1}{2\pi} r \frac{d}{dr} \int_0^{2\pi} \log \sqrt{\{1+|f(re^{i\theta})|^2\}}\,d\theta+n(r,f) = \frac{1}{\pi} \int_0^r \int_0^{2\pi} \frac{|f'(\rho e^{i\theta})|^2\rho\,d\rho d\theta}{\{1+|f(\rho e^{i\theta})|^2\}^2}.$$

We denote the right-hand side by $A(r)$, divide by r and integrate the resulting identity from 0 to r. This yields

$$\int_0^r \frac{A(t)\,dt}{t} = N(r,f)+\frac{1}{2\pi} \int_0^{2\pi} \log \sqrt{\{1+|f(re^{i\theta})|^2\}}\,d\theta-\log \sqrt{\{1+|f(0)|^2\}}.$$

$$(1.13)$$

We now make a transformation

$$W = \frac{1+\bar{a}w}{w-a}, \qquad (1.14)$$

where $w = f(z)$, and denote the resulting function by $W = F(z)$. Set

$$\frac{1}{k(w,a)} = \sqrt{\left\{1+\left|\frac{1+\bar{a}w}{w-a}\right|^2\right\}} = \frac{\sqrt{\{|w-a|^2+|1+\bar{a}w|^2\}}}{|w-a|}$$

$$= \frac{\sqrt{\{(1+|a|^2)(1+|w|^2)\}}}{|w-a|},$$

so that

$$k(w, a) = \frac{|w-a|}{\sqrt{\{(1+|a|^2)(1+|w|^2)\}}} \quad (w, a \text{ both finite}),$$

$$k(a, \infty) = k(\infty, a) = \frac{1}{\sqrt{(1+|a|^2)}}.$$

Clearly $k(w, a) \leqslant 1$ always. Again

$$\frac{dW}{dz} = -\frac{(1+|a|^2)}{(w-a)^2} \frac{dw}{dz},$$

so that

$$\frac{1}{1+|W|^2} \left|\frac{dW}{dz}\right| = \frac{(1+|a|^2)}{|w-a|^2} k(w, a)^2 \left|\frac{dw}{dz}\right| = \frac{1}{1+|w|^2} \left|\frac{dw}{dz}\right|.$$

Thus

$$A(r) = \frac{1}{\pi} \int_0^r \rho \, d\rho \int_0^{2\pi} \frac{|f'(\rho e^{i\theta})|^2 \, d\theta}{(1+|f|^2)^2} = \frac{1}{\pi} \int_0^r \rho \, d\rho \int_0^{2\pi} \frac{|F'(\rho e^{i\theta})|^2 \, d\theta}{(1+|F|^2)^2}.$$

We write

$$T_0(r) = \int_0^r \frac{A(t) \, dt}{t},$$

$$m_0(r, a) = \frac{1}{2\pi} \int_0^{2\pi} \log \frac{1}{k\{f(re^{i\theta}), a\}} \, d\theta,$$

and apply (1.13) to $F(z)$. Clearly

$$N(r, F(z)) = N\left(r, \frac{1}{f(z)-a}\right) = N(r, a),$$

since $f(z)-a$ has a zero of order p at a pole of $F(z)$ of order p. Thus we obtain the first fundamental theorem in the form of Ahlfors and Shimizu.

THEOREM 1.4. *Suppose that $f(z)$ is meromorphic in $|z| < R$, where $0 < R < \infty$. Then we have for every a, finite or infinite, and $0 < r < R$*

$$T_0(r) = \int_0^r \frac{A(t) \, dt}{t} = N(r, a) + m_0(r, a) - m_0(0, a),$$

provided $f(0) \neq a$.

We note that

$$\log^+|f| \leqslant \log \sqrt{(1+|f|^2)} \leqslant \log^+|f| + \tfrac{1}{2}\log 2.$$

Thus $m(r, \infty) \leqslant m_0(r, \infty) \leqslant m(r, \infty) + \tfrac{1}{2}\log 2.$

Hence, by (1.13),

$$|T(r)-T_0(r)-\log^+|f(0)\|| \leqslant \tfrac{1}{2}\log 2.$$

Thus $T(r)$ and $T_0(r)$ differ by a bounded term and this means that in most applications they can be used interchangeably. If confusion is likely $T_0(r)$ will be called the Ahlfors–Shimizu characteristic and $T(r)$ the Nevanlinna characteristic.

1.5.1. Theorem 1.4 possesses an interesting geometric interpretation. Let S be the Riemann sphere, a sphere of unit diameter lying on the complex plane and touching the plane at the origin O. Let N be the other end of the diameter of S through O. Then to any point z in the plane there corresponds a unique point P on the sphere such that NPz is a straight line and $z = \infty$ corresponds to N. By means of this correspondence we may identify the complex plane with the Riemann sphere. It is not difficult to see that if z_1, z_2 are two points in the complex plane, then $k(z_1, z_2)$ is precisely the length of the chord or chordal distance between the corresponding points P_1, P_2 on the Riemann sphere. Also if $d\alpha$ is an element of area in the z plane near a point z and dA the corresponding element of area on the sphere, then

$$dA = \frac{d\alpha}{(1+|z|^2)^2}.$$

Thus $\pi A(r)$ is precisely the area with due regard to multiplicity of the image on the Riemann sphere of $|z| < r$ by $w = f(z)$. Using these geometrical ideas we obtain another deduction of Theorem 1.4 from (1.13) since we may rotate the Riemann sphere (in fact the transformations (1.14) correspond to such rotations on the Riemann sphere) so that N goes to the point corresponding to $w = a$. Such a rotation leaves $A(r)$ invariant and replaces $m_0(r, \infty)$, $N(r, \infty)$ by $m_0(r, a)$, $N(r, a)$.

1.6. An application: average and maximum of $n(r, a)$

For functions $f(z)$ meromorphic and not constant in the plane, $T_0(r, f)$ is evidently a positive, convex, and strictly increasing function of $\log r$, and hence $T_0(r, f) \to \infty$ with r. For a fixed a, Theorem (1.2) shows that

$$N(r, a) < T_0(r) + O(1) \quad \text{as } r \to \infty,$$

and hence
$$n(r, a) < A(r) + o(1) \tag{1.15}$$

for a sequence of $r \to \infty$. Since

$$A(r) = \frac{\text{area of image of } |z| < r \text{ on Riemann sphere}}{\text{area of Riemann sphere}}$$

we may interpret $A(r)$ as being the average number of times points on the Riemann sphere are covered by the image of $|z| < r$ by $f(z)$, or again as the average number of roots in $|z| < r$ of the equation $f(z) = a$ for varying a. Then the equation (1.15) shows that for every fixed $a = a_0$ the number of roots of the equation $f(z) = a_0$ in $|z| < r$ is for a sequence of $r \to \infty$ not much larger than the average number of roots of this equation for all a.

One drawback of this result is that the corresponding sequence of r depends on a. It is reasonable to ask whether we can find a sequence of r independent of a, or again, whether if

$$n(r) = \sup_a n(r, a)$$

we have necessarily

$$\lim_{r \to \infty} \{n(r) - A(r)\} < +\infty.$$

Nothing as strong as this is known. However, by reasonably elementary methods we can prove (Hayman and Stewart [1]):

THEOREM 1.5. *With the above notation we have*

$$1 \leqslant \lim_{r \to \infty} \frac{n(r)}{A(r)} \leqslant e.$$

We need the following lemmas about real functions.

LEMMA 1.2. *Suppose that $\phi(x)$ is positive for $x \geqslant x_0$ and bounded in every interval $[x_0, x_1]$ when $x_0 < x_1 < \infty$. Then given $K > 1$ there exists a sequence $x_n \to \infty$, such that*

$$\phi(x) < K\phi(x_n) \quad \textit{for } x_n < x < x_n + \frac{1}{\log^+\{\phi(x_n)\}^K} + \frac{1}{\phi(x_n)}.$$

Suppose first that $\phi(x)$ is bounded for $x \geqslant x_0$. Then given $n > x_0$, the least upper bound M_n of $\phi(x)$ in $n \leqslant x < \infty$ is positive and finite. We can choose x_n such that $x_n \geqslant n$, and $\phi(x_n) > M_n/K$ and then x_n satisfies the required hypothesis.

Next suppose that $\phi(x)$ is unbounded for $x \geqslant x_0$ and that our conclusion is false. Then for all sufficiently large x we can find ξ, such that

$$x < \xi < x + \{\log^+\phi(x)\}^{-K} + \{\phi(x)\}^{-1} \quad \text{and} \quad \phi(\xi) \geqslant K\phi(x).$$

Suppose this holds for $x \geqslant x_1$. Then if x_n has already been defined we define x_{n+1}, so that

$$x_n \leqslant x_{n+1} \leqslant x_n + \{\log^+\phi(x_n)\}^{-K} + \{\phi(x_n)\}^{-1} \quad \text{and} \quad \phi(x_{n+1}) \geqslant K\phi(x_n).$$

We assume $\phi(x_1) \geqslant K$, which is possible since $\phi(x)$ is unbounded for large x. Then

$$\phi(x_{n+1}) \geqslant K\phi(x_n) \geqslant K^n\phi(x_1) \geqslant K^{n+1}.$$

Thus

$$\log^+\phi(x_n) \geqslant n\log K,$$

$$x_{n+1}-x_n \leqslant (n\log K)^{-K}+K^{-(n+1)} \quad (n \geqslant 1).$$

Thus $\sum (x_{n+1}-x_n)$ converges so that x_n is bounded above, while $\phi(x_n) \to \infty$ as $n \to \infty$. This contradicts our hypothesis and proves our result.

LEMMA 1.3. *Suppose that $g(x)$ is a positive strictly increasing and convex function of x for $x \geqslant x_0$. Then given $K > 1$ there exists a sequence $x_n \to \infty$ such that if $f(x)$ is any other positive increasing and convex function of x such that $f(x) < g(x)$ for $x \geqslant x_0$, we have*

$$f'(x_n) < e^K g'(x_n) \quad (n = 1, 2, \ldots).$$

Here $f'(x)$ denotes the right derivative of $f(x)$ and $g'(x)$ the left derivative of $g(x)$.

Since $g(x)$ is convex, $g'(x)$ is non-decreasing. Since $g(x)$ is strictly increasing, $g'(x) > 0$ for $x > x_0$. Also $g'(x)$ is bounded above in any finite interval (x_0, x_1) for $x_1 > x_0$. Thus we may apply the previous lemma to the function $\phi(x) = g'(x)/g(x)$, and so we can find a sequence $x_n \to \infty$ such that

$$\phi(x) < K\phi(x_n), \quad \text{for } x_n \leqslant x \leqslant x_n+\frac{1}{\phi(x_n)}.$$

Also if

$$x'_n = x_n+\frac{1}{\phi(x_n)},$$

we have

$$\log g(x'_n)-\log g(x_n) = \int_{x_n}^{x'_n} \frac{g'(x)}{g(x)}\,dx < (x'_n-x_n)K\phi(x_n) = K.$$

Thus

$$g(x'_n) < e^K g(x_n).$$

Then since $f'(x)$ is increasing we have

$$f'(x_n) \leqslant \frac{1}{x'_n-x_n}\int_{x_n}^{x'_n} f'(x)\,dx = \frac{f(x'_n)-f(x_n)}{x'_n-x_n} \leqslant \phi(x_n)f(x'_n)$$

$$\leqslant \phi(x_n)g(x'_n) < e^K\phi(x_n)g(x_n) = e^K g'(x_n).$$

This proves Lemma 1.3.

We now apply Theorem 1.4 with a fixed $r = r_0 > 0$ and a variable r and subtract. This gives

$$T_0(r)-T_0(r_0) = N(r,a)-N(r_0,a)+m_0(r,a)-m_0(r_0,a),$$

or $N(r,a)-N(r_0,a) = T_0(r)-m_0(r,a)+m_0(r_0,a)-T_0(r_0).$

We suppose now that $f(z)$ is not constant and choose r_0 so that $f(z) \neq f(0)$ on $|z| = r_0$. Thus

$$k\{f(z), f(0)\} \geqslant \delta > 0 \quad (|z| = r_0).$$

Hence if $k\{f(0), a\} \leqslant \frac{1}{2}\delta$ we deduce that

$$k\{f(z), a\} \geqslant \frac{1}{2}\delta \quad (|z| = r_0)$$

and so

$$m_0(r_0, a) \leqslant \log(2/\delta).$$

Thus in this case

$$\int_{r_0}^{r} \frac{n(t, a)\, dt}{t} = N(r, a) - N(r_0, a) \leqslant T_0(r) + \log(2/\delta) \quad (r > r_0).$$

On the other hand, if $k\{f(0), a\} \geqslant \frac{1}{2}\delta$, we deduce that

$$m_0(0, a) \leqslant \log(2/\delta),$$

and so

$$\int_{r_0}^{r} \frac{n(t, a)\, dt}{t} \leqslant N(r, a) \leqslant T_0(r) + \log(2/\delta),$$

by Theorem 1.4. Hence this inequality holds for $r > r_0$ and all a.

We set $C = \log(2/\delta)$. Since $N(r, a) - N(r_0, a)$, $T_0(r) + C$ are both positive increasing convex functions of $\log r$ for $\log r > \log r_0$ and $T_0(r)$ is strictly increasing we can find a sequence of $r_m \to \infty$ and depending only on $T(r)$ but not on a such that

$$r \frac{d}{dr} N(r, a) < e^K r \frac{d}{dr} \{T_0(r) + C\} \quad (r = r_m, \text{ all } a),$$

i.e.

$$n(r_m, a) < e^K A(r_m) \quad (m = 1, 2, ..., \text{ all } a).$$

Thus

$$\lim_{r \to \infty} \frac{n(r)}{A(r)} \leqslant e^K,$$

and since K may be chosen as near 1 as we please, the right-hand inequality of Theorem 1.5 follows. The left-hand inequality is obvious, since $A(r) \leqslant n(r)$ for all r.

1.7. Orders of growth

Let $S(r)$ be a real and non-negative function increasing for

$$r_0 < r < \infty, \quad \text{where } r_0 > 0.$$

The *order* k and the *lower order* λ of the function $S(r)$ are defined as

$$k = \varlimsup_{r \to \infty} \{\log S(r)\}/\log r, \qquad \lambda = \varliminf_{r \to \infty} \{\log S(r)\}/\log r.$$

The order and the lower order of the function always satisfy the relation $0 \leqslant \lambda \leqslant k \leqslant \infty$.

If $0 < k < \infty$ we set

$$C = \overline{\lim_{r \to \infty}} \frac{S(r)}{r^k}$$

and distinguish the following possibilities:

(a) $S(r)$ has *maximal* type if $C = +\infty$;
(b) $S(r)$ has *mean* type if $0 < C < +\infty$;
(c) $S(r)$ has *minimal* type if $C = 0$;
(d) $S(r)$ has *convergence class* if

$$\int_{r_0}^{\infty} \frac{S(t)\,dt}{t^{k+1}} \quad \text{converges.}$$

Note that if $S(r)$ is of order k, where $0 < k < \infty$ and $\epsilon > 0$ then

$$S(r) < r^{k+\epsilon} \quad \text{for all large } r,$$

and

$$S(r) > r^{k-\epsilon} \quad \text{for some large } r.$$

It can be seen that, if $S(r)$ is of order k and of convergence class, i.e. (d) holds, then it is of minimal type (c). In fact in this case

$$\int_{r_0}^{\infty} \frac{S(r)}{r^{k+1}}\,dr < \epsilon \quad \text{if } r_0 > t(\epsilon).$$

Then

$$\int_{r_0}^{2r_0} \frac{S(r)}{r^{k+1}}\,dr < \epsilon,$$

and since $S(r)$ increases with r,

$$\int_{r_0}^{2r_0} \frac{S(r)}{r^{k+1}}\,dr \geqslant \frac{S(r_0)}{(2r_0)^{k+1}}\,r_0,$$

so that

$$S(r_0)2^{-(k+1)}/r_0^k < \epsilon \quad \text{for } r_0 > t(\epsilon),$$

that is

$$\overline{\lim_{r \to \infty}} \frac{S(r)}{r^k} = 0.$$

Thus (d) implies (c). We also note that if k' is greater than the order k of $S(r)$, then

$$\int_{r_0}^{\infty} \frac{S(r)}{r^{k'+1}}\,dr \quad \text{converges,}$$

and if k' is less than k, then

$$\int_{r_0}^{\infty} \frac{S(r)}{r^{k'+1}}\,dr \quad \text{diverges.}$$

1.7.1. We next prove the following fundamental inequality.

THEOREM 1.6. *If $f(z)$ is regular for $|z| \leqslant R$ and*

$$M(r,f) = \max_{|z|=r} |f(z)|,$$

then $\qquad T(r,f) \leqslant \log^+ M(r,f) \leqslant \dfrac{R+r}{R-r} T(R,f) \quad (0 \leqslant r < R).$

Since $f(z)$ is regular we have

$$T(r,f) = m(r,f) = \frac{1}{2\pi} \int_0^{2\pi} \log^+ |f(re^{i\theta})|\, d\theta \leqslant \log^+ M(r,f).$$

To prove the second inequality, note that the result is trivial if $M(r,f) \leqslant 1$. Suppose then $M(r,f) > 1$ and choose $z_0 = re^{i\theta}$ so that $|f(z_0)| = M(r,f)$. Since $f(z)$ has no poles in $|z| < R$, Theorem 1.1 yields

$$\log^+ M(r,f) = \log|f(z_0)| \leqslant \frac{1}{2\pi} \int_0^{2\pi} \log|f(Re^{i\phi})|\, \frac{(R^2 - r^2)\, d\phi}{R^2 - 2Rr\cos(\theta - \phi) + r^2}$$

$$\leqslant \frac{1}{2\pi} \int_0^{2\pi} \frac{R+r}{R-r} \log^+ |f(Re^{i\phi})|\, d\phi = \frac{R+r}{R-r} m(R,f) = \frac{R+r}{R-r} T(R,f).$$

This proves Theorem 1.6.

We deduce immediately the following:

THEOREM 1.7. *If $f(z)$ is an integral function then the order k of the functions $S_1(r) = \log^+ M(r,f)$ and $S_2(r) = T(r,f)$ is the same. Further if $0 < k < \infty$, $S_1(r)$ and $S_2(r)$ belong to the same classes (a), (b), (c), or (d).*

In fact we have from Theorem 1.6, setting $R = 2r$,

$$S_2(r) \leqslant S_1(r) \leqslant 3S_2(2r).$$

We deduce at once that the order of $S_2(r)$ is not greater than that of $S_1(r)$ and also that the order of $S_1(r)$ is not greater than that of $S_2(r)$. Suppose now for instance that $S_2(r)$ has convergence class of order k. Then

$$\int_{r_0}^{\infty} \frac{S_1(r)\, dr}{r^{k+1}} \leqslant 3 \int_{r_0}^{\infty} \frac{S_2(2r)\, dr}{r^{k+1}} = 3 \cdot 2^k \int_{2r_0}^{\infty} \frac{S_2(t)\, dt}{t^{k+1}} < \infty.$$

Thus $S_1(r)$ has convergence class also. The converse is also obvious. The other results are proved similarly.

We shall say in the sequel that a function $f(z)$ meromorphic in the plane has order k and maximal, minimal, mean type or convergence class if the function $T(r,f)$ has this property. For integral functions this coincides by Theorem 1.7 with the corresponding definition in terms of $\log^+ M(r)$ which is classical.

1.8. Comparative growth of $T(r)$ and $\log M(r)$

It is to be noted that although for an integral function

$$C_1 = \varlimsup_{r \to \infty} \frac{T(r)}{r^k} \quad \text{and} \quad C_2 = \varlimsup_{r \to \infty} \frac{\log^+ M(r)}{r^k}$$

are zero, finite, or infinite together, C_1 and C_2 need not have the same value. Thus for $f(z) = e^z$, $C_1 = 1/\pi$ (see section 1.3, example (ii)), $C_2 = 1$. We evidently always have $C_1 \leqslant C_2$.

Setting $R = r(1+1/k)$ in Theorem 1.6 we deduce that, if C_1 is finite, we have for all large r

$$\log M(r) < \frac{r(2+1/k)}{r/k}(C_1+\epsilon)\left(1+\frac{1}{k}\right)^k r^k,$$

so that

$$C_2 \leqslant (2k+1)\left(1+\frac{1}{k}\right)^k C_1 < e(2k+1)C_1. \tag{1.16}$$

On the other hand, for $k > \frac{1}{2}$ and $\alpha = 1/k$ Mittag–Leffler's function

$$E_\alpha(z) = \sum_{n=0}^{\infty} \frac{z^n}{\Gamma(1+\alpha n)}$$

is bounded for† $\pi/2k < |\arg z| < \pi$, and is such that

$$\log|f(re^{i\theta})| \sim r^k \cos k\theta \quad (r \to \infty)$$

uniformly for $|\theta| < \pi/2k - \delta$, where $\delta > 0$. For this function

$$T(r,f) \sim \frac{1}{2\pi} \int_{-\pi/(2k)}^{\pi/(2k)} r^k \cos k\theta \, d\theta = \frac{r^k}{\pi k},$$

while

$$\log M(r,f) \sim r^k.$$

For $k = 1$, $f(z)$ reduces to e^z.

Thus $e(2k+1)$ cannot be replaced by any constant less than πk in (1.16). It seems probable that πk is in fact the correct value for $k > \frac{1}{2}$.‡

1.8.1. For functions of infinite order it is possible that

$$\frac{T(r,f)}{\log M(r)} \to 0, \quad \text{as } r \to \infty.$$

An example of this is provided by the function $f(z) = e^{e^z}$. Here

$$\log^+|f(re^{i\theta})| \leqslant e^{r\cos\theta}.$$

Thus

$$T(r,f) \leqslant \frac{1}{2\pi} \int_{-\pi}^{\pi} e^{r\cos\theta} \, d\theta = \frac{e^r}{\pi} \int_{0}^{\pi} e^{-r(1-\cos\theta)} \, d\theta.$$

† See e.g. Cartwright [1, Theorem 35, p. 50].
‡ See Wahlund [1] for $k < \frac{1}{2}$.

We note that

$$1-\cos\theta = 2\sin^2\tfrac{1}{2}\theta > \frac{2\theta^2}{\pi^2} \quad (0 < \theta < \pi).$$

Thus

$$T(r,f) \leqslant \frac{e^r}{\pi}\int_0^\pi e^{-2r\theta^2/\pi^2}\,d\theta < \frac{e^r}{\pi}\int_0^\infty e^{-2r\theta^2/\pi^2}\,d\theta = \frac{e^r}{\pi}\sqrt{\left(\frac{\pi^3}{8r}\right)} = e^r\sqrt{\left(\frac{\pi}{8r}\right)};$$

while

$$\log M(r,f) = e^r.$$

(By section 1.3, exercise (iv), we have actually $T(r,f) \sim e^r(2\pi^3 r)^{-\frac{1}{2}}$.)

1.8.2. In the opposite direction to that of the above example we have the following theorem due to T. Shimizu [1].

THEOREM 1.8. *Suppose that $f(z)$ is a non-constant integral function and $K > 1$. Then*

$$\lim_{r\to\infty} \frac{\log M(r)}{T(r)\{\log T(r)\}^K} = 0.$$

We apply Lemma 1.2 with $\phi(x) = T(e^x, f)$. This is possible since f is non-constant and so unbounded in the plane. Hence $\log M(r) \to \infty$ with r by Liouville's theorem, and so does $T(r)$ by Theorem 1.6. Accordingly we can find a sequence x_n such that

$$\phi(x) < K\phi(x_n) \quad \text{for } x_n < x < x_n + \{\log^+\phi(x_n)\}^{-K},$$

and such that $x_n \to \infty$ and hence $\phi(x_n) \to \infty$ as $n \to \infty$. We choose $\log r = x_n$, $\log R = x_n + \{\log^+\phi(x_n)\}^{-K}$ in Theorem 1.6. This gives

$$\log M(r) < \frac{R+r}{R-r}T(r) < K\frac{\exp[\{\log\phi(x_n)\}^{-K}]+1}{\exp[\{\log\phi(x_n)\}^{-K}]-1}T(r)$$

$$\sim 2KT(r)\{\log T(r)\}^K$$

and $r \to \infty$ through the sequence $\exp(x_n)$. Thus

$$\lim_{r\to\infty} \frac{\log M(r)}{T(r)\{\log T(r)\}^K} < +\infty.$$

Since we may replace K by $\tfrac{1}{2}(1+K)$ in the above argument and $T(r) \to \infty$ with r, Theorem 1.8 follows.

Hayman and Stewart [1] have shown that if $f(z) \neq 0$ in the plane the conclusion of Theorem 1.8 holds for $K > \tfrac{1}{2}$. The example of $f(z) = e^{e^z}$, which we have just discussed, shows that this result is no longer true for $K = \tfrac{1}{2}$ even in this special case. The function of Lemma 4.1 for which $\log M(r) \sim e^r$, $T(r) = O(e^r/r)$, shows that Theorem 1.8 no longer holds in general with $K = 1$.

1.9. Representation of a meromorphic function in terms of its zeros and poles

The fundamental theorem of algebra allows us to write any polynomial $P(z)$ in the form

$$P(z) = cz^p \prod_{r=p+1}^{n} \left(1 - \frac{z}{z_r}\right),$$

where z_r are the zeros of $P(z)$ other than those at the origin. It is possible to extend this theorem to integral functions and this was done by Weierstrass [1] and Hadamard [1]. The finite product becomes an infinite product to which it is in general necessary to add other factors in order to make the product converge. The results are particularly simple for functions of finite order when the factorization is still almost unique.

For meromorphic functions a corresponding expression of a function as a product in terms of its zeros and poles is possible, and Nevanlinna's theory allowed him to obtain conclusions which even in the case of integral functions go farther than those previously known and are essentially best possible.

We define for any positive integer q the Weierstrass primary factor

$$E(z, q) = (1 - z)e^{z + \frac{1}{2}z^2 + \dots + (1/q)z^q}$$

and $$E(z, 0) = 1 - z.$$

Then we have the following:

THEOREM 1.9. *Suppose that $f(z)$ is meromorphic in the plane and has there zeros a_μ and poles b_ν, and satisfies one of the conditions*

(a) $\overline{\lim_{R \to \infty}} \dfrac{T(R, f)}{R^q} = 0,$

(b) $\lim_{R \to \infty} \dfrac{T(R, f)}{R^q} = 0,$

where q is a positive integer. Then

$$f(z) = z^p e^{P_{q-1}(z)} \lim \left\{ \prod_{|a_\mu| < R} E\left(\frac{z}{a_\mu}, q-1\right) \middle/ \prod_{|b_\nu| < R} E\left(\frac{z}{b_\nu}, q-1\right) \right\},$$

where the limit takes place as $R \to \infty$ through all values in case (a) and through a suitable sequence of values in case (b). Here p is an integer and $P_{q-1}(z)$ is a polynomial of degree $q-1$ at most.†

---

† More precisely $P_{q-1}(z)$ consists of the terms of degree less than q in the power series expansion of $\log\{f(z)/z^p\}$ near $z = 0$.

1.9.1. Note that the theorem only asserts that the limit on the right exists, but does not indicate whether the products are separately convergent.

To start with let us assume that $f(0) \neq 0, \infty$. Then Theorem 1.1 gives, for $z = re^{i\theta}$,

$$\log|f(z)| = \frac{1}{2\pi} \int_0^{2\pi} \frac{(R^2-r^2)\log|f(Re^{i\phi})|\,d\phi}{R^2-2Rr\cos(\phi-\theta)+r^2} +$$
$$+ \sum_{|a_\mu|<R} \log\left|\frac{R(z-a_\mu)}{R^2-\bar{a}_\mu z}\right| + \sum_{|b_\nu|<R} \log\left|\frac{R^2-\bar{b}_\nu z}{R(z-b_\nu)}\right|.$$

Both the sides are equal harmonic functions $v(z)$ (say) of z near any point $z = re^{i\theta}$, where $f(re^{i\theta}) \neq 0, \infty$. Let us apply the operator $\partial/\partial x - i\partial/\partial y$ to both sides of the above equation.

Differentiating under the integral sign and observing that

$$\mathscr{R}\left(\frac{Re^{i\phi}+z}{Re^{i\phi}-z}\right) = \frac{R^2-r^2}{R^2-2Rr\cos(\phi-\theta)+r^2}$$

we deduce that

$$\frac{f'(z)}{f(z)} = \frac{1}{2\pi} \int_0^{2\pi} \log|f(Re^{i\phi})| \frac{2Re^{i\phi}}{(Re^{i\phi}-z)^2}\,d\phi -$$
$$- \sum_{|a_\mu|<R}\left(\frac{1}{a_\mu-z}-\frac{\bar{a}_\mu}{R^2-\bar{a}_\mu z}\right) + \sum_{|b_\nu|<R}\left(\frac{1}{b_\nu-z}-\frac{\bar{b}_\nu}{R^2-\bar{b}_\nu z}\right),$$

provided that there are no zeros or poles on $|z| = R$, which we assume. Differentiating this $q-1$ times we obtain

$$\left(\frac{d}{dz}\right)^{q-1}\left(\frac{f'(z)}{f(z)}\right) = \frac{q!}{\pi}\int_0^{2\pi}\frac{\log|f(Re^{i\phi})|Re^{i\phi}\,d\phi}{(Re^{i\phi}-z)^{q+1}} +$$
$$+(q-1)!\sum_{|b_\nu|<R}\left(\frac{1}{(b_\nu-z)^q}-\frac{\bar{b}_\nu^q}{(R^2-\bar{b}_\nu z)^q}\right) -$$
$$-(q-1)!\sum_{|a_\mu|<R}\left(\frac{1}{(a_\mu-z)^q}-\frac{\bar{a}_\mu^q}{(R^2-\bar{a}_\mu z)^q}\right). \quad (1.17)$$

Suppose now that $T(2r)/r^q \to 0$ as $r \to \infty$ either through all values or through a suitable sequence of values, say R_k (which tends to ∞ with k). Such a sequence of values exists by our assumptions. Also by decreasing R_k slightly if necessary, we may assume that $f(z) \neq 0, \infty$ on $|z| = R_k$. We take $R = R_k$ in (1.17). Then, since $m(r,f) \geqslant 0$,

$$T(2R_k,f) \geqslant N(2R_k,f) \geqslant \int_{R_k}^{2R_k}\frac{n(t,f)\,dt}{t} \geqslant n(R_k,f)\log 2.$$

Thus
$$n(R_k, f)/R_k^q \to 0 \quad \text{as } k \to \infty.$$

Similarly
$$n(R_k, 1/f)R_k^q \to 0, \quad \text{as } k \to \infty,$$

since
$$T(R_k, 1/f) = T(R_k, f) + O(1)$$

by (1.10).

Our next aim now is to show that some of the terms on the right of the equation (1.17) including the integral tend to zero uniformly for z on any bounded set as k tends to infinity. Then letting k tend to infinity we shall obtain a modified equation which will yield our result after integrating q times.

Suppose then that $|z| < \frac{1}{2}R_k$. Then $|\bar{b}_\nu z| < \frac{1}{2}R_k \cdot R_k$ for $|b_\nu| < R_k$ and
$$|R_k^2 - \bar{b}_\nu z| \geqslant R_k^2 - |\bar{b}_\nu z| > \tfrac{1}{2}R_k^2.$$

Hence
$$\left| \frac{\bar{b}_\nu^q}{(R_k^2 - \bar{b}_\nu z)^q} \right| < \frac{R_k^q}{(\frac{1}{2}R_k^2)^q} = \frac{2^q}{R_k^q},$$

this inequality being true for all poles b_ν with $|b_\nu| < R_k$. Therefore, summing up for all poles b_ν in $|z| < R_k$

$$\left| \sum \frac{\bar{b}_\nu^q}{(R_k^2 - \bar{b}_\nu z)^q} \right| \leqslant \sum \left| \frac{\bar{b}_\nu^q}{(R_k^2 - \bar{b}_\nu z)^q} \right| < \frac{2^q n(R_k, f)}{R_k^q},$$

and here the right-hand side tends to zero uniformly as k tends to infinity for z in any bounded set. A similar result holds good for the zeros of the function.

We now consider the integral in (1.17). We have
$$|R_k e^{i\phi} - z| > \tfrac{1}{2}R_k \quad \text{for } |z| < \tfrac{1}{2}R_k.$$

Hence the modulus of the integral on the right of (1.17) is at most

$$q! \frac{R_k}{\pi} \frac{2^{q+1}}{R_k^{q+1}} \int_0^{2\pi} \left| \log|f(R_k e^{i\phi})| \right| d\phi$$

$$= \frac{q!}{\pi} \frac{2^{q+1}}{R_k^q} \left\{ \int_0^{2\pi} \log^+ |f(R_k e^{i\phi})| \, d\phi + \int_0^{2\pi} \log^+ \left| \frac{1}{f(R_k e^{i\phi})} \right| d\phi \right\}$$

$$= \frac{q!}{\pi} \frac{2^{q+1}}{R_k^q} \{ m(R_k, f) + m(R_k, 1/f) \}$$

$$= O\left\{ \frac{T(R_k, f)}{R_k^q} \right\} = O\left\{ \frac{T(2R_k, f)}{R_k^q} \right\} \to 0, \quad \text{as } k \to \infty.$$

Thus the equation (1.17) takes the form

$$\left(\frac{d}{dz}\right)^{q-1}\frac{f'(z)}{f(z)} = \lim_{k\to\infty} S_k(z),$$

where
$$S_k(z) = (q-1)!\left\{\sum_{|b_\nu|<R_k}\frac{1}{(b_\nu-z)^q} - \sum_{|a_\mu|<R_k}\frac{1}{(a_\mu-z)^q}\right\},$$

the convergence being uniform for any bounded set of values of z not containing any of the zeros or poles of $f(z)$.

By the uniform convergence we may therefore integrate both sides $(q-1)$ times along a suitable path from 0 to z to get

$$\frac{f'(z)}{f(z)} = \lim_{k\to\infty}\left[\sum_{|b_\nu|<R_k}\left\{\frac{1}{b_\nu-z}-\frac{1}{b_\nu}-\frac{z}{b_\nu^2}-\cdots-\frac{z^{q-2}}{b_\nu^{q-1}}\right\}-\right.$$

$$\left.-\sum_{|a_\mu|<R_k}\left\{\frac{1}{a_\mu-z}-\frac{1}{a_\mu}-\frac{z}{a_\mu^2}-\cdots-\frac{z^{q-2}}{a_\mu^{q-1}}\right\}\right]+P_{q-2}(z),$$

where $P_{q-2}(z)$ is a polynomial of degree at most $q-2$.

Now integrate both sides once more from 0 to z, and take exponentials. This yields Theorem 1.9 in the case when $f(0) \neq 0, \infty$. In case zero is a pole of order $-p$ or a zero of $f(z)$ of order p, consider the function $f(z)/z^p$ and apply the result just obtained to get Theorem 1.9 in its final form.

Exercise. If $f(z)$ is meromorphic with only a finite number of zeros and poles in the plane and satisfies

$$\lim_{r\to\infty}\frac{T(r,f)}{r} = 0$$

prove that $f(z)$ is rational.

1.10. Behaviour of Weierstrass products

We next investigate the converse problem to that of Theorem 1.9, namely that of the behaviour of the Weierstrass products

$$\prod_{\nu=1}^{\infty}E\left(\frac{z}{a_\nu}, q-1\right)$$

for given sequences a_ν. In this way we shall be able to construct meromorphic functions of given order with zeros and poles that are arbitrary, subject only to the conditions implied by Theorem 1.10.

We shall need a number of preliminary results. Let $a_1,..., a_n,...$ be a sequence of non-zero complex numbers arranged in the order of increasing moduli and such that $a_n \to \infty$ as $n \to \infty$. Let $n(r)$ be the number of the a_n lying in the circle $|z| < r$, and set

$$N(r) = \int_0^r \frac{n(t)\, dt}{t}.$$

We shall call $n(r)$ the counting function of the sequence a_n.

LEMMA 1.4. *The functions $n(r)$ and $N(r)$ have the same order and type-class and for any k such that $0 < k < \infty$, we have further*

$$\sum_{\nu=1}^{\infty} |a_\nu|^{-k} = k \int_0^\infty \frac{n(r)\, dr}{r^{k+1}} = k^2 \int_0^\infty \frac{N(r)\, dr}{r^{k+1}}$$

in the sense that all three expressions are infinite, or all are finite and equal.

The order and type-class of $n(r)$ and $N(r)$ will be called the order and type-class of the sequence a_n.

To prove the lemma, suppose that

$$n(r) < Cr^k \quad (r > r_0).$$

Then
$$N(r) < \int_{r_0}^r Ct^k \frac{dt}{t} + O(1) = \frac{C}{k} r^k + O(1) \quad (r > r_0).$$

This shows at once that the order and type-class of $N(r)$ cannot exceed that of $n(r)$. Again, if
$$N(r) < Cr^k \quad (r > r_0),$$

we have
$$n(r) \log 2 \leqslant \int_r^{2r} \frac{n(t)\, dt}{t} \leqslant N(2r) \leqslant C(2r)^k \quad (r > r_0),$$

so that the order and type-class of $n(r)$ cannot exceed that of $N(r)$.

Next we have
$$\sum_{|a_\nu| < R} |a_\nu|^{-k} = \int_0^R \frac{dn(t)}{t^k}$$

since $n(t)$ increases by p at r if p of the a_ν lie on $|z| = r$. We integrate the Riemann–Stieltjes integral on the right-hand side by parts and obtain

$$\sum_{|a_\nu| < R} |a_\nu|^{-k} = \frac{n(R)}{R^k} + k \int_0^R \frac{n(t)\, dt}{t^{k+1}}$$

$$= \frac{n(R)}{R^k} + k \int_0^R \frac{dN(t)}{t^k} = \frac{n(R)}{R^k} + \frac{kN(R)}{R^k} + k^2 \int_0^R \frac{N(r)\, dr}{r^{k+1}}.$$

Making $R \to \infty$ we deduce at once that if

$$I_1 = \int\limits_0^\infty \frac{N(r)\,dr}{r^{k+1}}$$

diverges then so do

$$I_2 = \int\limits_0^\infty \frac{n(r)\,dr}{r^{k+1}} \quad\text{and}\quad I_3 = \sum\limits_{\nu=1}^\infty |a_\nu|^{-k}.$$

Next if I_1 converges $N(R)$ has at most convergence class of order k, and hence at most minimal type of order k, so that

$$\frac{N(R)}{R^k} \to 0 \quad\text{as}\quad R \to \infty.$$

Thus also

$$\frac{n(R)}{R^k} \to 0 \quad\text{as}\quad R \to \infty,$$

and so by making $R \to \infty$, we see that $k^2 I_1 = k I_2 = I_3$ in this case, as required.

We deduce at once

THEOREM 1.10. *If $f(z)$ is a non-constant meromorphic function, then for any complex a the order and type-class of the roots of the equation $f(z) = a$ do not exceed the order and type-class†of $f(z)$.*

In fact we have, by Theorem 1.2,

$$N(r, a) \leqslant T(r, f) + O(1).$$

Since the order and type-class of $f(z)$ and the roots of $f(z) = a$ can be defined in terms of $N(r, a)$ and $T(r, f)$, the result follows.

1.10.1. We next need some estimates for $E(z, q)$.

LEMMA 1.5. *If $|z| \leqslant \tfrac{1}{2}$, then, taking the principal value of the logarithm, we have*

$$|\log E(z, q)| \leqslant 2|z|^{q+1}. \tag{1.18}$$

Further we have for all z,

$$\log|E(z, q)| \leqslant \log(1 + |z|), \tag{1.19}$$

if $q = 0$, and for $q \geqslant 1$

$$\log|E(z, q)| \leqslant A(q)\min(|z|^q, |z|^{q+1}), \tag{1.20}$$

where $A(q) = 2(2 + \log q)$.

Suppose first that

$$|z| < 1 - \frac{1}{2(q+1)}.$$

---

† i.e. the order of the roots of $f(z) = a$ does not exceed the order of $f(z)$ and if the two orders are the same, the corresponding result holds for type classes.

Then

$$|\log E(z,q)| = \left|\log(1-z)+z+\tfrac{1}{2}z^2+\dots+\frac{1}{q}z^q\right| = \left|\frac{z^{q+1}}{q+1}+\frac{z^{q+2}}{q+2}+\dots\right|$$

$$\leqslant \frac{|z|^{q+1}}{q+1}(1+|z|+|z|^2+\dots) = \frac{|z|^{q+1}}{(q+1)(1-|z|)} \leqslant 2|z|^{q+1}.$$

Thus our lemma holds in this case. The inequality (1.19) is trivial if $q = 0$, so we assume henceforth $q \geqslant 1$. Consider next the range $|z| \geqslant 1$. Then

$$\log|E(z,q)| \leqslant \log(1+|z|)+|z|+\frac{|z|^2}{2}+\dots+\frac{|z|^q}{q} \leqslant 2|z|+\frac{|z|^2}{2}+\dots+\frac{|z|^q}{q}$$

$$\leqslant |z|^q\left(2+\tfrac{1}{2}+\dots+\frac{1}{q}\right) \leqslant (2+\log q)|z|^q.$$

In particular it follows that we have for $|z| = 1$

$$\log|E(z,q)| \leqslant 2+\log^+ q,$$

and this inequality remains valid for $|z| < 1$ by the maximum modulus theorem. In the range $1-\{2(q+1)\}^{-1} < |z| \leqslant 1$, we have

$$|z|^{q+1} \geqslant \left\{1-\frac{1}{2(q+1)}\right\}^{q+1} \geqslant \tfrac{1}{2}, \quad \text{for } q \geqslant 0,$$

so that

$$\log|E(z,q)| \leqslant 2(2+\log^+ q)|z|^{q+1}$$

in this range. This completes the proof of our lemma.

1.10.2. We are now able to prove our result.

THEOREM 1.11. *Let a_ν be a sequence of non-zero complex numbers having counting function $n(t)$ and let q be the least integer such that $\sum\limits_{\nu=1}^{\infty}|a_\nu|^{-q}$ converges. Then the product*

$$\prod_{\nu=1}^{\infty} E\!\left(\frac{z}{a_\nu},\,q-1\right)$$

converges absolutely and uniformly in any bounded part of the plane to an integral function $\Pi(z)$ having the same order ρ as the sequence a_n, and the same type-class if ρ is not an integer. Further $\Pi(z)$ satisfies the inequality

$$\log|\Pi(z)| \leqslant qA(q)\left\{|z|^{q-1}\int_0^{|z|}\frac{n(t)\,dt}{t^q}+|z|^q\int_{|z|}^{\infty}\frac{n(t)\,dt}{t^{q+1}}\right\}, \qquad (1.21)$$

where $A(q) = 1$ *if* $q = 1$, $A(q) = 2(2+\log q)$, *for* $q > 1$.

We have by Lemma 1.5 for $|z| < \tfrac{1}{2}R \leqslant \tfrac{1}{2}|a_n|$

$$\left|\log E\!\left(\frac{z}{a_n},\,q-1\right)\right| < 2\,\frac{|z|^q}{|a_n|^q} < \frac{2R^q}{|a_n|^q}.$$

Thus the series
$$\sum_{n=n_0}^{\infty} \log E\left(\frac{z}{a_n}, q-1\right)$$
converges uniformly for $|z| < \frac{1}{2}R$ if n_0 is large enough, and hence so does the product $\Pi(z)$.

We next establish the inequality (1.21). Suppose first that $q = 1$. Then
$$\log|\Pi(z)| \leqslant \sum_{\nu=1}^{\infty} \log\left(1+\left|\frac{z}{a_\nu}\right|\right) = \int_0^{\infty} \log\left(1+\frac{|z|}{t}\right) dn(t)$$
$$= \lim_{R\to\infty}\left[n(R)\log\left(1+\frac{|z|}{R}\right) + \int_0^R \frac{|z|n(t)\, dt}{t(t+|z|)}\right].$$

Since the a_ν have order 1 convergence class at most and so
$$\frac{n(R)}{R} \to 0 \quad\text{as } R \to \infty,$$
$$\log|\Pi(z)| \leqslant |z| \int_0^{\infty} \frac{n(t)\, dt}{t(t+|z|)} \leqslant \int_0^{|z|} \frac{n(t)\, dt}{t} + |z| \int_{|z|}^{\infty} \frac{n(t)\, dt}{t^2}.$$

This proves (1.21) if $q = 1$.

Suppose next that $q > 1$. In this case we have, by Lemma 1.5,
$$\log|\Pi(z)| \leqslant A(q)\left\{\sum_{|a_\nu|\leqslant|z|} \frac{|z|^{q-1}}{|a_\nu|^{q-1}} + \sum_{|a_\nu|>|z|} \frac{|z|^q}{|a_\nu|^q}\right\}$$
$$= A(q)\left\{\int_0^{|z|} \frac{|z|^{q-1}\, dn(t)}{t^{q-1}} + \int_{|z|}^{\infty} \frac{|z|^q\, dn(t)}{t^q}\right\}.$$

We integrate by parts and obtain
$$\log|\Pi(z)| \leqslant A(q)\left\{|z|^{q-1}\int_0^{|z|} \frac{(q-1)n(t)\, dt}{t^q} + |z|^q \int_{|z|}^{\infty} \frac{qn(t)\, dt}{t^{q+1}}\right\}.$$

This proves (1.21).

Suppose now that
$$n(t) < ct^\rho \quad (t > t_0), \tag{1.22}$$
where $q-1 < \rho < q$. Then (1.21) gives for $|z| = r > t_0$,
$$\log^+|\Pi(z)| \leqslant qA(q)\left[r^{q-1}\left\{\int_0^r ct^{\rho-q}\, dt + O(1)\right\} + cr^q\left\{\int_r^{\infty} t^{\rho-q-1}\, dt\right\}\right]$$
$$= qA(q)c\left\{\frac{r^\rho}{\rho-q+1} + \frac{r^\rho}{q-\rho}\right\} + O(r^{q-1}).$$

Thus if $n(t)$ has order ρ mean type or minimal type at most so does $\Pi(z)$, where $q-1 < \rho < q$.

If $n(t)$ has order $q-1$, then (1.22) is satisfied for every $\rho > q-1$ and a suitable c and so $\Pi(z)$ has order at most ρ, i.e. at most $q-1$. Finally, if $n(t)$ has order q convergence type and hence minimal type, then (1.21) yields

$$\log^+|\Pi(z)| \leqslant qA(q)\left\{|z|^{q-1}\int_0^{|z|} o(1)\,dt + |z|^q \int_{|z|}^{\infty} \frac{n(t)\,dt}{t^{q+1}}\right\} = o\left(|z|^q\right).$$

Thus $\Pi(z)$ has order q minimal type at most. This completes the proof of Theorem 1.11.

1.10.3. If q is the quantity occurring in Theorem 1.11, then $q-1$ is called the *genus* of the Weierstrass product $\Pi(z)$.

If ρ is the order of the sequence of zeros then the genus satisfies the inequality $q-1 \leqslant \rho \leqslant q$. If ρ is an integer, so that $\rho = q$ or $\rho = q-1$, then $\Pi(z)$ need not have the same type-class as the sequence a_n.

Exercise. Consider

$$\Pi(z) = \prod_{n=1}^{\infty}\left(1+\frac{z}{n}\right)e^{-z/n}.$$

Then†

$$\log \Pi(z) = \sum_{n=1}^{\infty}\left\{\log\left(1+\frac{z}{n}\right)-\frac{z}{n}\right\} = \int_0^{\infty}\left\{\log\left(1+\frac{z}{t}\right)-\frac{z}{t}\right\}d[t]$$

$$= -z^2\int_0^{\infty}\frac{[t]\,dt}{t^2(z+t)} = -z^2\int_1^{\infty}\frac{dt}{t(t+z)}+O(z) = -z\log z+O(z)$$

uniformly as $z \to \infty$ for $|\arg z| < \pi-\delta$. Thus

$$\log M(r,\Pi) > (1-\epsilon)r\log r$$

for large r, so that $\Pi(z)$ has maximal type, but the sequence of zeros has mean type. Here $q = 2$, and the genus $q-1$ is 1, $\rho = 1$.

If $\rho = q$, then $n(t)$ has convergence class and so minimal type of order q. In this case we saw that $\Pi(z)$ also has order q minimal type at most, but the example

$$\Pi(z) = \prod_{n=2}^{\infty}\left(1+\frac{z}{n(\log n)^2}\right)$$

shows that $\Pi(z)$ need not have convergence class of order 1. In this case

$$T(r,\Pi) \sim \frac{r}{\log r}, \qquad n\left(r,\frac{1}{\Pi}\right) \sim \frac{r}{(\log r)^2}.$$

† $[x]$ denotes the largest integer not greater than x.

If in Theorem 1.9 $f(z)$ has at most convergence class of order q then Theorems 1.10 and 1.11 show that the products

$$\Pi_1(z) = \prod_{\mu=1}^{\infty} E\left(\frac{z}{a_\mu}, q-1\right) \quad \text{and} \quad \Pi_2(z) = \prod_{\nu=1}^{\infty} E\left(\frac{z}{b_\nu}, q-1\right)$$

converge absolutely, and so

$$f(z) = z^p e^{P_{q-1}} \frac{\Pi_1(z)}{\Pi_2(z)}$$

by Theorem 1.9. However, under the more general hypotheses of Theorem 1.9 these products need not converge absolutely and in fact need not converge separately at all.

2

NEVANLINNA'S SECOND FUNDAMENTAL THEOREM

2.0. Introduction

WE have in the previous chapter defined Nevanlinna's characteristic function and have seen (Theorem 1.2) that for every complex a we have $m(r,a)+N(r,a) = T(r)+O(1)$. It follows that the sum $m+N$ is largely independent of a. This is the result of the first fundamental theorem. The second fundamental theorem (Theorem 2.4) shows that in general it is the term $N(r,a)$ which is dominant in the sum $m+N$ and further that in $N(r,a)$ we do not decrease the sum much if multiple roots are counted simply. Thus for most values of a the equation $f(z) = a$ has nearly as many roots as the first fundamental theorem permits and, moreover, the majority of these roots are simple. The result contains as a special case Picard's theorem that a transcendental meromorphic function assumes infinitely often all values in the plane except at most two. However, Nevanlinna's result goes much farther as we shall see.

In this chapter we prove Nevanlinna's second fundamental theorem† and give some of the more immediate applications. Further extensions and applications are reserved for later chapters.

2.1. The fundamental inequality

For the sake of simplicity we shall write $m(r,a)$ for $m\{r, 1/(f-a)\}$ and $m(r,\infty)$ for $m(r,f)$ if this notation is unlikely to give rise to ambiguity. Then we have†

THEOREM 2.1. *Suppose that $f(z)$ is a non-constant meromorphic function in $|z| \leqslant r$. Let $a_1, a_2, ..., a_q$, where $q > 2$, be distinct finite complex numbers, $\delta > 0$, and suppose that $|a_\mu - a_\nu| \geqslant \delta$ for $1 \leqslant \mu < \nu \leqslant q$. Then*

$$m(r,\infty) + \sum_{\nu=1}^{q} m(r,a_\nu) \leqslant 2T(r,f) - N_1(r) + S(r),$$

---

† The name second fundamental theorem is usually given to the inequality of Theorem 2.1 subject to a suitable estimate of $S(r)$ and also to Theorem 2.4 which is an immediate consequence of this.

where $N_1(r)$ is positive and is given by

$$N_1(r) = N(r, 1/f') + 2N(r,f) - N(r,f'),$$

and

$$S(r) = m\left(r, \frac{f'}{f}\right) + m\left\{r, \sum_{\nu=1}^{q} \frac{f'}{(f-a_\nu)}\right\} - q\log^+\frac{3q}{\delta} + \log 2 + \log\frac{1}{|f'(0)|},$$

with modifications if $f(0) = \infty$, or $f'(0) = 0$.

The quantity $S(r)$ will in general play the role of an unimportant error term. The combination of this fact with Theorem 2.1 yields the second fundamental theorem. It shows that the sum of any number of the terms $m(r, a_\nu)$ cannot in general be much bigger than $2T(r)$. If $f(z) \neq 0, 1, \infty$, $m(r, a) = T(r,f) + O(1)$ for $a = 0, 1, \infty$, so that

$$m(r, 0) + m(r, 1) + m(r, \infty) = 3T(r) + O(1)$$

and this would give us a contradiction. This gives Picard's theorem.

We first prove the relatively simple Theorem 2.1 before tackling the much more complicated estimation of $S(r)$.

2.1.1. *Proof of Theorem 2.1*

Consider

$$F(z) = \sum_{\nu=1}^{q} \left(\frac{1}{f(z) - a_\nu}\right)$$

and suppose that for some ν, $|f(z) - a_\nu| < \delta/3q$. Then for $\mu \neq \nu$,

$$|f(z) - a_\mu| \geqslant |a_\mu - a_\nu| - |f(z) - a_\nu| \geqslant \delta - \delta/3q \geqslant \tfrac{2}{3}\delta.$$

Therefore for $\mu \neq \nu$

$$\frac{1}{|f(z) - a_\mu|} \leqslant \frac{3}{2\delta} \leqslant \frac{1}{2q}\left\{\frac{1}{|f(z) - a_\nu|}\right\}.$$

Again,

$$|F(z)| \geqslant \frac{1}{|f(z) - a_\nu|} - \sum_{\mu \neq \nu} \frac{1}{|f(z) - a_\mu|}$$

$$\geqslant \left\{\frac{1}{|f(z) - a_\nu|}\right\}\left\{\left(1 - \frac{q-1}{2q}\right)\right\} \geqslant \frac{1}{2|f(z) - a_\nu|}.$$

Hence

$$\log^+|F(z)| \geqslant \log^+\frac{1}{|f(z) - a_\nu|} - \log 2.$$

In this case

$$\log^+|F(z)| \geqslant \sum_{\mu=1}^{q} \log^+\frac{1}{|f(z) - a_\mu|} - q\log^+\frac{2}{\delta} - \log 2$$

$$\geqslant \sum_{\mu=1}^{q} \log^+\frac{1}{|f(z) - a_\mu|} - q\log^+\frac{3q}{\delta} - \log 2,$$

since all the terms for $\mu \neq \nu$ are at most $\log^+(2/\delta)$. This is true if $|f(z)-a_\nu| < \delta/3q$ for some $\nu \leqslant q$. This inequality is true evidently for at most one ν. If it is not true for any value ν then we have trivially

$$\log^+|F(z)| \geqslant \sum_{\nu=1}^{q} \log^+ \frac{1}{|f(z)-a_\nu|} - q\log^+\frac{3q}{\delta} - \log 2.$$

So the last relationship holds good in all cases.

Taking integrals we deduce

$$m(r, F) \geqslant \sum_{\nu=1}^{q} m(r, a_\nu) - q\log^+\frac{3q}{\delta} - \log 2. \tag{2.1}$$

Again, to get an inequality in the other direction we note that

$$m(r, F) = m\left(r, \frac{1}{f}\frac{f}{f'}f'F\right) \leqslant m\left(r, \frac{1}{f}\right) + m\left(r, \frac{f}{f'}\right) + m(r, f'F).$$

By (1.10) we have

$$T(r, f) = T\left(r, \frac{1}{f}\right) + \log|f(0)|,$$

$$m\left(r, \frac{f}{f'}\right) = m\left(r, \frac{f'}{f}\right) + N\left(r, \frac{f'}{f}\right) - N\left(r, \frac{f}{f'}\right) + \log\left|\frac{f(0)}{f'(0)}\right|$$

and

$$m\left(r, \frac{1}{f}\right) = T(r, f) - N\left(r, \frac{1}{f}\right) + \log\frac{1}{|f(0)|}.$$

Hence we get finally

$$m(r, F) \leqslant T(r, f) - N\left(r, \frac{1}{f}\right) + \log\frac{1}{|f(0)|} + m\left(r, \frac{f'}{f}\right) +$$

$$+ N\left(r, \frac{f'}{f}\right) - N\left(r, \frac{f}{f'}\right) + m(r, f'F) + \log\left|\frac{f(0)}{f'(0)}\right|.$$

The above inequality combined with (2.1) gives

$$\sum_{\nu=1}^{q} m(r, a_\nu) + m(r, \infty) \leqslant m(r, F) + m(r, f) + q\log^+\frac{3q}{\delta} + \log 2$$

$$\leqslant T(r, f) - N\left(r, \frac{1}{f}\right) + N\left(r, \frac{f'}{f}\right) - N\left(r, \frac{f}{f'}\right) +$$

$$+ m\left(r, \frac{f'}{f}\right) + m(r, f'F) + \log\frac{1}{|f'(0)|} +$$

$$+ T(r, f) - N(r, f) + q\log^+\left(\frac{3q}{\delta}\right) + \log 2.$$

Again, by Jensen's formula

$$N\left(r,\frac{f'}{f}\right)-N\left(r,\frac{f}{f'}\right) = \frac{1}{2\pi}\int_0^{2\pi}\log\left|\frac{f(re^{i\theta})}{f'(re^{i\theta})}\right|d\theta-\log\left|\frac{f(0)}{f'(0)}\right|$$

$$= \frac{1}{2\pi}\int_0^{2\pi}\log|f(re^{i\theta})|\,d\theta-\log|f(0)|-$$

$$-\frac{1}{2\pi}\int_0^{2\pi}\log|f'(re^{i\theta})|\,d\theta+\log|f'(0)|$$

$$= N\left(r,\frac{1}{f}\right)-N(r,f)-N\left(r,\frac{1}{f'}\right)+N(r,f').$$

Thus we obtain finally

$$\sum_{\nu=1}^q m(r,a_\nu)+m(r,\infty) \leqslant 2T(r,f)-\left\{2N(r,f)-N(r,f')+N\left(r,\frac{1}{f'}\right)\right\}+S(r),$$

where $S(r)$ is defined as in Theorem 2.1, and the proof of Theorem 2.1 is complete.

2.2. The estimation of $S(r)$

The second fundamental theorem is a consequence of the following:

THEOREM 2.2. *Suppose that $f(z)$ is meromorphic and not constant in $|z| < R_0 \leqslant +\infty$, and that $S(r,f)$ is defined as in Theorem 2.1. Then we have*

(i) *If $R_0 = +\infty$,*

$$S(r,f) = O\{\log T(r,f)\}+O(\log r),$$

as $r \to \infty$ through all values if $f(z)$ has finite order and as $r \to \infty$ outside a set E of finite linear measure otherwise.

(ii) *If $0 < R_0 < +\infty$,*

$$S(r,f) = O\left\{\log^+T(r,f)+\log\frac{1}{R_0-r}\right\}$$

as $r \to R_0$ outside a set E such that

$$\int_E \frac{dr}{R_0-r} < +\infty.$$

Further there is a point r outside E for which $\rho < r < \rho'$ provided that $0 < R-\rho' < e^{-2}(R-\rho)$.

2.2.1. The proof of Theorem 2.2 is rather lengthy. We prove first

LEMMA 2.1. *Let z be any complex number and $0 < r < \infty$. Let E_k be the set of all θ such that $|z - re^{i\theta}| < kr$, and $0 \leqslant |\theta| < \pi$, where $0 < k \leqslant 1$. Then*

$$\int_{E_k} \log\left|\frac{r}{z - re^{i\theta}}\right| d\theta < \pi k \left\{\log\left(\frac{1}{k}\right) + 1\right\}.$$

We may assume without loss of generality that z is real and positive. Then for θ in E_k, we have

$$|z - re^{i\theta}| \geqslant r \sin\theta,$$

and E_k lies in the interval $|\theta| \leqslant \theta_0$, where θ_0 is the smallest positive root of the equation $\sin\theta_0 = k$, since for $\frac{1}{2}\pi \leqslant |\theta| \leqslant \pi$ we clearly have $|z - re^{i\theta}| > r$, when $z > 0$. Thus

$$\int_{E_k} \log\frac{r}{|z - re^{i\theta}|} d\theta \leqslant 2\int_0^{\theta_0} \log\left(\frac{1}{\sin\theta}\right) d\theta \leqslant 2\int_0^{\theta_0} \log\left(\frac{\pi}{2\theta}\right) d\theta$$

$$= 2\theta_0\left\{\log\left(\frac{\pi}{2\theta_0}\right) + 1\right\}.$$

Here the right-hand side increases with increasing θ_0 in $0 < \theta_0 < \frac{1}{2}\pi$, and so, since $\sin\theta_0 = k$, we may replace θ_0 by the larger number $\frac{1}{2}\pi k$. This proves the lemma.

We have next:

LEMMA 2.2. *Let $z_1, z_2, ..., z_n$ be $n \geqslant 1$ points in the plane and let $\delta(z)$ be the least of the distances $|z - z_\nu|$, $\nu = 1$ to n. Then*

$$\frac{1}{2\pi}\int_0^{2\pi} \log^+\frac{r}{\delta(re^{i\theta})} d\theta \leqslant 2\log n + \frac{1}{2}.$$

Let E_ν be the set of all θ where $|re^{i\theta} - z_\nu| < r/n$, and let $E = \bigcup_{\nu=1}^n E_\nu$. Set $\log_0 x = \log x$ if $x \geqslant n$, $\log_0 x = 0$ otherwise. Then in E, $\delta(re^{i\theta}) < r/n$, and so

$$\log^+\frac{r}{\delta(re^{i\theta})} = \log_0\frac{r}{\delta(re^{i\theta})} \leqslant \sum_{\nu=1}^n \log_0\left|\frac{r}{re^{i\theta} - z_\nu}\right|.$$

Hence, by Lemma 2.1 with $k = 1/n$, we have

$$\int_E \log^+\frac{r}{\delta(re^{i\theta})} d\theta \leqslant \sum_{\nu=1}^n \int_0^{2\pi} \log_0\frac{r}{|re^{i\theta} - z_\nu|} d\theta \leqslant \frac{n\pi}{n}(\log n + 1).$$

Also in the complement CE of E we have $\delta(re^{i\theta}) \geqslant r/n$, and hence

$$\int_{CE} \log^+ \frac{r}{\delta(re^{i\theta})} \, d\theta \leqslant \int_{CE} \log n \, d\theta \leqslant 2\pi \log n.$$

Thus

$$\int_0^{2\pi} \log^+ \frac{r}{\delta(re^{i\theta})} \, d\theta \leqslant 2\pi \log n + \pi(\log n + 1) = \pi(3 \log n + 1).$$

This proves the lemma.

2.2.2. We are now ready to estimate $m(r, f'/f)$ in terms of $T(R, f)$ where $R > r$. Our result is:

LEMMA 2.3. *Suppose that $f(z)$ is meromorphic in $|z| \leqslant R$, that $0 < r < R$, and that $f(0) \neq 0, \infty$. Then*

$$m\left(r, \frac{f'}{f}\right) < 4 \log^+ T(R, f) + 4 \log^+ \log^+ \frac{1}{|f(0)|} +$$

$$+ 5 \log^+ R + 6 \log^+ \frac{1}{R-r} + \log^+ \frac{1}{r} + 14.$$

We use again the formula (1.17) obtained by logarithmic differentiation from the Poisson–Jensen formula, with $\rho = \frac{1}{2}(R+r)$ instead of R and $q = 1$. This gives

$$\frac{f'(z)}{f(z)} = \frac{1}{2\pi} \int_0^{2\pi} \log|f(\rho e^{i\phi})| \frac{2\rho e^{i\phi}}{(\rho e^{i\phi} - z)^2} \, d\phi +$$

$$+ \sum_\mu \left(\frac{\bar{a}_\mu}{\rho^2 - \bar{a}_\mu z} - \frac{1}{a_\mu - z} \right) + \sum_\nu \left(\frac{1}{b_\nu - z} - \frac{\bar{b}_\nu}{\rho^2 - \bar{b}_\nu z} \right), \quad (2.2)$$

where the sums run over the zeros a_μ and poles b_ν of $f(z)$ in $|z| < \rho$. We set $|z| = r$ and $\delta(z)$ for the distance of z from the nearest of the numbers a_μ and b_ν, and

$$n = n(\rho, f) + n\left(\rho, \frac{1}{f} \right)$$

for the total number of these zeros and poles in $|z| < \rho$. Then

$$|\rho^2 - \bar{a}_\mu z| \geqslant \rho^2 - \rho r = \rho(\rho - r).$$

Thus
$$\left| \frac{a_\mu}{\rho^2 - \bar{a}_\mu z} \right| \leqslant \frac{\rho}{\rho(\rho - r)} = \frac{1}{\rho - r}, \qquad \left| \frac{b_\nu}{\rho^2 - \bar{b}_\nu z} \right| \leqslant \frac{1}{\rho - r}.$$

Also
$$\left| \frac{1}{a_\mu - z} \right| \leqslant \frac{1}{\delta(z)}, \qquad \left| \frac{1}{b_\nu - z} \right| \leqslant \frac{1}{\delta(z)}.$$

Further,

$$\left| \frac{1}{2\pi} \int_0^{2\pi} \log |f(\rho e^{i\phi})| \frac{2\rho e^{i\phi}}{(\rho e^{i\phi} - z)^2} \, d\phi \right|$$

$$\leqslant \frac{2\rho}{(\rho - r)^2} \frac{1}{2\pi} \int_0^{2\pi} |\log |f(\rho e^{i\phi})|| \, d\phi = \frac{2\rho}{(\rho - r)^2} \left\{ m(\rho, f) + m\left(\rho, \frac{1}{f}\right) \right\}.$$

Thus (2.2) gives

$$\left| \frac{f'(z)}{f(z)} \right| \leqslant \frac{2\rho}{(\rho - r)^2} \left\{ m(\rho, f) + m\left(\rho, \frac{1}{f}\right) \right\} + n \left\{ \frac{1}{\delta(z)} + \frac{1}{\rho - r} \right\}.$$

Using (1.9) and (1.10) we obtain

$$\left| \frac{f'}{f} \right| \leqslant \frac{4\rho}{(\rho - r)^2} \left\{ T(\rho, f) + \log^+ \left| \frac{1}{f(0)} \right| \right\} + \frac{n}{r} \left\{ \frac{r}{\delta(z)} + \frac{r}{\rho - r} \right\}.$$

Thus, using the inequalities

$$\log^+ ab \leqslant \log^+ a + \log^+ b, \qquad \log^+(a + b) \leqslant \log^+ a + \log^+ b + \log 2,$$

we have

$$\log^+ \left| \frac{f'(z)}{f(z)} \right| \leqslant \log^+ \rho + 2 \log^+ \frac{1}{\rho - r} + 2 \log 2 + \log^+ T(\rho, f) + \log^+ \log^+ \left| \frac{1}{f(0)} \right| +$$

$$+ \log 2 + \log^+ \frac{n}{r} + \log^+ \frac{r}{\delta(z)} + \log^+ \frac{r}{\rho - r} + 2 \log 2.$$

We proceed to integrate with respect to z on $|z| = r$ and use Lemma 2.2. Thus we obtain

$$m\left(r, \frac{f'}{f}\right) \leqslant \log^+ T(\rho, f) + 3 \log^+ n + \log^+ \frac{1}{r} + 5 \log 2 + \tfrac{1}{2} + \log^+ \log^+ \frac{1}{|f(0)|} +$$

$$+ \log^+ \rho + 2 \log^+ \frac{1}{\rho - r} + \log^+ r + \log^+ \frac{1}{\rho - r}. \qquad (2.3)$$

We next estimate n. To do this, note that

$$N(R, f) \geqslant \int_\rho^R \frac{n(t, f) \, dt}{t} \geqslant n(\rho, f) \frac{R - \rho}{R}, \qquad N\left(R, \frac{1}{f}\right) \geqslant n\left(\rho, \frac{1}{f}\right) \frac{R - \rho}{R}.$$

Thus

$$n = n(\rho, f) + n\left(\rho, \frac{1}{f}\right) \leqslant \frac{R}{R - \rho} \left\{ N(R, f) + N\left(R, \frac{1}{f}\right) \right\}$$

$$\leqslant \frac{R}{R - \rho} \left\{ 2T(R, f) + \log \frac{1}{|f(0)|} \right\} \leqslant \frac{2R}{R - \rho} \left\{ T(R, f) + \log^+ \frac{1}{|f(0)|} \right\}.$$

Thus

$$\log^+ n \leqslant \log^+ R + \log^+ \frac{1}{R - \rho} + \log^+ T(R, f) + \log^+ \log^+ \frac{1}{|f(0)|} + 2 \log 2.$$

We substitute this in (2.3) and remember that $\rho-r = R-\rho = \frac{1}{2}(R-r)$ and $r < \rho < R$. Thus monotonic functions of ρ can be replaced by corresponding functions of r or R in (2.3). This gives finally

$$m\left(r,\frac{f'}{f}\right) < 4\log^+ T(R,f)+4\log^+\log^+\frac{1}{|f(0)|}+$$

$$+5\log^+ R+6\log^+\frac{1}{R-r}+\log^+\frac{1}{r}+17\log 2+\tfrac{1}{2}.$$

This proves Lemma 2.3.

2.2.3. In order to complete our proof of Theorem 2.2 we have to show that it is in general possible to select $R > r$ so that neither $\log^+ T(R,f)$ nor $\log^+\{1/(R-r)\}$ are much larger than $\log^+ T(r,f)$. This result follows from the following lemma going back essentially to Borel [1].

LEMMA 2.4.

(i) *Suppose that* $T(r)$ *is continuous, increasing and* $T(r) \geqslant 1$ *for* $r_0 \leqslant r < +\infty$. *Then we have*

$$T\left\{r+\frac{1}{T(r)}\right\} < 2T(r) \tag{2.4}$$

outside a set E_0 *of* r *which has linear measure at most* 2.

(ii) *If* $T(r)$ *is continuous and increasing for* $r_0 \leqslant r < R_0 < +\infty$ *and* $T(r) \geqslant 1$ *there, then we have*

$$T[r+(R_0-r)/\{eT(r)\}] < 2T(r) \tag{2.5}$$

outside a set E_0 *of* r *such that* $\int_{E_0} dr/(R_0-r) \leqslant 2$. *In particular* (2.5) *holds for some* r *in the interval* $\rho < r < \rho'$ *provided that* $r_0 < \rho < R_0$ *and* $R_0-\rho' < (R_0-\rho)/e^2$.

We prove first (i). Let r_1 be the lower bound of all $r > r_0$ for which (2.4) is false. If there are no such r there is nothing to prove. We now define by induction a sequence of numbers r_n. Suppose that r_n has been defined and write $r'_n = r_n+1/T(r_n)$. Define then r_{n+1} as the lower bound of all $r \geqslant r'_n$ for which (2.4) is false. We have already defined r_1 and so we obtain the sequence $\{r_n\}$. Note that by the continuity of $T(r)$ (2.4) is false for $r = r_n$ for $n = 1, 2, 3,...$. Thus r_n belongs to the exceptional set E_0. From the definition of r_{n+1} it follows that there are no points of E_0 in (r'_n, r_{n+1}) so that the set of closed intervals $[r_n, r'_n]$ contains E_0. In fact if there are an infinity of r_n, r_n cannot tend to a finite limit r. For otherwise since $r_n < r'_n \leqslant r_{n+1}$, $r'_n \to r$ also. But then we have for all n

$$r'_n-r_n = 1/T(r_n) \geqslant 1/T(r) > 0$$

since $T(r)$ is increasing which gives a contradiction. It remains to be shown that $\sum (r'_n - r_n) \leqslant 2$. Now

$$T(r'_n) = T\{r_n + 1/T(r_n)\} \geqslant 2T(r_n)$$

since r_n belongs to E_0. Thus

$$T(r_{n+1}) \geqslant T(r'_n) \geqslant 2T(r_n).$$

Hence

$$T(r_{n+1}) \geqslant 2T(r_n) \geqslant \ldots \geqslant 2^n T(r_1) \geqslant 2^n, \quad \text{since } T(r) \geqslant 1.$$

Thus

$$\sum_{n=1}^{\infty} (r'_n - r_n) = \sum_{n=1}^{\infty} 1/T(r_n) \leqslant \sum_{n=1}^{\infty} 2^{1-n} = 2.$$

This proves Lemma 2.4 (i).

To prove (ii) set

$$\rho = \log \frac{1}{R_0 - r}, \qquad r = R_0 - e^{-\rho}, \qquad \rho_0 = \log \frac{1}{R_0 - r_0},$$

and apply the first part to

$$T_1(\rho) = T(R_0 - e^{-\rho}), \qquad \rho_0 \leqslant \rho < +\infty.$$

Let E be the set of ρ for which $\rho_0 \leqslant \rho < +\infty$ and

$$T_1\{\rho + 1/T_1(\rho)\} \geqslant 2T_1(\rho).$$

Then if E_0 is the corresponding set of values of r, we have by (i)

$$\int_{E_0} \frac{dr}{R_0 - r} = \int_E d\rho \leqslant 2.$$

For values of r not in E_0, we have

$$T(r') < 2T(r),$$

where r' is given by

$$\log \frac{1}{R_0 - r'} = \log \frac{1}{R_0 - r} + \frac{1}{T(r)}$$

so that

$$r' = r + (R_0 - r)\{1 - e^{-1/T(r)}\} \geqslant r + \frac{R_0 - r}{eT(r)},$$

since for $0 \leqslant x \leqslant 1$, we have $1 - e^{-x} = xe^{-\theta} \geqslant x/e$ by the mean value theorem. This proves (2.5). Also if $r_0 < \rho < \rho' \leqslant R_0$, we have

$$\int_{\rho}^{\rho'} \frac{dt}{R_0 - t} = \log \frac{R_0 - \rho}{R_0 - \rho'} > 2, \quad \text{if } R_0 - \rho' < (R_0 - \rho)/e^2.$$

Thus in this case the set E_0 cannot occupy the whole interval (ρ, ρ'), and so we can find r such that $\rho < r < \rho'$ and r lies outside E_0, i.e.

$$T\left(r + \frac{R_0 - r}{eT(r)}\right) < 2T(r).$$

This completes the proof of Lemma 2.4.

2.2.4. *Proof of Theorem* 2.2. Suppose now that $S(r,f)$ is defined as in Theorem 2.1. Then as r varies

$$S(r,f) = m\left(r,\frac{f'}{f}\right) + m\left(r,\frac{\phi'}{\phi}\right) + \text{const},$$

where

$$\phi(z) = \prod_{\nu=1}^{q} \{f(z) - a_\nu\}.$$

Suppose first that $R_0 = +\infty$ and $f(z)$ has finite order in the plane. Then

$$T(r,f) = O(r^k) \quad \text{as } r \to +\infty.$$

Also we have in all cases

$$T(r,\phi) \leqslant \sum_{\nu=1}^{q} T(r,f-a_\nu) \leqslant qT(r,f) + O(1). \tag{2.6}$$

In this case we choose $R = 2r$ in Lemma (2.3) and obtain

$$m\left(r,\frac{f'}{f}\right) = O(\log r), \qquad m\left(r,\frac{\phi'}{\phi}\right) = O(\log r) \quad \text{as } r \to +\infty,$$

so that (i) is proved in this case.

Next suppose that $f(z)$ has infinite order in the plane. Then we choose $R - r = 1/T(r,f)$ and apply Lemmas 2.3 and 2.4 (i). Using (2.6) we deduce that outside a set E_0 of r of finite length we have

$$m\left(r,\frac{\phi'}{\phi}\right) \leqslant 4\log^+\{2T(r,\phi)\} + 5\log^+(2r) + 6\log^+T(r,f) + O(1)$$

$$\leqslant 10\{\log^+T(r,f) + \log^+r\}$$

for large r, and similarly

$$m\left(r,\frac{f'}{f}\right) \leqslant 10\log^+T(r,f) + 10\log r.$$

This completes the proof of case (i) of Theorem 2.2.

To prove case (ii) we again apply Lemma 2.3 and set

$$R = r + \frac{R_0 - r}{eT(r,f)}.$$

Then it follows from Lemma 2.4 that outside the exceptional set E_0 of that lemma $T(R) < 2T(r)$. Thus in this case Lemma 2.3 gives as $r \to R_0$ outside E_0,

$$m\left(r,\frac{\phi'}{\phi}\right) \leqslant 4\log^+\{2T(r,\phi)\} + 6\log^+\frac{eT(r,f)}{R_0 - r} + O(1)$$

$$\leqslant 10\log^+T(r,f) + 7\log^+\frac{1}{R_0 - r},$$

if r is sufficiently near R_0. A similar inequality holds for $m(r,f'/f)$. This completes the proof of Theorem 2.2.

We note that in the above analysis the exceptional set E_0 depends only on $T(r,f)$ and not on the number or values of the constants a_ν.

2.3. Conditions for $S(r)$ to be small

We have as an immediate deduction from Theorem 2.2:

THEOREM 2.3. *Suppose that $f(z)$ is meromorphic and not constant in $|z| < R_0$. Then if $S(r,f)$ is defined as in Theorem 2.1*

$$\frac{S(r,f)}{T(r,f)} \to 0 \quad as \ r \to R_0, \tag{2.7}$$

with the following provisos:

(*a*) *(2.7) holds without restrictions if $R_0 = +\infty$ and $f(z)$ is meromorphic of finite order in the plane.*

(*b*) *If $f(z)$ has infinite order in the plane (2.7) still holds as $r \to \infty$ outside a certain exceptional set E_0 of finite length. Here E_0 depends on $f(z)$ but not on the a_ν or on q.*

(*c*) *If $R_0 < +\infty$ and*

$$\overline{\lim_{r \to R_0}} \frac{T(r,f)}{\log\{1/(R_0-r)\}} = +\infty, \tag{2.8}$$

then (2.7) holds as $r \to R_0$ through a suitable sequence r_n, which depends on f but not on the a_ν or on q.

Suppose first that $R_0 = +\infty$. If $f(z)$ is a rational function $f'/f \to 0$, $\phi'/\phi \to 0$ as $z \to \infty$. Thus in this case (2.7) holds trivially. If $f(z)$ is not rational,

$$\frac{T(r,f)}{\log r} \to +\infty \quad as \ r \to +\infty,$$

by the example in section 1.9. Thus our results now follow at once from Theorem 2.2.

If $R_0 < +\infty$ and (2.8) holds let $\rho_n \to R_0$ so that

$$\frac{T(\rho_n,f)}{\log\{1/(R_0-\rho_n)\}} \to +\infty.$$

Then by Lemma 2.4 we can find r_n outside the exceptional set E and such that

$$R_0-\rho_n > R_0-r_n > \frac{R_0-\rho_n}{9}.$$

It follows that $r_n \to R_0$ and also that

$$\log\frac{1}{R_0-r_n} = \log\frac{1}{R_0-\rho_n} + O(1) = o\{T(\rho_n,f)\} = o\{T(r_n,f)\}.$$

Thus by Theorem 2.2 (ii) it follows that

$$\frac{S(r_n,f)}{T(r_n,f)} \to 0, \quad \text{as } n \to \infty.$$

This completes the proof of Theorem 2.3.

2.4. Nevanlinna's theory of deficient values: the second fundamental theorem

Theorem 2.3 gives conditions for (2.7) to hold so that $S(r,f)$ in Theorem 2.1 plays the role of an unimportant error term. In the sequel we shall say that $f(z)$ is *admissible* in $|z| < R_0$ (for the Nevanlinna theory) if either $R_0 < +\infty$ and (2.8) holds, or if $R_0 = +\infty$ and $f(z)$ is not constant. In this case (2.7) holds, at least as $r \to R_0$ through a suitable sequence of values, and it is only then that we can make effective use of Theorem 2.1. We denote again by $n(t,a) = n(t,a,f)$ the number of roots of the equation $f(z) = a$ in $|z| \leqslant t$, multiple roots being counted multiply, and by $\bar{n}(t,a)$ the number of distinct roots of $f(z) = a$ in $|z| \leqslant t$. Correspondingly we define

$$N(r,a) = N(r,a,f) = \int_0^r \frac{n(t,a)-n(0,a)}{t}\,dt + n(0,a)\log r,$$

$$\bar{N}(r,a) = \bar{N}(r,a,f) = \int_0^r \frac{\bar{n}(t,a)-\bar{n}(0,a)}{t}\,dt + \bar{n}(0,a)\log r.$$

As before, we write $N(r,f)$, $T(r,f)$, etc., for $N(r,\infty,f)$, $T(r,\infty,f)$, etc., wherever this notation does not give rise to ambiguity. We shall suppose that $f(z)$ is meromorphic in $|z| < R_0$, and that

$$T(r,f) \to +\infty, \quad \text{as } r \to R_0,$$

so that by Theorem 1.2

$$m(r,a)+N(r,a) = T(r,f)+O(1)$$

as $r \to R_0$. We set

$$\delta(a) = \delta(a,f) = \varliminf_{r \to R_0} \frac{m(r,a)}{T(r)} = 1 - \varlimsup_{r \to R_0} \frac{N(r,a)}{T(r)};$$

$$\Theta(a) = \Theta(a,f) = 1 - \varlimsup_{r \to R_0} \frac{\bar{N}(r,a)}{T(r)};$$

$$\theta(a) = \theta(a,f) = \varliminf_{r \to R_0} \frac{N(r,a)-\bar{N}(r,a)}{T(r)}.$$

Evidently, given $\epsilon > 0$, we have for r sufficiently close to R_0,

$$N(r,a) - \overline{N}(r,a) > \{\theta(a) - \epsilon\}T(r), \qquad N(r,a) < \{1 - \delta(a) + \epsilon\}T(r),$$

and hence $\qquad \overline{N}(r,a) < \{1 - \delta(a) - \theta(a) + 2\epsilon\}T(r),$

so that $\qquad\qquad\qquad \Theta(a) \geqslant \delta(a) + \theta(a).$

The quantity $\delta(a)$ is called the *deficiency* of the value a, and $\theta(a)$ is called the *index of multiplicity* (*Verzweigungsindex*). Evidently $\delta(a)$ is positive only if there are relatively few roots of the equation $f(z) = a$, while $\theta(a)$ is positive if there are relatively many multiple roots.

We can now prove the basic result of Nevanlinna's theory, namely Nevanlinna's theorem on deficient values.

THEOREM 2.4. *Suppose that $f(z)$ is admissible in $|z| < R_0$. Then the set of values a for which $\Theta(a) > 0$ is countable, and we have, on summing over all such values*† a

$$\sum_a \{\delta(a) + \theta(a)\} \leqslant \sum_a \Theta(a) \leqslant 2.$$

We choose a sequence $r_n \to R_0$, such that

$$S(r_n, f) = o\{T(r_n, f)\}.$$

Then we add $N(r_n, \infty) + \sum_{\nu=1}^{q} N(r_n, a_\nu)$ to both sides of the inequality of Theorem 2.1 and obtain

$$(q+1)T(r_n, f) \leqslant \sum_{\nu=1}^{q} N(r_n, a_\nu) + N(r_n, \infty) - N_1(r_n) + \{2 + o(1)\}T(r_n, f),$$

or $\quad \{(q-1) + o(1)\}T(r_n, f) < \sum_{\nu=1}^{q} N(r_n, a_\nu) + \overline{N}(r_n, \infty) - N(r_n, 1/f').$

Now a root of the equation $f(z) = a_\nu$ of order p is also a zero of order $p-1$ of $f'(z)$ and so contributes only 1 to $n(t, a_\nu) - n(t, 1/f')$. Thus we may write our inequality as

$$\{q - 1 + o(1)\}T(r_n, f) \leqslant \sum_{\nu=1}^{q} \overline{N}(r_n, a_\nu) + \overline{N}(r_n, \infty) - N_0(r_n, 1/f'), \quad (2.9)$$

where $N_0(r, 1/f')$ refers to those zeros of f' which occur at points other than roots of the equation $f(z) = a_\nu$ ($\nu = 1$ to q). Ignoring this latter

† Much weaker results only are true if $\delta(a)$ is replaced by

$$\Delta(a) = \varlimsup_{r \to R_0} \frac{m(r, a)}{T(r)}.$$

See R. Nevanlinna [3, pp. 260–9] and Ahlfors [2].

term and dividing by $T(r_n, f)$ we deduce that

$$\sum_{\nu=1}^{q} \varlimsup_{r \to R_0} \frac{\overline{N}(r, a_\nu)}{T(r)} + \varlimsup_{r \to R_0} \frac{\overline{N}(r, \infty)}{T(r)} \geqslant \varlimsup_{r \to R_0} \frac{\sum_{\nu=1}^{q} \overline{N}(r, a_\nu) + \overline{N}(r, \infty)}{T(r)} \geqslant q - 1,$$

i.e.
$$\sum_{\nu=1}^{q} \{1 - \Theta(a_\nu)\} + 1 - \Theta(\infty) \geqslant q - 1,$$

or
$$\sum_{1}^{q} \Theta(a_\nu) + \Theta(\infty) \leqslant 2.$$

The result shows that $\Theta(a) > 1/N$ for at most $2N-1$ distinct finite values a. Thus the values a for which $\Theta(a) > 0$ may be arranged in a sequence, in order of decreasing $\Theta(a)$, by taking first those for which $\Theta(a) = 1$, then those, if any, for which $\Theta(a) > \frac{1}{2}$, then those of the remainder for which $\Theta(a) > \frac{1}{3}$, etc. If a_ν is the resulting sequence together with $a_0 = \infty$, we deduce that

$$\sum_{\nu=0}^{q} \Theta(a_\nu) \leqslant 2$$

for any finite q and hence if the sequence a_ν is infinite we deduce that

$$\sum_{\nu=0}^{\infty} \Theta(a_\nu) \leqslant 2.$$

This proves Theorem 2.4.

2.5. Some examples

Suppose that the equation $f(z) = a$ has no roots. Then $N(r, a) = 0$, for all r, and $\delta(a) = 1$. The same conclusion holds if

$$N(r, a) = o\{T(r)\}, \quad \text{as } r \to R_0.$$

By Theorem 2.4 there can be at most two distinct such values a or, more generally, at most two distinct values a for which $\delta(a) > \frac{2}{3}$.

Suppose next that the value a is such that the equation $f(z) = a$ has only multiple roots. Then

$$\overline{N}(r, a) \leqslant \tfrac{1}{2} N(r, a) < \tfrac{1}{2} T(r) + O(1),$$

so that
$$\Theta(a) \geqslant \tfrac{1}{2}.$$

Theorem 2.4 shows that there can be at most four distinct such values a. An example of a meromorphic function having in fact four distinct such values is given by Weierstrass's elliptic function $\wp(z)$. It satisfies the equation

$$\wp'(z)^2 = \{\wp(z) - a_1\}\{\wp(z) - a_2\}\{\wp(z) - a_3\},$$

where a_1, a_2, a_3 are distinct finite numbers. Clearly $\wp'(z) = 0$ wherever $\wp(z) = a_\nu$ ($\nu = 1$ to 3), so that all the roots of these three equations are multiple. Similarly $\wp(z)$ has only double poles.

If $f(z)$ is an integral function, $\Theta(\infty) = 1$, and $\sum \Theta(a) \leqslant 1$, where the sum is taken over finite values a. In this case the equation $f(z) = a$

has some roots for all but at most one value of a, and some simple roots for all but at most two values of a. The functions e^z, for which $\delta(0) = 1$, and $\sin z$ for which $\theta(1) = \theta(-1) = \frac{1}{2}$, show that these results are also best possible.

2.5.1. Let us consider some further examples. Set

$$z = \phi(w) = \int\limits_0^w (t-a)^{(1/m)-1}(t-b)^{(1/n)-1}(t-c)^{(1/p)-1}\, dt,$$

where a, b, c are distinct complex numbers and m, n, p are positive integers such that $1/m+1/n+1/p = 1$. In these circumstances $\phi(w)$ maps the circle through the points $w = a$, b, c on to a triangle in the z-plane having angles π/m, π/n, π/p. The inverse function can be analytically continued over the whole plane as a one-valued meromorphic function by Schwarz's reflection principle and the resulting function $w = f(z)$ is doubly periodic.

The points a, b, c correspond to corners of triangles only and these roots are taken with multiplicity m, n, p respectively. In fact, if $z = z_1$ corresponds to $w = a$, then

$$dz/dw \sim k(w-a)^{(1/m)-1}, \qquad (z-z_1) \sim km(w-a)^{1/m},$$
$$(w-a) \sim \{(z-z_1)/(km)\}^m$$

as $z \to z_1$. Thus we have

$$\bar{N}(r,f,a) = (1/m)\, N(r,f,a), \qquad \Theta(a) \geqslant 1-1/m,$$

and similarly $\Theta(b) \geqslant 1-1/n, \qquad \Theta(c) \geqslant 1-1/p.$

Since $\Theta(a)+\Theta(b)+\Theta(c) \leqslant 2$ we must have

$$\Theta(a) = 1-1/m, \qquad \Theta(b) = 1-1/n, \qquad \Theta(c) = 1-1/p.$$

Thus

$$\varlimsup_{r\to\infty} \frac{\bar{N}(r,a)}{T(r)} = \frac{1}{m} = \varlimsup_{r\to\infty} \frac{1}{m}\frac{N(r,a)}{T(r)}.$$

Hence $\delta(a) = 0$, and similarly $\delta(b) = \delta(c) = 0$. Also for $z \neq a, b, c$ $\Theta(z) = 0$ and so $\delta(z) = 0$.

Three cases are effectively possible apart from permutations, (i) $p = 2$, $m = 3$, $n = 6$, (ii) $p = 2$, $m = 4$, $n = 4$, and (iii) $p = m = n = 3$.

These examples have a certain theoretical interest. Suppose we say that a value a_ν has multiplicity at least m_ν if all the roots of the equation $f(z) = a_\nu$ have multiplicity at least m_ν. In this case

$$\bar{N}(r, a_\nu, f) \leqslant \frac{1}{m_\nu} N(r, a_\nu, f) \leqslant \frac{1}{m_\nu} T(r,f)+O(1),$$

so that

$$\Theta(a_\nu) \geqslant 1 - \frac{1}{m_\nu}.$$

Thus Theorem 2.4 shows that

$$\sum \left(1 - \frac{1}{m_\nu}\right) \leqslant 2.$$

Here $1 - 1/m_\nu \geqslant \frac{1}{2}$, so that at most four values a_ν can exist, and if there are four such values we must have $m_\nu = 2$ for each of them. The elliptic function $\wp(z)$ gives an example of this case.

Next, if there are three values a_ν we must have $1/m_1 + 1/m_2 + 1/m_3 \geqslant 1$. Possible sets of positive integers satisfying this inequality are given by $(2, 2, m)$, $(2, 3, 3)$, $(2, 3, 4)$, $(2, 3, 5)$, $(2, 3, 6)$, $(2, 4, 4)$, and $(3, 3, 3)$. The functions $\cos z$, $\sin z$ have the value ∞ of multiplicity at least m for every m, and the values ∓ 1 with multiplicity 2. The cases $(2, 3, 6)$, $(2, 4, 4)$, and $(3, 3, 3)$ effectively exist as is shown by our previous examples and if the equation $f(z) = c$ has only roots of multiplicity at least 6, then it will certainly have roots of multiplicity at least 3, 4, or 5. Thus the extreme cases can effectively occur.

2.5.2. Consider next the function

$$f(z) = \int_0^z e^{-t^q}\, dt, \quad \text{where } q \geqslant 2.$$

We set

$$a_k = e^{2\pi k i/q} \int_0^\infty e^{-t^q}\, dt \quad (k = 1, 2, \ldots, q).$$

Then $f(z) \to a_k$ uniformly as $z \to \infty$ in the angle $|\arg z - (2\pi k/q)| \leqslant \pi/(2q)$. We have, for $|\arg z - (2\pi k/q)| \leqslant \pi/(2q)$,

$$f(z) - a_k = -\int_z^\infty e^{-t^q}\, dt = \frac{-e^{-z^q}}{qz^{q-1}} + \frac{q-1}{q} \int_z^\infty \frac{e^{-t^q}}{t^q}\, dt = -\frac{e^{-z^q}}{qz^{q-1}}\{1 + o(1)\}.$$

Thus

$$m\left(r, \frac{1}{f(z) - a_k}\right) \geqslant \frac{1}{2\pi}\{1 + o(1)\} r^q \int_{-\pi/(2q)}^{\pi/(2q)} \cos q\theta\, d\theta$$

$$= \{1 + o(1)\}\frac{r^q}{q\pi} \quad (k = 1 \text{ to } q).$$

By a similar argument we obtain for $|\arg z - (2k-1)\pi/q| \leqslant \pi/(2q)$

$$f(z) = \int_0^z e^{-t^q}\, dt = \frac{-e^{-z^q}\{1 + o(1)\}}{qz^{q-1}} + O(1),$$

so that

$$m(r, f) = \{1 + o(1)\}\frac{r^q}{\pi}.$$

Thus for this function we have

$$\Theta(a_k) = \delta(a_k) = \lim_{r \to \infty} \frac{m(r, a_k)}{T(r, f)} = \frac{1}{q} \quad (k = 1, 2, ..., q),$$

and $\delta(\infty) = 1$. Here again it follows from the second fundamental theorem that $\Theta(a) = 0$ for every other value of a. The consideration of some further results concerning the possible deficiencies of meromorphic functions will be deferred until Chapter 4.

2.6. Deficient functions

We conclude the chapter by giving some rather simple extensions and applications of the previous theory. We shall denote by $S(r, f)$ any quantity satisfying the conclusions of Theorem 2.2, not necessarily the same each time. We have the following result of Nevanlinna.

THEOREM 2.5. *If $f(z)$ is meromorphic and admissible in $|z| < R_0$ and $a_1(z)$, $a_2(z)$, $a_3(z)$ are distinct meromorphic functions satisfying for $\nu = 1$, 2, and 3*

$$T\{r, a_\nu(z)\} = o\{T(r, f)\}, \quad \text{as } r \to R_0, \tag{2.10}$$

then

$$\{1 + o(1)\} T(r, f) \leqslant \sum_{\nu=1}^{3} \overline{N}\left(r, \frac{1}{f - a_\nu(z)}\right) + S(r, f), \tag{2.11}$$

as $r \to R_0$, where $S(r, f)$ satisfies the conclusions of Theorem 2.2.

To prove Theorem 2.5, we set

$$\phi(z) = \frac{f(z) - a_1(z)}{f(z) - a_3(z)} \frac{a_2(z) - a_3(z)}{a_2(z) - a_1(z)},$$

and apply (2.9) to $\phi(z)$, with $a_1 = 0$, $a_2 = 1$. This gives

$$T(r, \phi) \leqslant \overline{N}(r, \phi) + \overline{N}\left(r, \frac{1}{\phi}\right) + \overline{N}\left(r, \frac{1}{\phi - 1}\right) + S(r, \phi). \tag{2.12}$$

Now

$$T(r, f) \leqslant T(r, f - a_3) + T(r, a_3) + O(1)$$

$$\leqslant T\left(r, \frac{1}{f - a_3}\right) + o\{T(r, f)\} \leqslant T\left(r, \frac{a_3 - a_1}{f - a_3}\right) + o\{T(r, f)\}$$

$$\leqslant T\left(r, 1 + \frac{a_3 - a_1}{f - a_3}\right) + o\{T(r, f)\} = T\left(r, \frac{f - a_1}{f - a_3}\right) + o\{T(r, f)\},$$

in view of (2.10).

Similarly

$$T\left(r, \frac{a_2(z) - a_1(z)}{a_2(z) - a_3(z)}\right) = o\{T(r, f)\},$$

and so

$$T(r, f) \leqslant \{1 + o(1)\} T\left(r, \frac{f - a_1}{f - a_3}\right) \leqslant \{1 + o(1)\}\left\{T(r, \phi) + T\left(r, \frac{a_2 - a_1}{a_2 - a_3}\right)\right\}$$

$$\leqslant \{1 + o(1)\} T(r, \phi), \quad \text{as } r \to R_0.$$

It follows that $S(r, \phi)$ satisfies the conditions for $S(r, f)$ as $r \to R_0$. Finally the equations $\phi(z) = 0, 1, \infty$ have roots only if either

$$f(z) - a_\nu(z) = 0$$

for $\nu = 1, 2$, or 3 or if two of the functions $a_\nu(z)$ become equal. Thus

$$\bar{N}(r, \phi) + \bar{N}\left(r, \frac{1}{\phi}\right) + \bar{N}\left(r, \frac{1}{\phi - 1}\right)$$

$$\leqslant \sum_{\nu=1}^{3} \bar{N}\left(r, \frac{1}{f - a_\nu}\right) + \bar{N}\left(r, \frac{1}{a_1 - a_2}\right) + \bar{N}\left(r, \frac{1}{a_2 - a_3}\right) + \bar{N}\left(r, \frac{1}{a_3 - a_1}\right)$$

$$\leqslant \sum_{\nu=1}^{3} \bar{N}\left(r, \frac{1}{f - a_\nu}\right) + o\{T(r, f)\} \quad \text{as } r \to R_0.$$

Now (2.11) follows from (2.12). It is an interesting open problem† whether Theorem 2.5 can be extended to more than three functions $a_\nu(z)$ thus resulting in an analogue of Theorem 2.5 with exceptional functions $a_\nu(z)$ of slower growth than $f(z)$ instead of constants a_ν. Theorem 2.5 shows that at most two such functions can have 'deficiency' greater than $\frac{2}{3}$ but gives no limitation on the number of functions with deficiency less than or equal to $\frac{2}{3}$. (See, however, example, section 4.1.6.)

2.7. Functions taking the same values at the same points

Under what circumstances can two different functions $f_1(z), f_2(z)$ take the same value at the same points? We prove the following result of Nevanlinna.

THEOREM 2.6. *Suppose that $f_1(z), f_2(z)$ are meromorphic in the plane and let $E_j(a)$ be the set of points z such that $f_j(z) = a$ ($j = 1, 2$). Then if $E_1(a) = E_2(a)$ for five distinct values of a, $f_1(z) \equiv f_2(z)$, or f_1, f_2 are both constant.*

The functions $f_1(z) = e^{-z}, f_2(z) = e^z$, with $a = 0, 1, -1, \infty$, show that here 5 cannot be replaced by 4. R. Nevanlinna [1, chapter 5], has also shown that three or four sets of $E_j(a)$ are apart from certain exceptional cases sufficient to determine $f(z)$, if we know in addition the multiplicity of the roots of the equation $f(z) = a$. We proceed to prove Theorem 2.6.

We suppose that $f_1(z), f_2(z)$ are neither both constant nor identical. Let a_1 to a_5 be distinct and such that the sets $E_1(a_\nu), E_2(a_\nu)$ are identical for $\nu = 1$ to 5, and write

$$N_\nu(r) = \bar{N}\left(r, \frac{1}{f_1(z) - a_\nu}\right) = \bar{N}\left(r, \frac{1}{f_2(z) - a_\nu}\right) \quad (\nu = 1 \text{ to } 5).$$

Then if $f_1(z)$ is constant, $f_2(z)$ omits at least four values and so is also

† An almost complete answer to this problem has now been given by Chuang [1].

constant, which is excluded by our hypothesis. Thus we have by (2.9) as $r \to \infty$ through a suitable sequence of values

$$\{4+o(1)\}T(r,f_j) \leqslant \sum_{\nu=1}^{5} N_\nu(r) + \bar{N}(r,f_j), \quad \text{for } j = 1, 2,$$

and hence
$$\{3+o(1)\}T(r,f_j) \leqslant \sum_{\nu=1}^{5} N_\nu(r).$$

Thus since $f_1(z)$, $f_2(z)$ are not identical, we have as $r \to \infty$ through this sequence

$$T[r, \{f_1(z)-f_2(z)\}^{-1}] = T(r, f_1-f_2) + O(1)$$
$$\leqslant T(r,f_1) + T(r,f_2) + O(1) \leqslant \{\tfrac{2}{3}+o(1)\} \sum_{\nu=1}^{5} N_\nu(r).$$

On the other hand, each common root of the equations $f_j(z) = a$ for $j = 1, 2$ is a pole of $\{f_1(z)-f_2(z)\}^{-1}$ and so

$$\sum_{\nu=1}^{5} N_\nu(r) \leqslant \bar{N}\{r, (f_1-f_2)^{-1}\} \leqslant T\{r, (f_1-f_2)^{-1}\} + O(1).$$

This gives a contradiction, unless

$$\sum_{\nu=1}^{5} N_\nu(r) = O(1),$$

which is impossible if $f_1(z)$ and $f_2(z)$ are not constant. Thus Theorem 2.6 is proved.

A refinement of the argument will show that Theorem 2.6 remains valid if $f_1(z)$ and $f_2(z)$ are admissible in a finite circle $|z| < R_0$. Suppose that $f_1(z)$, $f_2(z)$ are distinct. In this case we shall have outside a set E for which

$$\int_E \frac{dr}{R_0-r} < +\infty,$$

$$\sum_{\nu=1}^{5} N_\nu(r) \leqslant \{1+o(1)\}\{T(r,f_1)+T(r,f_2)+O(1)\}$$
$$\leqslant \{\tfrac{2}{3}+o(1)\} \sum_{\nu=1}^{5} N_\nu(r) + O\left\{\log\frac{1}{R_0-r}\right\},$$

on using Theorems 2.1 and 2.2 (ii). This contradicts (2.8) so that $f_1(z)$ and $f_2(z)$ cannot be admissible.

2.8. Fix-points of integral functions

Let $f(z)$ be an integral function. Set $f_1(z) = f(z)$, and inductively

$$f_{\nu+1}(z) = f\{f_\nu(z)\} \quad (\nu \geqslant 1).$$

The solutions of the equation $f_\nu(z) = z$ are called fix-points of $f(z)$ of order ν. If ζ is a fix-point of $f(z)$ of order ν, but of no lower order, then ζ is called a fix-point of exact order ν. Evidently the functions $f(z) = e^{g(z)} + z$, where $g(z)$ is an integral function, have no fix-points of order 1. If $f(z) = z^2 - z$, then the fix-points of $f(z)$ of order 1 are given by $f(z) = z$, i.e. $z^2 - 2z = 0$, $z = 0$, 2, and those of order 2 by

$$f_2(z) = (z^2 - z)^2 - (z^2 - z) = z,$$

i.e. $z^4 - 2z^3 = 0$, so that the fix-points $z = 0$, 2 of order 1 are the only fix-points of order 2 and there are no fix-points of exact order 2.

We note that if z_0 is a fix-point of exact order ν and if we set $z_p = f(z_{p-1})$ $(p = 1, 2, ...)$, then z_0, z_1, z_2,..., $z_{\nu-1}$ are different, but $z_{p+\nu} = z_p$, so that the z_p form a cycle of ν points. We prove the following result of I. N. Baker.†

THEOREM 2.7. *If $f(z)$ is a transcendental integral function then $f(z)$ possesses infinitely many fix-points of exact order n, except for at most one value of n.*

2.8.1. We shall need to quote a lemma of H. Bohr [1], the proof of which we defer (Theorem 6.9, Chapter 6).

LEMMA 2.5. *Suppose that $w = f(z)$ is regular in $|z| \leqslant 1$ and satisfies $f(0) = 0$ and*

$$\mu = \max_{|z| = \frac{1}{2}} |f(z)| \geqslant 1.$$

Then $f(z)$ assumes in $|z| < 1$ all values w on some circle $|w| = r$, where $r > A$ and A is a positive absolute constant.

In fact the correct value of A is $\frac{1}{8}$ (Hayman [1]), but we shall not need this result.

We deduce

LEMMA 2.6. *If $f(z)$, $g(z)$ are transcendental integral functions and $\phi(z) = g\{f(z)\}$, then*

$$\frac{T\{r, g(z)\}}{T\{r, \phi(z)\}} \to 0, \quad as \ r \to +\infty.$$

We set $f(0) = C$ and apply Lemma 2.5 with

$$f_1(z) = \frac{f(\frac{1}{2}rz) - C}{M(\frac{1}{4}r, f(z) - C)} \quad \text{instead of } f(z).$$

Thus $f_1(z)$ assumes in $|z| < 1$ all values w on a circle $|w| = R \geqslant A$. Hence $f(z)$ assumes in $|z| \leqslant \frac{1}{2}r$ all values w on some circle

$$|w - C| = R_0 \geqslant AM(\tfrac{1}{4}r, f - C) \geqslant AM(\tfrac{1}{4}r, f) - A|C|.$$

---

† Baker [1]. Rosenbloom [1] had previously shown that $f(z)$ always has fix-points of exact order one or two.

Let θ be so chosen that

$$g(C+R_0 e^{i\theta}) = \max_{|w-C|=R_0} |g(w)|.$$

Then there exists z_0, with $|z_0| \leqslant \frac{1}{2}r$, so that $f(z_0) = C + R_0 e^{i\theta}$,

$$|\phi(z_0)| = |g\{f(z_0)\}| = |g(C+R_0 e^{i\theta})| = \max_{|w-C|=R_0} |g(w)|$$
$$\geqslant \max_{|w|=R_0-|C|} |g(w)| = M\{R_0-|C|, g(w)\},$$

by the maximum modulus principle. Thus, using Theorem 1.6, we have

$$T(r,\phi) \geqslant \tfrac{1}{3}\log M(\tfrac{1}{2}r,\phi) \geqslant \tfrac{1}{3}\log M(R_0-|C|,g) \geqslant \tfrac{1}{3}T(R_1,g),$$

where $\qquad\qquad R_1 = R_0-|C| \geqslant AM(\tfrac{1}{4}r,f)-(A+1)|C|.$

Now since f is a transcendental integral function we have for any fixed N and sufficiently large r

$$AM(\tfrac{1}{4}r,f) \geqslant r^{N+1}+(A+1)|C|,$$

and thus $\qquad\qquad T(r,\phi) \geqslant \tfrac{1}{3}T(r^{N+1},g).$ \hfill (2.13)

Now by Theorem 1.3 we know that $T(r,g)$ is an increasing convex function of $\log r$, so that $T(r,g)/\log r$ is finally increasing and hence

$$T(r^{N+1},g) \geqslant (N+1)T(r,g),$$

for sufficiently large r. Thus

$$T(r,\phi) \geqslant \frac{N+1}{3} T(r,g),$$

and this proves Lemma 2.6.

2.8.2. We are now ready to prove Theorem 2.7. Suppose that $f(z)$ has only a finite number of fix-points of exact order k, $\zeta_1, \zeta_2,..., \zeta_p$ say, and assume $n > k$. Let z_0 be a root of the equation $f_n(z_0) = f_{n-k}(z_0)$. Then

$$f_k\{f_{n-k}(z_0)\} = f_{n-k}(z_0),$$

so that $\zeta = f_{n-k}(z_0)$ is a fix-point of order k of the function $f(z)$. Thus either $\zeta = \zeta_\nu$, for some ν, or ζ is a fix-point of exact order j less than k, so that $f_j(\zeta) = \zeta$, i.e.

$$f_{n-k+j}(z_0) = f_{n-k}(z_0), \quad \text{and} \quad 1 \leqslant j \leqslant k-1.$$

Thus

$$\overline{N}\left\{r, \frac{1}{f_n(z)-f_{n-k}(z)}\right\} \leqslant \sum_{j=1}^{k-1} \overline{N}\left\{r, \frac{1}{f_{n-k+j}(z)-f_{n-k}(z)}\right\} + \sum_{\nu=1}^{p} \overline{N}\left\{r, \frac{1}{f_{n-k}(z)-\zeta_\nu}\right\}$$
$$= O\left[\sum_{l=1}^{n-1} T\{r,f_l(z)\}\right] = o[T\{r,f_n(z)\}]$$

by Lemma 2.6. In fact $f_n(z) = f_l\{f_{n-l}(z)\}$, so that we may apply Lemma

2.6 with $f_l(z)$, $f_{n-l}(z)$, $f_n(z)$ instead of $g(z)$, $f(z)$, $\phi(z)$. We now apply Theorem 2.5 to $f_n(z)$ with $a_1(z) \equiv z$, $a_2(z) \equiv f_{n-k}(z)$, and $a_3(z) \equiv \infty$ and obtain for a sequence of $r \to \infty$,

$$\{1+o(1)\}T\{r,f_n(z)\} \leqslant \overline{N}\left(r, \frac{1}{f_n(z)-z}\right).$$

If we denote the right-hand side by $N_n(r)$, then the contribution of fix-points of order less than n to $N_n(r)$ is at most

$$\sum_{p=1}^{n-1} N_p(r) = O\left[\sum_{p=1}^{n-1} T\{r,f_p(z)\}\right] = o[T\{r,f_n(z)\}].$$

Thus $f(z)$ has infinitely many fix-points of exact order n, and so there can be at most one value of k for which $f(z)$ has only finitely many fix-points of exact order k. This proves Theorem 2.7.

2.8.3. We conclude by considering the case of polynomials. Following Baker [1] we prove

THEOREM 2.8. *If $f(z)$ is a polynomial of degree at least 2, then $f(z)$ has at least one fix-point of exact order n, for every positive integer n, with at most one exception.*

Suppose that $f(z)$ has degree $d \geqslant 2$. Then $f_n(z)$ has degree d^n and so $f(z)$ has fix-points of every order n. In particular $f(z)$ has a fix-point of exact order 1. Suppose that $f(z)$ has no fix-points of exact orders n, k where $n > k \geqslant 2$. We consider

$$\phi(z) = \frac{f_n(z)-z}{f_{n-k}(z)-z}.$$

Then the equation $\phi(z) = 0$ has roots only where $f_n(z) = z$, and these roots occur only when $f_j(z) = z$ for some $j < n$. Also if j is the exact order of z, then the numbers $z_l = f_l(z)$ form a cycle of j points and so if $z_n = z_0 = z$, $j \mid n$.† If $n = 3$, we must have $j = 1$, so that there are at most d distinct zeros of $\phi(z)$. If $n = 4$, any fix-point of exact order 1 is a fix-point of order 2, so that since $j = 1$ or 2, $\phi(z)$ has at most d^2 distinct zeros. If $n > 4$, we must have $j \leqslant n-3$, and so $\phi(z)$ has at most

$$\sum_{j=1}^{n-3} d^j < d^{n-2}$$

distinct zeros. Thus in all cases $\phi(z)$ has at most d^{n-2} distinct zeros.

Again $\phi(z) = 1$ implies $f_{n-k}(z) = f_n(z) = f_k\{f_{n-k}(z)\}$, so that $\zeta = f_{n-k}(z)$ is a fix-point of f_k and so a fix-point of f_j, for some divisor j of k with $1 \leqslant j < k$. Thus

$$f_j\{f_{n-k}(z)\} = f_{n-k+j}(z) = f_{n-k}(z).$$

† $j \mid n$ means that n is an integral multiple of j.

The polynomial $f_{n-k+j}(z)-f_{n-k}(z)$ has degree d^{n-k+j} so that the number of different 1-points of $\phi(z)$ is at most

$$\sum_j d^{n-k+j} \leqslant \sum_{j=1}^{k-2} d^{n-k+j} \leqslant d^{n-1}, \quad \text{if } k \geqslant 3,$$

and

$$\sum_j d^{n-k+j} = d^{n-1}, \quad \text{if } k = 2.$$

Let N be the number of zeros of $\phi'(z)$ with due count of multiplicity. Then we deduce that the total number of distinct solutions of the equations $\phi(z) = 0, 1$ is at most $d^{n-1}+d^{n-2}$ and so the total number of solutions counting multiplicity is at most

$$N+d^{n-1}+d^{n-2}.$$

Suppose that $\phi(z)$ has q finite poles (multiple poles being counted multiply). Then $\phi(z)$ has a pole of order d^n-d^{n-k} at ∞, and $\phi(z)$ has $d^n-d^{n-k}+q$ poles and so $2(d^n-d^{n-k}+q)$ zeros and ones altogether in the closed plane, counting multiplicity. Also $\phi'(z)$ has a pole of order $d^n-d^{n-k}-1$ at ∞ and at most $2q$ finite poles. Thus

$$N \leqslant d^n-d^{n-k}+2q-1.$$

Hence

$$2(d^n-d^{n-k}+q) \leqslant N+d^{n-1}+d^{n-2} \leqslant d^n-d^{n-k}+d^{n-1}+d^{n-2}+2q-1.$$

Thus $$d^n \leqslant d^{n-1}+d^{n-2}+d^{n-k}-1 \leqslant 2d^{n-1}-1 \leqslant d^n-1,$$

giving a contradiction, which proves Theorem 2.8.

2.9. A theorem of Pólya

Pólya [2] used the ideas of section 2.8.1 to prove

THEOREM 2.9. *Suppose that $f(z)$, $g(z)$ are integral functions and that $\phi(z) = g\{f(z)\}$ has finite order. Then either $f(z)$ is a polynomial or $g(z)$ has zero order.*

Suppose that $f(z)$ and $g(z)$ are transcendental, since otherwise there is nothing to prove. In this case it follows from (2.13) that

$$T(r, \phi) \geqslant \tfrac{1}{3}T(r^{N+1}, g)$$

for all sufficiently large r, when N is a fixed positive integer. Since $\phi(z)$ has finite order k, say, we deduce that, for all sufficiently large r, we have by (2.13) $$T(r^{N+1}, g) < 3r^{k+1},$$

and setting $\rho = r^{N+1}$ we deduce for all sufficiently large ρ

$$T(\rho, g) < 3\rho^{(k+1)/(N+1)}.$$

Since k is fixed and N can be chosen as large as we please, $g(z)$ must have zero order. This proves Theorem 2.9.

Exercise (i). Prove that if $f(z)$ is a non-constant integral function, $g(z)$ a polynomial of degree N, and $\phi(z) = g\{f(z)\}$, then

$$\frac{T(r,\phi)}{T(r,g)} \to N, \quad \text{as } r \to \infty.$$

Exercise (ii).† If $f(z)$ and $g(z)$ are transcendental integral functions and $\phi(z) = g\{f(z)\}$ prove that

$$\frac{T(r,\phi)}{T(r,f)} \to \infty, \quad \text{as } r \to \infty.$$

[If $g(z)$ has distinct zeros at $w_1, w_2, ..., w_n$ prove that

$$N\left(r, \frac{1}{\phi}\right) \geqslant \sum_{\nu=1}^{n} N\left(r, \frac{1}{f(z)-w_\nu}\right),$$

$$m\left(r, \frac{1}{\phi}\right) \geqslant \sum_{\nu=1}^{n} m\left(r, \frac{1}{f(z)-w_\nu}\right) - O(1).$$

If $g(z)$ has infinitely many zeros the result follows. If not, we apply the above argument to $1 + g(z)$ instead of $g(z)$.]

† This result and its proof is due to J. G. Clunie [2]. He also notes that the corresponding theorem for $\log M(r)$ is false. It is possible to construct an integral function $f(z)$ such that

$$\lim_{r \to \infty} \frac{\log M(r, e^f)}{\log M(r, f)} = 0.$$

3

DISTRIBUTION OF THE VALUES OF
MEROMORPHIC FUNCTIONS AND THEIR
DERIVATIVES

3.0. Introduction

I N this chapter we consider some further applications of Nevanlinna's theory. For the sake of simplicity we shall confine ourselves to the study of functions meromorphic in the plane although most of the results extend to functions of sufficiently rapid growth in the unit circle.

Let $f(z)$ be meromorphic and not constant in the plane. We shall call an *error term* and denote by $S(r,f)$ any quantity satisfying

$$S(r, f) = o\{T(r, f)\} \tag{3.1}$$

as $r \to +\infty$, possibly outside a set of r of finite linear measure. Throughout this chapter we shall denote by $a(z)$, $a_0(z)$, $a_1(z)$, etc., functions meromorphic in the plane and satisfying

$$T\{r, a(z)\} = S(r, f), \quad \text{as } r \to +\infty. \tag{3.2}$$

3.1. Milloux theory

For our estimations a basic role will be played by the following result of Milloux [1].

THEOREM 3.1. *Let l be a positive integer and*

$$\psi(z) = \sum_{\nu=0}^{l} a_\nu(z) f^{(\nu)}(z). \tag{3.3}$$

Then
$$m\left(r, \frac{\psi(z)}{f(z)}\right) = S(r, f), \tag{3.4}$$

and
$$T(r, \psi) \leqslant (l+1)T(r, f) + S(r, f). \tag{3.5}$$

We consider first the case $\psi(z) = f^{(l)}(z)$ and prove Theorem 3.1 in this case by induction on l. We have by Theorem 2.2 that

$$m\left(r, \frac{f'}{f}\right) = S(r, f)$$

in this case. Suppose we have already proved that

$$m\left(r, \frac{f^{(l)}}{f}\right) = S(r, f)$$

for some integer l. We deduce that

$$m(r, f^{(l)}) \leqslant m\left(r, \frac{f^{(l)}}{f}\right) + m(r, f) = m(r, f) + S(r, f).$$

Also if $f(z)$ has a pole of order k at z_0, $f^{(l)}(z)$ has a pole of order

$$k+l \leqslant (l+1)k$$

there, so that $N(r, f^{(l)}) \leqslant (l+1)N(r, f).$

Thus by addition we deduce that

$$T(r, f^{(l)}) = m(r, f^{(l)}) + N(r, f^{(l)}) \leqslant m(r, f) + (l+1)N(r, f) + S(r, f)$$
$$\leqslant (l+1)T(r, f) + S(r, f),$$

and this proves (3.5) in this case.

We deduce that

$$m\left(r, \frac{f^{(l+1)}}{f^{(l)}}\right) = S(r, f^{(l)}) = o\{T(r, f^{(l)})\} = o\{T(r, f)\},$$

as $r \to \infty$ outside a set of finite linear measure. Thus

$$m\left(r, \frac{f^{(l+1)}}{f}\right) \leqslant m\left(r, \frac{f^{(l+1)}}{f^{(l)}}\right) + m\left(r, \frac{f^{(l)}}{f}\right) = S(r, f) + S(r, f) = S(r, f).$$

This completes the inductive proof in case $\psi(z) = f^{(l)}(z)$.

To deal with the general case note that

$$m\left(r, \frac{\psi(z)}{f}\right) \leqslant \sum_{\nu=0}^{l} m\left(r, \frac{a_\nu(z)f^{(\nu)}(z)}{f}\right) + \log(l+1)$$
$$\leqslant \sum_{\nu=0}^{l} \left[m\{r, a_\nu(z)\} + m\left(r, \frac{f^{(\nu)}(z)}{f}\right) \right] + \log(l+1)$$
$$\leqslant \sum_{\nu=0}^{l} S(r, f) + O(1) = S(r, f).$$

This proves (3.4). Further we have

$$m(r, \psi) \leqslant m\left(r, \frac{\psi}{f}\right) + m(r, f) \leqslant m(r, f) + S(r, f).$$

Also if $f(z)$ has a pole of order p at z_0 and the $a_\nu(z)$ have poles of order at most q there, then $\psi(z)$ has a pole of order at most

$$p+l+q \leqslant (l+1)p+q$$

at z_0. Thus

$$N(r, \psi) \leqslant (l+1)N(r, f) + \sum_{\nu=0}^{l} N\{r, a_\nu(z)\} \leqslant (l+1)N(r, f) + S(r, f).$$

Now we deduce (3.5) and the proof of Theorem 3.1 is complete.

3.2. Milloux's basic results

It was shown by Milloux† that in the second fundamental theorem we can replace the counting functions for certain roots of $f(z) = a$ by roots of equations $\psi(z) = b$, where $\psi(z)$ is given by (3.3). In this connexion we have the following:

THEOREM 3.2. *Suppose that $f(z)$ is meromorphic and non-constant in the plane and $\psi(z)$ is given by (3.3) and is not constant. Then*

$$T(r, f) < \overline{N}(r, f) + N\left(r, \frac{1}{f}\right) + \overline{N}\left(r, \frac{1}{\psi - 1}\right) - N_0\left(r, \frac{1}{\psi'}\right) + S(r, f),$$

where in $N_0(r, 1/\psi')$ only zeros of $\psi'(z)$ not corresponding to the repeated roots of $\psi(z) = 1$ are to be considered.

Note that this result reduces to Theorem 2.1 when $\psi(z) = f(z)$ and $q = 3$. We apply Theorem 2.1 to $\psi(z)$ and obtain

$$m(r, \psi) + m\left(r, \frac{1}{\psi}\right) + m\left(r, \frac{1}{\psi - 1}\right) < 2T(r, \psi) - N_1(r, \psi) + S(r, \psi).$$
$$(3.6)$$

Now

$$2T(r, \psi) - N_1(r, \psi) = m(r, \psi) + m\left(r, \frac{1}{\psi - 1}\right) + N(r, \psi) + N\left(r, \frac{1}{\psi - 1}\right) -$$
$$- N\left(r, \frac{1}{\psi'}\right) - 2N(r, \psi) + N(r, \psi') + O(1). \quad (3.7)$$

Again at a pole of $\psi(z)$ of order l, $\psi'(z)$ has a pole of order $(l+1)$. Such poles occur only at poles of $f(z)$ or of the $a_\nu(z)$. Thus

$$N(r, \psi') - N(r, \psi) = \overline{N}(r, \psi) \leqslant \overline{N}(r, f) + \sum_{\nu=0}^{l} \overline{N}\{r, a_\nu(z)\} \leqslant \overline{N}(r, f) + S(r, f).$$

Further, at a zero of $\psi(z) - 1$ of order l, $\psi'(z)$ has a zero of order $l-1$, so that

$$N\left(r, \frac{1}{\psi - 1}\right) - N\left(r, \frac{1}{\psi'}\right) = \overline{N}\left(r, \frac{1}{\psi - 1}\right) - N_0\left(r, \frac{1}{\psi'}\right).$$

Again, by (3.5) $S(r, \psi) = o\{T(r, \psi)\} = o\{T(r, f)\}$

outside a set of finite linear measure, so that

$$S(r, \psi) = S(r, f).$$

Thus (3.6) and (3.7) yield

$$m\left(r, \frac{1}{\psi}\right) < \overline{N}(r, f) + \overline{N}\left(r, \frac{1}{\psi - 1}\right) - N_0\left(r, \frac{1}{\psi'}\right) + S(r, f). \qquad (3.8)$$

† See Milloux [1] for a slightly weaker version of Theorem 3.2 and other results of this general nature.

Again we have

$$T(r,f) = m\left(r,\frac{1}{f}\right)+N\left(r,\frac{1}{f}\right)+O(1)$$

$$\leqslant m\left(r,\frac{1}{\psi}\right)+m\left(r,\frac{\psi}{f}\right)+N\left(r,\frac{1}{f}\right)+O(1)$$

$$\leqslant m\left(r,\frac{1}{\psi}\right)+N\left(r,\frac{1}{f}\right)+S(r,f)$$

by (3.4) and now Theorem 3.2 follows from (3.8).

As an immediate consequence we have

THEOREM 3.3. *If $f(z)$ is meromorphic and transcendental in the plane and has only a finite number of zeros and poles, then every function $\psi(z)$ given by (3.3) assumes every finite complex value except possibly zero infinitely often, or else $\psi(z)$ is identically constant.*

The case when $\psi(z)$ is identically zero can in fact occur. We may take for instance $f(z) = e^{g(z)}$, and $\psi(z) = f'(z)-g'(z)f(z)$. Suppose now that $\psi(z)$ is not constant. Then Theorem 3.2 shows that

$$T(r,f) < \overline{N}\left(r,\frac{1}{\psi-1}\right)+S(r,f)+O(\log r),$$

or $$\{1+o(1)\}T(r,f) < \overline{N}\left(r,\frac{1}{\psi-1}\right), \tag{3.9}$$

as $r \to +\infty$ outside an exceptional set of finite linear measure. Thus the equation $\psi(z) = 1$ must have infinitely many roots, since otherwise we should deduce $$T(r,f) = O(\log r),$$

so that $f(z)$ would be rational. If w is any complex number other than zero the same conclusion holds with $\psi(z)/w$ instead of $\psi(z)$, so that the equation $\psi(z) = w$ has infinitely many roots.

It is worth noting that (3.9) in fact yields a good deal more than this. Since $f(z)$ has only a finite number of poles,

$$N(r,\psi) \leqslant (l+1)N(r,f)+o\{T(r,f)\} = o\{T(r,f)\},$$

$$m(r,\psi) \leqslant m\left(r,\frac{\psi}{f}\right)+m(r,f) \leqslant \{1+o(1)\}T(r,f)$$

by (3.4). Thus $$T(r,\psi) \leqslant \{1+o(1)\}T(r,f),$$

and so (3.9) shows that outside a set of finite linear measure,

$$\{1+o(1)\}T(r,f) \leqslant \overline{N}\left(r,\frac{1}{\psi-1}\right) \leqslant T(r,\psi)+O(1) \leqslant \{1+o(1)\}T(r,f).$$

Thus if w is any complex number other than zero,

$$\overline{N}\left(r, \frac{1}{\psi - w}\right) \sim T(r, \psi) \sim T(r, f)$$

as $r \to +\infty$ outside a possible exceptional set of finite linear measure. In particular either $\psi(z)$ is constant or $\psi(z)$ has no finite deficient values except possibly zero.

3.3. Exceptional values of meromorphic functions and their derivatives

In this section we consider the special case $\psi(z) = f^{(l)}(z)$, where l is a positive integer. We shall see that it is possible in this case to obtain the conclusion of Theorem 3.3 without making any assumptions about the poles of $f(z)$. However, we first prove the much more elementary†

THEOREM 3.4. *Suppose that $f(z)$ is a transcendental meromorphic function in the plane and $\psi(z) = f^{(l)}(z)$. Then in the notation of Theorem 2.4 we have*

$$\sum_{a \neq \infty} \Theta(a, \psi) \leqslant 1 + \frac{1}{l+1}.$$

In particular $\psi(z)$ assumes every finite value with at most one exception infinitely often.

At every pole of $f(z)$ of order p, $\psi(z)$ has a pole of order $p + l \geqslant l + 1$. Thus

$$\overline{N}(r, \psi) \leqslant \frac{1}{l+1} N(r, \psi) \leqslant \frac{1}{l+1} T(r, \psi),$$

and so, in the notation of Theorem 2.4,

$$\Theta(\infty, \psi) \geqslant \frac{l}{l+1}.$$

Now Theorem 3.4 follows from Theorem 2.4.

Exercise. If $f(z) = \tan z$, $l = 1$, $\psi(z) = \sec^2 z$, $\Theta(0) = 1$, since $\psi(z) \neq 0$, and $\Theta(1) = \frac{1}{2}$, since $1 - \sec^2 z = -\tan^2 z$ has only repeated zeros. Thus in this case the bound $1 + 1/(l+1)$ in Theorem 3.4 is sharp.

3.3.1. It follows from Theorem 3.3 that if $f(z)$ is transcendental and has only a finite number of zeros and poles then the exceptional value which is not taken infinitely often by $f^{(l)}(z)$ can only be zero. We shall see that in this result it is possible to suppress completely the hypothesis about the poles of $f(z)$. We have, in fact,†

† Hayman [5].

Theorem 3.5. *Suppose that $f(z)$ is meromorphic and transcendental in the plane. Then as $r \to \infty$*

$$T(r,f) \leqslant \left(2+\frac{1}{l}\right)N\left(r,\frac{1}{f}\right)+\left(2+\frac{2}{l}\right)\overline{N}\left(r,\frac{1}{f^{(l)}-1}\right)+S(r,f).$$

Corollary. *Either $f(z)$ assumes every finite value infinitely often or $f^{(l)}(z)$ assumes every finite value except possibly zero infinitely often.*

We shall need Theorem 3.2 together with the following:

Lemma 3.1. *If $\psi(z) = f^{(l)}(z)$, $N_0(r, 1/\psi')$ is defined as in Theorem 3.2 and $N_1(r,f)$, $\overline{N}_2(r,f)$ denote the N functions with respect to the simple and multiple poles of $f(z)$ respectively, each pole being counted only once, we have*

$$lN_1(r,f) \leqslant \overline{N}_2(r,f)+\overline{N}\left(r,\frac{1}{\psi(z)-1}\right)+N_0\left(r,\frac{1}{\psi'(z)}\right)+S(r,f).$$

We set
$$g(z) = \frac{\{f^{(l+1)}(z)\}^{l+1}}{\{1-f^{(l)}(z)\}^{l+2}} = \frac{\{\psi'(z)\}^{l+1}}{\{1-\psi(z)\}^{l+2}}.$$

Then we have at a simple pole z_0 of $f(z)$

$$f(z) = \frac{a}{z-z_0}+O(1),$$

where $a \neq 0$. Differentiating l times we deduce that

$$1-\psi(z) = 1-f^{(l)}(z) = \frac{(-1)^{l+1}al!}{(z-z_0)^{l+1}}+O(1)$$

$$= \frac{(-1)^{l+1}al!}{(z-z_0)^{l+1}}\{1+O(z-z_0)^{l+1}\}.$$

A further differentiation yields

$$f^{(l+1)}(z) = \frac{(-1)^{l+1}a(l+1)!}{(z-z_0)^{l+2}}\{1+O(z-z_0)^{l+2}\}.$$

Thus
$$g(z) = \frac{(-1)^{l+1}(l+1)^{l+1}}{al!}\{1+O(z-z_0)^{l+1}\},$$

so that $g(z_0) \neq 0, \infty$, but $g'(z)$ has a zero of order at least l at z_0.

Now Jensen's formula applied to $g'(z)/g(z)$ shows that

$$N\left(r,\frac{g}{g'}\right)-N\left(r,\frac{g'}{g}\right) = m\left(r,\frac{g'}{g}\right)-m\left(r,\frac{g}{g'}\right)+O(1).$$

The left-hand side is

$$N(r,g)+N\left(r,\frac{1}{g'}\right)-N(r,g')-N\left(r,\frac{1}{g}\right) = N\left(r,\frac{1}{g'}\right)-N\left(r,\frac{1}{g}\right)-\overline{N}(r,g)$$

$$= N_0\left(r,\frac{1}{g'}\right)-\overline{N}\left(r,\frac{1}{g}\right)-\overline{N}(r,g),$$

where in $N_0(r, 1/g')$ only zeros of g' which are not zeros of g are to be considered.

By our above analysis,

$$lN_1(r,f) \leqslant N_0\left(r, \frac{1}{g'}\right) \leqslant \bar{N}\left(r, \frac{1}{g}\right) + \bar{N}(r,g) + m\left(r, \frac{g'}{g}\right) + O(1).$$

Clearly zeros and poles of $g(z)$ can occur only at multiple poles of $f(z)$, or zeros of $\psi(z) - 1$, or zeros of $\psi'(z)$ other than zeros of $\psi(z) - 1$. Thus

$$\bar{N}\left(r, \frac{1}{g}\right) + \bar{N}(r,g) \leqslant \bar{N}\left(r, \frac{1}{\psi(z)-1}\right) + \bar{N}_2(r,f) + N_0\left(r, \frac{1}{\psi'}\right).$$

Again by Theorem 3.1 we have, outside a set of finite linear measure,

$$m\left(r, \frac{g'}{g}\right) = o\{T(r,g)\} = o\{T(r,f^{(l+1)})\} + o[T\{r, 1 - f^{(l)}(z)\}] = o\{T(r,f)\}.$$

This proves Lemma 3.1.

3.3.2. We can now complete the proof of Theorem 3.5. We apply Theorem 3.2 with $\psi(z) = f^{(l)}(z)$, and use the fact that in $N(r,f)$ multiple poles are counted at least twice. Thus

$$N_1(r,f) + 2\bar{N}_2(r,f) \leqslant N(r,f) \leqslant T(r,f)$$

$$\leqslant \bar{N}(r,f) + N\left(r, \frac{1}{f}\right) + \bar{N}\left(r, \frac{1}{\psi-1}\right) - N_0\left(r, \frac{1}{\psi'}\right) + S(r,f).$$

Since $\bar{N}(r,f) = N_1(r,f) + \bar{N}_2(r,f)$ this gives

$$\bar{N}_2(r,f) \leqslant N\left(r, \frac{1}{f}\right) + \bar{N}\left(r, \frac{1}{\psi-1}\right) - N_0\left(r, \frac{1}{\psi'}\right) + S(r,f).$$

On combining this with Lemma 3.1 we deduce

$$lN_1(r,f) \leqslant \bar{N}_2(r,f) + \bar{N}\left(r, \frac{1}{\psi-1}\right) + N_0\left(r, \frac{1}{\psi'}\right) + S(r,f)$$

$$\leqslant N\left(r, \frac{1}{f}\right) + 2\bar{N}\left(r, \frac{1}{\psi-1}\right) + S(r,f).$$

Thus

$$\bar{N}(r,f) = N_1(r,f) + \bar{N}_2(r,f)$$

$$\leqslant \left(1 + \frac{1}{l}\right)N\left(r, \frac{1}{f}\right) + \left(1 + \frac{2}{l}\right)\bar{N}\left(r, \frac{1}{\psi-1}\right) + S(r,f).$$

On substituting this inequality in Theorem 3.2 we obtain the inequality of Theorem 3.5.

Suppose now that w_1, w_2 are complex numbers such that $w_2 \neq 0$, and set

$$F(z) = \frac{f(z) - w_1}{w_2}.$$

Then we have

$$T(r, F) = T(r,f) + O(1), \qquad S(r, F) = S(r,f).$$

We may apply Theorem 3.5 to $F(z)$ and obtain

$$T(r,f) < T(r, F) + O(1)$$

$$< \left(2 + \frac{1}{l}\right) N\left(r, \frac{1}{F}\right) + \left(2 + \frac{2}{l}\right) \overline{N}\left(r, \frac{1}{F^{(l)} - 1}\right) + S(r, F)$$

$$= \left(2 + \frac{1}{l}\right) N\left(r, \frac{1}{f - w_1}\right) + \left(2 + \frac{2}{l}\right) \overline{N}\left(r, \frac{1}{f^{(l)} - w_2}\right) + S(r,f).$$

If the equations $f(z) = w_1$, $f^{(l)}(z) = w_2$ have only a finite number of roots, we deduce

$$\{1 + o(1)\} T(r,f) = O(\log r) \quad \text{as } r \to \infty,$$

so that $f(z)$ is rational, which contradicts our hypotheses. This proves the corollary to Theorem 3.5.

3.4. Zeros of meromorphic functions and their derivatives. A theorem of Pólya

We have seen that if $f(z)$ is transcendental and the equation $f(z) = a$ has only finitely many roots then all derivatives of $f(z)$ assume every finite value except possibly zero infinitely often. If $f(z)$ is rational, then $f(z)$ assumes in the closed plane every complex value equally often with due regard to multiplicity; hence $f(z)$ assumes in the open plane every complex value except perhaps $f(\infty)$. Thus if $f(z) \neq w$, where w is finite, then

$$f(z) = w + \frac{O(1)}{z}, \qquad \text{as } z \to \infty,$$

$$f'(z) = \frac{O(1)}{z^2}, \qquad f^{(l)}(z) = \frac{O(1)}{z^{l+1}}, \qquad \text{as } z \to \infty,$$

so that $f^{(l)}(z)$ assumes in the open plane every complex value except possibly zero.

The value zero does in fact play an exceptional role. If

$$f(z) = e^{Az+B} + w_0, \quad \text{or} \quad f(z) = (Az+B)^{-n} + w_0,$$

where A, B, w_0 are complex constants such that $A \neq 0$ and n is a positive integer, then $f(z) \neq w_0$, $f^{(l)}(z) \neq 0$ for $l = 1, 2, \ldots$. However, we shall see that these are the only functions with this property. We prove first the following result of Pólya [1].

THEOREM 3.6. *Suppose that $f(z)$ is meromorphic in $|z-z_0| < R$, where $0 < R \leqslant \infty$, and has at least two distinct poles there. Let r be the radius of the largest circle with centre z_0 containing no pole of $f(z)$ in its interior. Then*

(i) *if the circle $|z-z_0| = r$ contains at least two distinct poles of $f(z)$, then for every positive δ, the equation $f^{(l)}(z) = 0$ has roots in $|z-z_0| < \delta$, when l is sufficiently large;*

(ii) *if the circle $|z-z_0| = r$ contains only one pole of $f(z)$, then if δ is sufficiently small, $f^{(l)}(z) \to \infty$ as $l \to \infty$ uniformly in $|z-z_0| \leqslant \delta$.*

COROLLARY. *For all sufficiently large l, $f^{(l)}(z)$ has zeros in every disk in which $f(z)$ is meromorphic and has at least two distinct poles.*

3.4.1. *Proof of* (ii). Suppose without loss of generality that $z_0 = 0$. Take $\rho > r$ and such that $f(z)$ has no poles in $r < |z| \leqslant \rho$. Suppose first that $f(z)$ has exactly one pole $\zeta_0 = re^{i\theta}$ on $|z| = r$. Let $g_0(z)$ be the principal part of $f(z)$ at ζ_0. Then $\phi(z) = f(z) - g_0(z)$ remains regular in $|z| \leqslant \rho$. Suppose that $|\phi(z)| \leqslant M$ in $|z| \leqslant \rho$ and that $0 < 3\delta < \rho - r$. Then if $|z| \leqslant \delta$ we have $|\phi(\zeta)| \leqslant M$ for $|\zeta - z| \leqslant r + 2\delta$, and the Cauchy inequalities give

$$|\phi^{(l)}(z)| \leqslant \frac{M\,l!}{(r+2\delta)^l}. \tag{3.10}$$

On the other hand
$$g_0(z) = \sum_{\nu=1}^{p} \frac{a_\nu}{(z-\zeta_0)^\nu},$$

where $a_p \neq 0$. Thus
$$g_0^{(l)}(z) = \sum_{\nu=1}^{p} \frac{(-1)^l \nu(\nu+1)...(\nu+l-1)a_\nu}{(z-\zeta_0)^{\nu+l}}.$$

Also as $l \to \infty$,
$$\frac{\nu(\nu+1)...(\nu+l-1)}{p(p+1)...(p+l-1)} = \frac{\Gamma(\nu+l)\Gamma(p)}{\Gamma(p+l)\Gamma(\nu)} \sim \frac{\Gamma(p)}{\Gamma(\nu)} l^{\nu-p} \to 0$$

for $1 \leqslant \nu < p$. Thus we have uniformly for $|z| \leqslant \delta$, and all large l,
$$|g_0^{(l)}(z)| > \frac{1}{2} \frac{\Gamma(p+l)}{\Gamma(p)} \frac{|a_p|}{(r+\delta)^{p+l}}.$$

Now as $l \to \infty$,
$$\frac{\Gamma(p+l)}{(r+\delta)^{p+l}} \frac{(r+2\delta)^l}{l!} \geqslant \left(\frac{r+2\delta}{r+\delta}\right)^l \frac{1}{(r+\delta)^p} \to \infty.$$

Thus we have from (3.10) as $l \to \infty$ uniformly for $|z| \leqslant \delta$,
$$|f^{(l)}(z)| = |g_0^{(l)}(z) + \phi^{(l)}(z)| \geqslant \frac{|a_p|\Gamma(p+l)}{2\Gamma(p)(r+\delta)^{p+l}} - \frac{M\,l!}{(r+2\delta)^l}$$

$$\geqslant \{1+o\,(1)\} \frac{|a_p|}{2\Gamma(p)} \frac{\Gamma(p+l)}{(r+\delta)^{p+l}} \to +\infty.$$

This proves (ii) when $z_0 = 0$. The general case follows by considering $f(z_0 + z)$ instead of $f(z)$.

3.4.2. *Proof of* (i). Suppose next that the circle $|z| = r$ contains exactly two distinct poles of $f(z)$, $\zeta_0 = re^{i\theta_0}$ and $\zeta_1 = re^{i\theta_1}$, where $0 \leqslant \theta_0 < \theta_1 < 2\pi$. Let $g_0(z)$ be the principal part of $f(z)$ at z_0, and $g_1(z)$ be the principal part of $f(z)$ at z_1. We suppose that $f(z)$ has no singularities in $r < |z| \leqslant r + 3\delta$, so that

$$f(z) = g_0(z) + g_1(z) + \phi(z),$$

where $\phi^{(l)}(z)$ satisfies (3.10) uniformly for $|z| \leqslant \delta$. Our previous analysis shows that we have for $|z| \leqslant \delta$, uniformly as $l \to \infty$,

$$g_0^{(l)}(z) \sim \frac{(-1)^l A_0 \Gamma(p+l)}{\Gamma(p)(z-\zeta_0)^{p+l}}, \qquad g_1^{(l)}(z) \sim \frac{(-1)^l A_1 \Gamma(q+l)}{\Gamma(q)(z-\zeta_1)^{q+l}},$$

where A_0, A_1 are non-zero complex constants and p, q are positive integers. We now consider the equation

$$f^{(l)}(z) = g_0^{(l)}(z) + g_1^{(l)}(z) + \phi^{(l)}(z) = 0,$$

or $\quad \dfrac{A_0 \Gamma(p+l)\{1+\epsilon_1(z)\}}{\Gamma(p)(z-\zeta_0)^{p+l}} + \dfrac{A_1 \Gamma(q+l)\{1+\epsilon_2(z)\}}{\Gamma(q)(z-\zeta_1)^{q+l}} + (-1)^l \phi^{(l)}(z) = 0,$ (3.11)

where $\epsilon_1(z) \to 0$, $\epsilon_2(z) \to 0$ as $l \to \infty$, uniformly for $|z| \leqslant \delta$. We can write this as

$$-\left(\frac{z-\zeta_1}{z-\zeta_0}\right)^l \frac{A_0 \Gamma(q)\Gamma(p+l)(-\zeta_1)^q}{A_1 \Gamma(p)\Gamma(q+l)(-\zeta_0)^p}$$
$$= \frac{\{1-(z/\zeta_0)\}^p\{1+\epsilon_2(z)\}}{\{1-(z/\zeta_1)\}^q\{1+\epsilon_1(z)\}} + \frac{(-1)^l \phi^{(l)}(z)\Gamma(q)(z-\zeta_1)^l(-\zeta_1)^q(z-\zeta_0)^p}{A_1 \Gamma(q+l)\{1+\epsilon_1(z)\}(-\zeta_0)^p}.$$
(3.12)

Using (3.10) we see that the right-hand side of this equation tends to $\{1-(z/\zeta_0)\}^p\{1-(z/\zeta_1)\}^{-q}$, as $l \to \infty$, uniformly for $|z| \leqslant \delta$.

We now set $\quad w^l = -\left(\dfrac{z-\zeta_1}{z-\zeta_0}\right)^l \dfrac{A_0 \Gamma(q)\Gamma(p+l)(-\zeta_1)^q}{A_1 \Gamma(p)\Gamma(q+l)(-\zeta_0)^p},$

so that $\qquad\qquad w = c_l \dfrac{z-\zeta_1}{z-\zeta_0},$ (3.13)

where $\qquad\qquad c_l = \left\{-\dfrac{A_0 \Gamma(q)\Gamma(p+l)(-\zeta_1)^q}{A_1 \Gamma(p)\Gamma(q+l)(-\zeta_0)^p}\right\}^{1/l}$

is so chosen that $|\arg c_l(\zeta_1/\zeta_0)| \leqslant \pi/l$. Evidently $|c_l| \to 1$, so that $c_l \zeta_1/\zeta_0 \to 1$ as $l \to +\infty$.

We wish to show that given $\delta > 0$ the equation (3.11) has a root in $|z| < \delta$, if l is sufficiently large. Given $\delta > 0$, we choose η so small that for all sufficiently large l, the points satisfying $|w-1| < \eta$ correspond entirely to points in $|z| < \delta$ by (3.13). This is possible since $z = 0$ corresponds to $w = c_l \zeta_1/\zeta_0$, which tends to 1 as $l \to +\infty$, and ζ_0, ζ_1 are fixed. In terms of w the equation (3.12) can be written as

$$w^l = \left(1 - \frac{z}{\zeta_0}\right)^p \left(1 - \frac{z}{\zeta_1}\right)^{-q} + o(1) = 1 + \psi(w),$$

say, where $|\psi(w)| < \frac{1}{2}$ if $|z| < \delta_0$ and δ_0 is a sufficiently small positive number, depending on p, q, and δ, and if further l is sufficiently large. Thus $|\psi(w)| < \frac{1}{2}$, if $|w-1| < \eta_0$, and $l > l_0$.

3.4.3. To complete our proof we need to show that if l is sufficiently large the equation $w^l = 1 + \psi(w)$ has a root in $|w-1| < \eta_0$. This result is contained in

LEMMA 3.2. *Suppose that $\psi(w)$ is regular and satisfies $|\psi(w)| < \frac{1}{2}$ for $|w-1| < \eta_0$, where η_0 is a fixed positive number. Then there exists l_0 depending only on η_0, such that if $l > l_0$, the equation $w^l = 1 + \psi(w)$ has at least one root in $|w-1| < \eta_0$.*

Set $\theta_0 = \pi/l$, $r_1 = e^{-1/l}$, $r_2 = e^{1/l}$, $\phi(w) = 1 + \psi(w)$, and consider the variation of $\arg\{\phi(w) - w^l\}$ along the closed curve C consisting of C_1, C_2, C_3, C_4 described in turn, where:

C_1 is the arc $w = r_2 e^{i\theta}$ $(-\theta_0 \leqslant \theta \leqslant \theta_0)$;

C_2 is the straight line from $r_2 e^{i\theta_0}$ to $r_1 e^{i\theta_0}$;

C_3 is the arc $w = r_1 e^{-i\theta}$ $(-\theta_0 \leqslant \theta \leqslant \theta_0)$;

C_4 is the straight line from $r_1 e^{-i\theta_0}$ to $r_2 e^{-i\theta_0}$.

We suppose that l is so large that C lies in $|w-1| < \eta_0$. On C_1,

$$\arg\{\phi(w) - w^l\} = \arg(-1) + l \arg w + \arg\left(1 - \frac{\phi(w)}{w^l}\right);$$

also the variation of $l \arg w$ is precisely 2π, while

$$|\phi(w)/w^l| < \frac{3}{2e} < 1,$$

so that the variation of $\arg[1 - \{\phi(w)/w^l\}]$ is greater than $-\pi$. Thus the variation of $\arg\{\phi(w) - w^l\}$ on C_1 is greater than π. On C_2 and C_4, w^l is real and negative and on C_3, $|w^l| < \frac{1}{2}$. Thus on C_2, C_3, and C_4 $\phi(w) - w^l = 1 - w^l + \psi(w)$ has positive real part and so the variation of $\arg\{\phi(w) - w^l\}$ on the union of these arcs is greater than $-\pi$. Hence

$$\mathrm{var}_C \arg\{\phi(w) - w^l\} > \pi - \pi = 0,$$

and so $\phi(w) - w^l$ has at least one zero inside C, and Lemma 3.2 is proved.

F

It follows from Lemma 3.2 that if $f(z)$ is meromorphic in $|z| \leqslant r$, and has exactly two poles on the circle $|z| = r$ and none in $|z| < r$, then given $\delta > 0$, $f^{(l)}(z)$ has a zero in $|z| < \delta$ if l is sufficiently large. By applying this result to $f(z_0+z)$ we see that if the circle $|z_0-z| = r$ has two poles of $f(z)$ on its circumference and none in its interior then $f^{(l)}(z)$ has a zero in $|z-z_0| < \delta$ for all sufficiently large l.

Suppose finally that $f(z)$ has no poles in $|z-z_0| < r$ but $q > 2$ distinct poles on $|z-z_0| = r$, $z_n = z_0+re^{i\theta_n}$ say, where

$$0 \leqslant \theta_1 < \theta_2 < \dots < \theta_q < 2\pi.$$

Then if $z' = z_0+te^{\frac{1}{2}i(\theta_1+\theta_2)}$, where t is a small positive number, the disk $|z-z'| \leqslant |z_1-z'|$ has exactly two poles of $f(z)$ on its circumference and none in its interior and so the disk $|z-z'| < t$ contains a zero of $f^{(l)}(z)$ for sufficiently large l. Thus the disk $|z-z_0| < 2t$ contains a zero of $f^{(l)}(z)$ for sufficiently large l, and the proof of Theorem 3.6 is complete.

3.4.4. To prove the corollary, suppose that the disk $|z-z_0| < r$ contains at least two distinct poles of $f(z)$, and let z_1 be a pole of $f(z)$ nearest to z_0. If there is another pole z_2, such that $|z_2-z_0| = |z_1-z_0|$, the corollary follows from the main theorem. If not, let z_2 be a pole of $f(z)$ such that the disk $|z-z_0| < |z_2-z_0|$ contains no pole of $f(z)$ other than z_1. Set $z(t) = (1-t)z_0+tz_2$. Then $|z(0)-z_1| < |z(0)-z_2|$ and $|z(1)-z_1| > |z(1)-z_2| = 0$. Thus we can choose t such that $0 < t < 1$ and for $z' = z(t)$ we have $|z'-z_1| = |z'-z_2|$. For any other pole or singularity z_3 of $f(z)$ we have

$$|z_3-z'| \geqslant |z_3-z_0|-|z'-z_0| \geqslant |z_2-z_0|-|z'-z_0| = |z_2-z'|.$$

Thus the conditions (i) of Theorem 3.6 are satisfied with z' instead of z_0, and so any disk containing z' contains zeros of $f^{(l)}(z)$ for sufficiently large l. In particular the disk $|z-z_0| < r$ contains such zeros and the corollary is proved.

3.4.5. We can use Pólya's Theorem 3.6 to prove (Hayman [5]):

THEOREM 3.7. *If $f(z)$ is meromorphic in the plane and $f^{(l)}(z)$ has no zeros for $l = 0$, 1, 2,..., then $f(z) = e^{Az+B}$, or $f(z) = (Az+B)^{-n}$, where A, B are constants such that $A \neq 0$, and n is a positive integer.*

It follows from Theorem 3.6 that $f(z)$ has at most one pole. Set

$$g(z) = \frac{f(z)}{f'(z)}, \qquad g'(z) = \frac{\{f'(z)\}^2-f(z)f''(z)}{\{f'(z)\}^2}$$

so that

$$g'(z)-1 = -\frac{f(z)f''(z)}{\{f'(z)\}^2}$$

Clearly $g(z) = 0$ only at poles or zeros of $f(z)$, so that $g(z)$ has at most one zero. Further $g'(z) = 1$ only at zeros of $f(z)$ or $f''(z)$, so that $g'(z) \neq 1$. It now follows from Theorem 3.5 that $g(z)$ must be rational, and since $g'(z) \neq 1$,

$$g'(z) = 1 + \frac{1}{P(z)}, \tag{3.14}$$

where $P(z)$ is a polynomial. But since $f(z)$ has no zero and at most one pole z_0,

$$f(z) = (z-z_0)^{-n} e^{Q(z)}$$

$$\frac{1}{g(z)} = \frac{f'(z)}{f(z)} = -\frac{n}{z-z_0} + Q'(z),$$

where n is a positive integer or zero, and $Q'(z)$ is an integral function. Thus $Q'(z)$ is a polynomial. Suppose now that $Q(z)$ is not constant. Then if $Q'(z) = C \neq 0$, or $Q'(z) \to \infty$ as $z \to \infty$, $g(z)$ remains bounded at ∞ and $g'(z) \to 0$ as $z \to \infty$. This contradicts (3.14) unless $g'(z) = 0$ in which case $g(z) = $ constant and $f(z) = e^{Az+B}$.

Alternatively $Q(z) = $ constant and $f(z) = (z-z_0)^{-n} e^Q$, or

$$f(z) = (Az+B)^{-n}.$$

3.5. The theory of Tumura–Clunie

While Theorem 3.7 applies to all meromorphic functions the hypothesis that none of the derivatives of $f(z)$ has any zeros is rather strong. It is not known whether the conclusion holds under significantly weaker hypotheses for general meromorphic functions. If we assume that $f(z)$ has finite order, or more generally that

$$\lim_{r \to +\infty} \frac{\log n(r,f)}{\log r} < +\infty,$$

where $n(r,f)$ is the number of poles of $f(z)$ in $|z| \leqslant r$, then the conclusion of Theorem 3.7 holds when $ff'f'' \neq 0$ (Hayman [5]).

A corresponding result for functions having at most a finite number of poles was first proved by Saxer [1] and Pólya. For integral functions it was shown by Csillag [1] that if $f(z)f^{(p)}(z)f^{(m)}(z) \neq 0$, where $m > p > 0$, then $f(z) = e^{Az+B}$. However, these results are contained in the following even stronger

THEOREM 3.8. *Suppose that $f(z)$ is meromorphic and has only a finite number of poles in the plane, and that $f(z)$, $f^{(l)}(z)$ have only a finite number of zeros for some $l \geqslant 2$. Then*

$$f(z) = \frac{P_1(z)}{P_2(z)} e^{P_3(z)},$$

where P_1, P_2, P_3 are polynomials. If, further, $f(z)$ and $f^{(l)}(z)$ have no zeros, then $f(z) = e^{Az+B}$ or $f(z) = (Az+B)^{-n}$.

Theorem 3.8 was stated by Tumura [1] but his proof contained serious gaps. A proof in the case $l = 2$ using the approach given in the previous section was given by the author [5] and the theorem in its general form was first correctly proved by Clunie [1]. We shall proceed now to develop the Tumura–Clunie method. It is based on the study of the zeros of certain polynomials in $f(z)$ and the derivatives of $f(z)$. We remark that Theorem 3.8 is false when $l = 1$. If $f(z) = e^{g(z)}$, where $g'(z)$ is any integral function without zeros, then $f(z) \neq 0$ and

$$f'(z) = g'(z)f(z) \neq 0.$$

3.5.1. We recall the notation of section 3.1. We shall continue to suppose that $f(z)$ denotes a basic meromorphic function in the plane which we shall assume to be not constant, and that $a(z)$, $a_\nu(z)$, etc., denote functions meromorphic in the plane and satisfying

$$T(r, a_\nu(z)) = o\{T(r, f)\},$$

except possibly for a set of r having finite linear measure. We shall be concerned largely with meromorphic functions $h(z)$ which are polynomials in $f(z)$ and the derivatives of $f(z)$ with coefficients of the form $a(z)$. Such functions $h(z)$ will be called *differential polynomials in $f(z)$*.

The following lemma is fundamental to Clunie's theorems.

LEMMA 3.3. *Suppose that $f(z)$ is meromorphic and transcendental in the plane and that*
$$f(z)^n P(z) = Q(z)$$
there, where $P(z)$, $Q(z)$ are differential polynomials in $f(z)$ and the degree of $Q(z)$ is at most n. Then

$$m\{r, P(z)\} = S(r, f) \quad as \quad r \to +\infty.$$

We have

$$2\pi m\{r, P(z)\} = \int_0^{2\pi} \log^+ |P(re^{i\theta})|\, d\theta$$
$$\leqslant \int_{\mathscr{E}_1} \log^+ |P(re^{i\theta})|\, d\theta + \int_{\mathscr{E}_2} \log^+ |P(re^{i\theta})|\, d\theta,$$

where $\mathscr{E}_1$ is the set of θ in $0 \leqslant \theta \leqslant 2\pi$ for which $|f(re^{i\theta})| < 1$, and $\mathscr{E}_2$ is the complementary set. By hypothesis $P(z)$ is the sum of a finite number of terms of the type

$$F(z) = a(z)f(z)^{l_0}f'(z)^{l_1}\ldots f^{(\nu)}(z)^{l_\nu},$$

where $l_0, l_1, \ldots, l_\nu$ are non-negative integers. Hence, in $\mathscr{E}_1$,

$$|F(z)| \leqslant |a(z)|\left|\frac{f'}{f}\right|^{l_1}\ldots\left|\frac{f^{(\nu)}}{f}\right|^{l_\nu},$$

and hence

$$\log^+|F(z)| \leqslant \log^+|a(z)| + \sum_{t=1}^{\nu} l_t \log^+\left|\frac{f^{(t)}(z)}{f(z)}\right|.$$

Thus

$$\int_{\mathscr{E}_1} \log^+|F(re^{i\theta})|\,d\theta \leqslant m(r,a) + O\left\{\sum_{t=1}^{\nu} m\left(r,\frac{f^{(t)}(z)}{f(z)}\right)\right\}$$

$$\leqslant S(r,f)$$

by Theorem 3.1 and condition (3.2). Thus by addition

$$\int_{\mathscr{E}_1} \log^+|P(re^{i\theta})|\,d\theta = \sum_{F} \int_{\mathscr{E}_1} \log^+|F(re^{i\theta})|\,d\theta + O(1) = S(r,f).$$

Next let $\mathscr{E}_2$ be the set of θ where $|f(z)| \geqslant 1$. The polynomial $Q(z)$ is the sum of terms of the type

$$a(z)f(z)^{l_0}f'(z)^{l_1}\dots f^{(\nu)}(z)^{l_\nu}, \quad \text{where } \sum_{t=0}^{\nu} l_t \leqslant n.$$

Thus on $\mathscr{E}_2$

$$|P(z)| = \left|\frac{1}{f(z)^n} \sum a(z)f(z)^{l_0}f'(z)^{l_1}\dots f^{(\nu)}(z)^{l_\nu}\right|$$

$$\leqslant \sum |a(z)|\left|\frac{f'}{f}\right|^{l_1}\dots\left|\frac{f^{(\nu)}}{f}\right|^{l_\nu}.$$

Thus again

$$\int_{\mathscr{E}_2} \log^+|P(re^{i\theta})|\,d\theta \leqslant O\left[\sum_{t=1}^{\nu} m\left(r,\frac{f^{(t)}}{f}\right) + m\{r,a(z)\}\right] = S(r,f).$$

This proves the lemma.

3.5.2. We shall prove a slight generalization of previous results of Tumura [1] and Clunie [1].

THEOREM 3.9. *Suppose that $f(z)$ is meromorphic and not constant in the plane, that*

$$g(z) = f(z)^n + P_{n-1}(f), \tag{3.15}$$

where $P_{n-1}(f)$ is a differential polynomial of degree at most $n-1$ in f, and that

$$N(r,f) + N\left(r,\frac{1}{g}\right) = S(r,f).$$

Then $g(z) = h(z)^n$, $h(z) = f(z) + (1/n)a(z)$ and $h(z)^{n-1}a(z)$ is obtained by substituting $h(z)$ for $f(z)$, $h'(z)$ for $f'(z)$, etc., in the terms of degree $n-1$ in $P_{n-1}(f)$.

Thus $g(z)$ is of the form $(f+a/n)^n$, where a is determined by the terms of degree $n-1$ in $P_{n-1}(f)$ and by $g(z)$. We note the following special cases. If

$$P_{n-1}(f) = a_0(z)f^{n-1} + \text{terms of degree } n-2 \text{ at most,}$$

then
$$h^{n-1}a(z) = a_0(z)\,h^{n-1},$$

so that
$$a(z) = a_0(z),$$

and
$$g(z) = \left(f(z) + \frac{a_0(z)}{n}\right)^n.$$

The case which is relevant to Theorem 3.8 is that in which
$$P_{n-1}(f) = a_0(z)f'f^{n-2} + \text{terms of degree } (n-2) \text{ at most.}$$

In this case
$$h^{n-1}a(z) = a_0(z)\,h'h^{n-2}, \qquad a(z) = a_0(z)\frac{h'}{h} = \frac{a_0(z)}{n}\frac{g'(z)}{g(z)},$$

$$g(z) = \left(f(z) + \frac{a_0(z)}{n^2}\frac{g'(z)}{g(z)}\right)^n.$$

3.5.3. *Proof of Theorem* 3.9. We note that by (3.15) $g(z)$ can have poles only at poles of $f(z)$ or of the coefficients $a_\nu(z)$. Let l be the order of the highest derivative $f^{(l)}(z)$ occurring on the right-hand side of (3.15). At a pole of $f(z)$ of order p, $f^{(l)}(z)$ has a pole of order at most
$$p+l \leqslant (l+1)p,$$

and so $g(z)$ has a pole of order at most $n(l+1)p+k$, where k is the sum of the orders of the poles of all the coefficients $a_\nu(z)$. Thus
$$N(r,g) \leqslant n(l+1)N(r,f) + \sum N\{r, a_\nu(z)\} = S(r,f)$$

by hypothesis. Also
$$m(r,g) \leqslant O\Big[\sum_{\nu=1}^{l} m\{r, f^{(\nu)}(z)\} + \sum m\{r, a_\nu(z)\}\Big] = O\{T(r,f)\}$$

outside a set of finite linear measure, so that
$$T(r,g) = O\{T(r,f)\}$$

outside a set of finite linear measure and
$$N\left(r, \frac{1}{g}\right) = S(r,f)$$

by hypothesis. Thus
$$N\left(r, \frac{g'}{g}\right) \leqslant N(r,g) + N\left(r, \frac{1}{g}\right) = S(r,f)$$

and by Theorem 3.1
$$m\left(r, \frac{g'}{g}\right) = S(r,f),$$

so that $a_0(z) = g'(z)/g(z)$ satisfies (3.2).

We now differentiate (3.15) and obtain
$$nf^{n-1}f' + Q_{n-1}(f) = g'(z), \tag{3.16}$$

where $Q_{n-1} = dP_{n-1}/dz$ is a differential polynomial in f of degree $n-1$.

In fact if $a(z)$ satisfies (3.2) so does $a'(z)$ by Theorem 3.1. We multiply (3.15) by g'/g and subtract from (3.16). This gives

$$f^{n-1}\left(nf' - \frac{g'}{g}f\right) + T_{n-1}(f) = 0. \tag{3.17}$$

The polynomial $T_{n-1}(f)$ satisfies the conditions for $Q(z)$ of Lemma 3.3 with $n-1$ instead of n. Thus we deduce that

$$m\left(r, nf' - \frac{g'}{g}f\right) = S(r,f)$$

as $r \to +\infty$.

Again the function

$$F(z) = f'(z) - \frac{1}{n}\frac{g'(z)}{g(z)}f(z)$$

has poles only at poles of $f(z)$ or $g'(z)/g(z)$ and so we have

$$N(r, F) \leqslant 2N(r,f) + N\left(r, \frac{g'}{g}\right) = o\{T(r,f)\},$$

outside a set of finite linear measure. Thus

$$T(r, F) = S(r,f)$$

and so $F(z)$ satisfies the condition (3.2) for $a(z)$.

3.5.4. We need next

LEMMA 3.4. *If with the hypotheses of Theorem 3.9 $\pi_{n-1}(f)$ is a homogeneous differential polynomial of degree $n-1$ in f, and $h(z)$ is defined formally by the equation*

$$\frac{h'(z)}{h(z)} = \frac{1}{n}\frac{g'(z)}{g(z)},$$

then

$$\pi_{n-1}(f) = \left(\frac{f}{h}\right)^{n-1}\pi_{n-1}(h) + p_{n-2}(f),$$

where $p_{n-2}(f)$ is a differential polynomial in f of degree $n-2$ at most.†

We have just proved that

$$f'(z) = \psi(z)f(z) + a(z),$$

where

$$\psi(z) = \frac{h'(z)}{h(z)} = \frac{1}{n}\frac{g'(z)}{g(z)} \quad \text{and} \quad a(z) = F(z)$$

satisfy (3.2). We deduce that

$$f'' = \psi'f + \psi f' + a'(z) = \psi'f + \psi(\psi f + a) + a'$$
$$= (\psi' + \psi^2)f + a_1,$$

† In general $h(z)$ has complicated singularities, but $h^{1-n}\pi_{n-1}(h)$ is a differential polynomial in $h'/h = (1/n)g'/g$ and so is meromorphic and in fact an $a(z)$.

where $a_1(z)$ satisfies (3.2), since $\psi(z)$ and $a(z)$ do. By induction we obtain

$$f^{(l)} = T_l(\psi)f + a_l(z),$$

where $T_l(\psi)$ is a certain differential polynomial in ψ which is independent of $a(z)$, and $a_l(z)$ satisfies (3.2) and further $a_l(z) \equiv 0$ if $a(z) \equiv 0$. Writing $h(z)$ instead of $f(z)$ so that $h'(z) = \psi(z)h(z)$, we deduce that

$$h^{(l)} = T_l(\psi)h(z),$$

so that

$$f^{(l)} = \frac{h^{(l)}}{h}f(z) + a_l(z).$$

We deduce that if $n_0 + n_1 + \ldots + n_l = n - 1$,

$$f^{n_0}(f')^{n_1}\ldots(f^{(l)})^{n_l} = f^{n-1}\left(\frac{h'}{h}\right)^{n_1}\left(\frac{h''}{h}\right)^{n_2}\ldots\left(\frac{h^{(l)}}{h}\right)^{n_l} + p_{n-2}(f)$$

$$= \frac{f^{n-1}}{h^{n-1}}h^{n_0}(h')^{n_1}\ldots(h^{(l)})^{n_l} + p_{n-2}(f),$$

where $p_{n-2}(f)$ is a differential polynomial in f of degree at most $n-2$. Now Lemma 3.4 follows by addition.

3.5.5. We can now complete the proof of Theorem 3.9. We substitute

$$f'(z) = \frac{h'(z)}{h(z)}f(z) + F(z)$$

in (3.15) and use Lemma 3.4. Then

$$f^n + \frac{\pi_{n-1}(h)}{h^{n-1}}f^{n-1} + L_{n-2}(f) = g,$$

where $L_{n-2}(f)$ is a differential polynomial of degree at most $n-2$ in f. Setting

$$a(z) = h^{1-n}\pi_{n-1}(h),$$

$$H(z) = f(z) + \frac{a(z)}{n},$$

we may write this as

$$H(z)^n + M_{n-2}(H) = g(z), \tag{3.18}$$

where $M_{n-2}(H)$ is a differential polynomial of degree at most $n-2$ in H. We can now again differentiate (3.18) and eliminate $g(z)$. We obtain the analogue of (3.17), namely

$$H^{n-1}\left\{nH'(z) - \frac{g'}{g}H(z)\right\} = Q_{n-2}(H),$$

where we note that this time the polynomial Q_{n-2} has degree at most $n-2$. We may thus apply Lemma 3.3 to both

$$P(z) = nH'(z) - \frac{g'}{g}H(z)$$

and $P(z)H(z)$ instead of $P(z)$. We deduce as before that

$$T(r, P) = S(r,f)$$

and

$$T(r, PH) = S(r,f).$$

Hence if $P(z)$ is not identically zero we deduce

$$T(r, H) \leqslant T(r, PH) + T\left(r, \frac{1}{P}\right) = S(r,f).$$

This gives a contradiction since then also

$$T(r,f) \leqslant T(r, H) + T\left(r, \frac{a(z)}{n}\right) + O(1) = S(r,f).$$

Thus $P(z)$ must be identically zero and

$$n\,\frac{H'(z)}{H(z)} = \frac{g'(z)}{g(z)}, \qquad g(z) = c\{H(z)\}^n,$$

where c is a constant.

We can finally prove that $c = 1$. For otherwise we should deduce from (3.18) that

$$(1-c)H^n + M_{n-2}(H) = 0.$$

A further application of Lemma 3.3 now yields that

$$m\{r,(1-c)H\} = S(r, H) = S(r,f),$$

and since

$$N(r, H) \leqslant N(r,f) + N\left(r, \frac{a(z)}{h}\right) = S(r,f),$$

by hypothesis, this yields

$$T(r, H) = S(r,f)$$

giving a contradiction as before. Thus $c = 1$ and Theorem 3.9 is proved, since we can now set $H(z) = h(z)$.

3.5.6. We now return to the proof of Theorem 3.8. We need

LEMMA 3.5. *Suppose that $F(z)$ is meromorphic in a domain D and set $f(z) = F'(z)/F(z)$. Then we have for $n \geqslant 1$*

$$\frac{F^{(n)}(z)}{F(z)} = f^n + \frac{n(n-1)}{2}f^{n-2}f' + a_n f^{n-3}f'' + b_n f^{n-4}f'^2 + P_{n-3}(f),$$

where $a_n = \frac{1}{6}n(n-1)(n-2)$, $b_n = \frac{1}{8}n(n-1)(n-2)(n-3)$, and $P_{n-3}(f)$ is a differential polynomial with constant coefficients, which vanishes identically for $n \leqslant 3$ and has degree $n-3$ when $n > 3$.

We prove the result by induction. It is clearly true for $n = 1$, with $a_1 = b_1 = P_{-2}(f) = 0$. Suppose it is true for n. Then

$$F^{(n)}(z) = F(z)(f^n + \tfrac{1}{2}n(n-1)f^{n-2}f' + a_n f^{n-3}f'' + b_n f^{n-4}f'^2 + P_{n-3}).$$

We differentiate and set $F' = fF$. This yields

$$F^{(n+1)}(z) = F(z)(nf^{n-1}f' + \tfrac{1}{2}n(n-1)f^{n-2}f'' + \tfrac{1}{2}n(n-1)(n-2)f^{n-3}f'^2 +$$
$$+ f^{n+1} + \tfrac{1}{2}n(n-1)f^{n-1}f' + a_n f^{n-2}f'' + b_n f^{n-3}f'^2 + P_{n-2}),$$

where $P_{n-2} = (d/dz)(a_n f^{n-3}f'' + b_n f^{n-4}f'^2) + P'_{n-3} + fP_{n-3}$. Thus

$$\frac{F^{(n+1)}}{F} = f^{n+1} + \frac{n(n+1)}{2}f^{n-1}f' + \left(a_n + \frac{n(n-1)}{2}\right)f^{n-2}f'' +$$
$$+ \left(b_n + \frac{n(n-1)(n-2)}{2}\right)f^{n-3}f'^2 + P_{n-2}.$$

This completes our proof by induction. We also see that if $n = 1, 2$, $a_n = b_n = P_{n-3} = 0$, so that $P_{n-2} = 0$. Thus $P_0 \equiv 0$, $P_1 = a_3 f''' = f'''$, etc.

3.5.7. We can now prove Theorem 3.8 and in fact rather more.

THEOREM 3.10. *Suppose that $F(z)$ is meromorphic and not constant in the plane and that*

$$N(r, F) + N\left(r, \frac{1}{F}\right) + N\left(r, \frac{1}{F^{(l)}}\right) = S\left(r, \frac{F'}{F}\right)$$

for some $l \geqslant 2$. Then $F(z) = e^{az+b}$, where a, b are constants.

We set $f(z) = F'(z)/F(z)$ and assume that $f(z)$ is not constant, since otherwise there is nothing to prove.

Then we have by Lemma 3.5

$$\frac{F^{(l)}(z)}{F(z)} = f^l + \frac{l(l-1)}{2}f^{l-2}f' + a_l f^{l-3}f'' + b_l f^{l-4}f'^2 + P_{l-3}(f) = g(z),$$

$$\tag{3.19}$$

where $f = F'/F$,

$$N\left(r, \frac{1}{g}\right) = S(r, f), \qquad N(r, f) = S(r, f).$$

Thus Theorem 3.9 shows that $g(z) = \psi(z)^l$, where

$$\psi(z) = f(z) + \frac{l-1}{2l}\frac{g'(z)}{g(z)} = f(z) + \frac{l-1}{2}\frac{\psi'(z)}{\psi(z)}.$$

We set

$$\alpha(z) = \frac{l-1}{2}\frac{\psi'(z)}{\psi(z)}, \quad \psi' = \frac{2\alpha}{l-1}\psi, \quad \psi'' = \left(\frac{4\alpha^2}{(l-1)^2} + \frac{2\alpha'}{l-1}\right)\psi;$$

$$f(z) = \psi(z) - \alpha(z),$$

$$f' = \psi' - \alpha' = \frac{2\alpha}{l-1}\psi - \alpha',$$

$$f'' = \psi'' - \alpha'' = \left(\frac{4\alpha^2}{(l-1)^2} + \frac{2\alpha'}{l-1}\right)\psi - \alpha'', \text{ etc.}$$

Thus if $l \geqslant 2$ we obtain from (3.19)

$$(\psi-\alpha)^l+\frac{l(l-1)}{2}\,(\psi-\alpha)^{l-2}\Big(\frac{2\alpha}{l-1}\,\psi-\alpha'\Big)+$$

$$+\Big\{a_l\Big(\frac{4\alpha^2}{(l-1)^2}+\frac{2\alpha'}{l-1}\Big)+b_l\,\frac{4\alpha^2}{(l-1)^2}\Big\}\psi^{l-2}+Q_{l-3}(\psi)\equiv\psi^l,\quad(3.20)$$

where $Q_{l-3}(\psi)$ is a differential polynomial of degree at most $l-3$ in ψ. In fact the coefficients of Q_{l-3} are polynomials in α and its derivatives and the poles of α occur at the zeros and poles of $\psi(z)$, i.e. of $g(z)$, and so by hypothesis $N(r,\alpha)=S(r,f)$, and also

$$m(r,\alpha)=m\Big(r,\frac{\psi'}{\psi}\Big)+O(1)=m\Big(r,\frac{g'}{g}\Big)+O(1)=S(r,g)=S(r,f).$$

We collect terms in the powers of ψ in (3.20) and note that terms of degree l and $l-1$ go out. The equation becomes

$$a_0(z)\psi^{l-2}+\text{terms of degree } l-3 \text{ at most} \equiv 0,$$

where

$$a_0(z)=\frac{l(l-1)}{2}\,(\alpha^2-\alpha')-l(l-2)\alpha^2+a_l\Big(\frac{4\alpha^2}{(l-1)^2}+\frac{2\alpha'}{l-1}\Big)+b_l\,\frac{4\alpha^2}{(l-1)^2}$$

$$=\frac{l(l+1)}{6}\Big(\frac{\alpha^2}{l-1}-\alpha'\Big).$$

If $l=2$, we see at once that $a_0\psi^{l-2}\equiv 0$, so that† $a_0\equiv 0$. If $l>2$, we apply Lemma 3.3 with $n=l-3$, $f=\psi$, and $P=a_0\psi$. We deduce that

$$m(r,a_0\psi)=S(r,\psi)=S(r,f).$$

Since by hypothesis

$$N(r,\psi)=O\{N(r,g)\}=S(r,f),$$

we deduce

$$T(r,a_0\psi)=S(r,f)$$

and hence, if a_0 is not identically zero,

$$T(r,\psi)=S(r,f),\qquad T(r,f)\leqslant T(r,\psi)+T\Big(r,\frac{g'}{g}\Big)+O(1)=S(r,f),$$

giving a contradiction. Thus in any case

$$a_0(z)=\frac{l(l+1)}{6}\Big\{\frac{\alpha^2}{l-1}-\alpha'\Big\}\equiv 0.$$

---

† We cannot have $\psi\equiv 0$, since this yields $F^{(l)}\equiv 0$, which contradicts our hypotheses.

This gives on integration, either $\alpha(z) \equiv 0$, or

$$\frac{\alpha'}{\alpha^2} = \frac{1}{l-1}, \qquad \frac{1}{\alpha} = \frac{A-z}{l-1},$$

$$\alpha(z) = \frac{l-1}{2}\frac{\psi'}{\psi} = \frac{l-1}{A-z},$$

$$\psi(z) = B(A-z)^{-2}, \quad B \neq 0.$$

$$\frac{F'(z)}{F(z)} = f(z) = \psi(z) - \frac{l-1}{2}\cdot\frac{\psi'(z)}{\psi(z)} = B(A-z)^{-2} - \frac{l-1}{A-z};$$

$$F(z) = C(A-z)^{l-1}\exp\{B(A-z)^{-1}\}, \quad B \neq 0, \quad C \neq 0.$$

This function is not meromorphic in the plane, and so we must have $\alpha(z) = 0$, $\psi(z) \equiv \text{const} \equiv f(z)$.

$$F'/F = \text{const}, \qquad F(z) = e^{az+b}.$$

This completes the proof of Theorem 3.10.

3.5.8. We proceed to deduce Theorem 3.8. Suppose that $F(z)$, $F^{(l)}(z)$ have only a finite number of zeros and poles. Then

$$N(r, F) + N\left(r, \frac{1}{F}\right) + N\left(r, \frac{1}{F^{(l)}}\right) = O(\log r).$$

Thus Theorem 3.10 shows that if $f(z) = F'/F$, then

$$\lim_{r \to +\infty} \frac{T(r,f)}{\log r} < +\infty,$$

so that $f(z)$ is rational. We deduce easily that

$$F(z) = \frac{P_1(z)}{P_2(z)} e^{P_3(z)},$$

where P_1, P_2, P_3 are polynomials. Suppose further that $F(z)$ and $F^{(l)}(z)$ have no zeros. Then we may take $P_1 \equiv 1$;

$$f(z) = \frac{F'}{F} = P_3' - \frac{P_2'}{P_2}.$$

Thus, by Lemma 3.5, $\qquad \dfrac{F^{(l)}(z)}{F(z)} = f^l + Q_{l-1}(f),$

where $Q_{l-1}(f)$ is a polynomial of degree $l-1$ in f and its derivatives. If P_3' is not constant we see that near ∞,

$$\frac{F^{(l)}}{F} \sim f^l \sim (P_3')^l \to \infty, \quad \text{as } z \to \infty.$$

Since a non-constant rational function assumes every value in the closed plane, it follows that $F^{(l)}(z) = 0$ somewhere in the open plane, giving a contradiction. If $P_3' = c \neq 0$, and $f(z)$ is not constant, we see that $f(z) = c$, $f' = f'' = \ldots = 0$ at ∞. Now we see that on the right-hand side of (3.19) all the terms except the first vanish at ∞, so that $F^{(l)}/F = c^l$ at ∞, and $F^{(l)}/F$ must again have a zero in the open plane. Thus if $P_3' \neq 0$, we must have $P_3' = c = f(z)$, $F(z) = e^{cz+b}$.

Finally, if $P_3' \equiv 0$, $P_3 = \text{const}$, we may write

$$F(z) = \frac{1}{P_2(z)}.$$

Thus if $P_2(z)$ has degree n, $F(z)$ has a zero of order n at ∞ and no finite zeros. Suppose that $F(z)$ has distinct poles of multiplicity p_ν ($\nu = 1$ to N). Then $\sum p_\nu = n$. Also $F^{(l)}(z)$ has poles of multiplicity $p_\nu + l$, so that altogether $F^{(l)}(z)$ has $\sum (p_\nu + l) = n + lN$ poles. Also $F^{(l)}(z)$ has a zero of order $n + l$ at ∞. Thus $F^{(l)}(z)$ has $l(N-1)$ finite zeros, and so if $F^{(l)}(z)$ has no finite zeros, $N = 1$, and $F(z)$ has only one pole, so that

$$F(z) = (Az + B)^{-n}.$$

This completes the proof of Theorem 3.8.

3.6. Conclusion

The results of this chapter show that the derivatives $f^{(l)}(z)$ of a meromorphic function $f(z)$ assume all finite values with at most one exception (Theorem 3.4). If $f(z)$ itself fails to assume some finite value a, then $f^{(l)}(z)$ assumes all finite values except possibly zero (Theorem 3.5). If in addition $f(z)$ has only a finite number of poles and is not one of the functions e^{az+b} or $(az+b)^{-n}$, and if $l \geqslant 2$, then $f^{(l)}(z)$ assumes all finite values without exception (Theorem 3.8). We have seen that the proof of the latter theorem leads to the problem of whether certain differential polynomials in a function $f(z)$ necessarily have zeros. This problem is solved in Theorem 3.9 in the case when $f(z)$ is an integral function and the polynomial has a single highest term f^n.

The most interesting open problem appears to be the extension of Theorem 3.8 to general meromorphic functions by deleting the hypotheses about the poles. Are e^{az+b} and $(az+b)^{-n}$ the only meromorphic functions such that $f(z)f^{(l)}(z) \neq 0$, for a single $l \geqslant 2$? If we put $f(z) = \{g(z)\}^{-1}$, where $g(z)$ is an integral function, then $f''(z) = \{2g'^2 - gg''\}/g^3$ so that we are led to the problem of whether differential polynomials such as $G(z) = gg'' - 2g'^2$ in the integral function $g(z)$ necessarily have zeros except when $g(z) = e^{az+b}$ or $(az+b)^n$. Since $G(z)$ is a homogeneous differential polynomial in $g(z)$ this problem appears to be beyond the scope of the methods of this chapter.

Another problem of some interest concerns the question of whether we can eliminate the term $\overline{N}(r,f)$ in Theorem 3.2 under hypotheses a little more general than those of Theorem 3.5. We also do not know whether the coefficients of $N(r, 1/f)$, $\overline{N}\{r, 1/(f^{(l)}-1)\}$ in the inequality of Theorem 3.5 are best possible, or whether Theorem 3.4 is sharp for $l \geqslant 2$.

FURTHER RESULTS ABOUT DEFICIENCIES

4.0. Introduction

In this chapter we consider further the possible deficient values and the values of their deficiencies for functions $f(z)$ meromorphic in the plane. This subject has grown very considerably in the last decade and it is not possible to do more here than to make a selection of some results which seem interesting and which can be proved in a reasonably short space of time. For other results we shall refer the reader to original papers.

As we saw in Chapter 2, Theorem 2.4, the deficient values a of a function $f(z)$ meromorphic in the plane are countable in number and their deficiencies satisfy

$$\sum_i \delta(a) \leqslant 2. \tag{4.1}$$

It has been shown by Le Van Thiem [1], completing an earlier result of R. Nevanlinna [2], that if the δ_n $(n = 1$ to $N)$ form a finite set of rational numbers such that

$$\sum_1^N \delta_n \leqslant 2,$$

and if a_1 to a_N are arbitrary distinct numbers in the closed plane, then there exists a meromorphic function $f(z)$ such that

$$\delta(a_n, f) = \delta_n \quad (n = 1 \text{ to } N). \tag{4.2}$$

The first example of a meromorphic function with irrational deficiency was constructed by Wittich (see, for example, [1], p. 128). Subsequently Gol'dberg [1] removed the restriction that the δ_n have to be rational in the theorem of Le Van Thiem, provided that

$$\sum_1^N \delta_n < 2.$$

Gol'dberg [2, 4] then provided a further major break-through by constructing the first examples of meromorphic functions $f(z)$ with infinitely many deficient values. His functions $f(z)$ could have arbitrary positive and finite order and the set of deficient values could be any countable set. By a theorem of Valiron [2] (see Theorem 4.11) a meromorphic function of order zero can have at most one deficient value.

Thus the set of deficient values of a meromorphic function of order ρ can be any countable set if $\rho > 0$ and consists of at most one point if $\rho = 0$.

We shall start this chapter by giving an example due to W. H. J. Fuchs and the author [1] of an integral function (of infinite order) having a completely arbitrary countable set of deficient values, and, with completely arbitrary deficiencies of these values, subject only to the condition (4.1) and $\delta(\infty) = 1$. Thus for integral functions of infinite order the inequality of Nevanlinna

$$\sum_{a \neq \infty} \delta(a) \leqslant 1$$

contains the only general restriction on the deficiencies.

We next show, however, that for meromorphic functions of finite order the inequality

$$\sum \delta(a)^\alpha < +\infty \tag{4.3}$$

holds for every $\alpha > \frac{1}{3}$. The case $\alpha = \frac{1}{2}$ is due to Fuchs [1]. By examples rather similar to those of Gol'dberg quoted above we show that (4.3) need not be true when $\alpha < \frac{1}{3}$. The case $\alpha = \frac{1}{3}$ remains in doubt.

We continue the chapter by proving some results about integral functions of finite non-integral order.

Finally, by using a general inequality of Gol'dberg, we shall prove a theorem of Edrei and Fuchs [3] giving the possible limitations on the pair of deficiencies $\delta(0,f)$, $\delta(\infty,f)$ when $f(z)$ is a meromorphic function of assigned order ρ, where $0 \leqslant \rho < 1$. Various earlier results follow as consequences of this general theorem. For other important recent results by Edrei, Fuchs, and others we shall have to refer the reader to the original papers.

4.1. An integral function with assigned deficiencies

The next few sections will be occupied with the proof of†

THEOREM 4.1. *Let a_ν be an arbitrary sequence of distinct complex numbers and δ_ν a sequence of positive numbers, $1 < \nu \leqslant N \leqslant \infty$, subject only to*

$$\sum_{\nu=1}^{N} \delta_\nu \leqslant 1.$$

Then there exists an integral function $f(z)$ such that

$$\delta(a_\nu, f) = \delta_\nu \quad (\nu = 1 \text{ to } N)$$

and such that $f(z)$ has no deficient values other than the a_ν.

---

† Fuchs and Hayman [1].

Our proof will be based on the general method of Gol'dberg [2, 4]. If

$$f(z) = \frac{\sum a_n \phi_n(z)}{\phi(z)}$$

and if $\phi_m(z)$ and $\phi(z)$ are both large and nearly equal on certain sets F_m which are disjoint for different m, while $\phi_m(z)$ is small outside F_m, then $f(z) \simeq a_m$ on F_m. If $f(z)$ is to be an integral function we must choose $\phi(z)$ without zeros and the $\phi_n(z)$ without poles. We shall choose

$$\phi(z) = \exp(e^z + z). \tag{4.4}$$

4.1.1. For the $\phi_n(z)$ we need the following:

LEMMA 4.1.† *There exists an integral function $E_0(z)$, such that in the strip*
$$A_0: \quad x > 0, \quad |y| \leqslant \pi \qquad (z = x + iy)$$
we have
$$E_0(z) = \phi(z) + O(z^{-2}), \tag{4.5}$$
while outside A_0 we have
$$E_0(z) = O(z^{-2}) \tag{4.6}$$
uniformly as $z \to \infty$, where $\phi(z)$ is given by (4.4).

Let L be the contour given by $x = 0$, $|y| \leqslant \pi$, and $y = \mp\pi$, $x \geqslant 0$ described in the clockwise direction and consider

$$E(z) = \frac{1}{2\pi i} \int\limits_L \frac{e^{e^\zeta} d\zeta}{\zeta - z}.$$

Clearly $E(z)$ represents a regular function $E_1(z)$ for z inside L, i.e. in A_0, and a (possibly) different regular function $E_2(z)$ for z outside A_0.

We next note that if $L(a)$ is the contour, given by $x = a$, $|y| \leqslant \pi$, $x \geqslant a$, $y = \mp\pi$, then, by Cauchy's theorem,

$$I = \frac{1}{2\pi i} \int\limits_{L(a)} e^{e^\zeta} d\zeta$$

is independent of a. Since the integrals along the rays $y = \mp\pi$, $x \geqslant a$, cancel out we have

$$I = \frac{1}{2\pi} \int\limits_{-\pi}^{\pi} e^{e^{a+iy}} dy.$$

This tends to one as $a \to -\infty$, so that $I = 1$. Thus

$$E(z) + \frac{1}{z} = \frac{1}{2\pi i} \int\limits_L \frac{e^{e^\zeta} \zeta \, d\zeta}{z(\zeta - z)}.$$

Suppose now that $R = |z| \geqslant 2\pi$. We divide the latter integral into

† Pólya and Szegö [1, chapter iii, problems 158–60, pp. 115–16] introduce the function $E_2(z)$ such that $E_0(z) = E_2'(z)$.

those parts for which $|\zeta| < \frac{1}{2}R$, $\frac{1}{2}R \leqslant |\zeta| \leqslant 2R$, and $|\zeta| > 2R$, and denote the corresponding integrals by I_1, I_2, and I_3, respectively. Then

$$|I_1| + |I_3| < \frac{A}{R^2} \int_L |\zeta e e^\zeta| |d\zeta| \leqslant \frac{A}{R^2}\left\{ \int_0^\infty xe^{-e^x}\, dx + O(1) \right\} < \frac{A}{R^2}.$$

Also we indent L away from z by an arc of a circle of radius $\frac{1}{4}$, so that on the new contour L', $|\zeta - z| \geqslant \frac{1}{4}$ everywhere. This does not affect the value of I_2 by Cauchy's theorem, provided the endpoints of L are kept fixed. On L' we have, setting $\zeta = \xi + i\eta$,

$$\left| \frac{\zeta e e^\zeta}{z(\zeta - z)} \right| \leqslant A\exp(e^\xi \cos\eta) \leqslant A\exp(-\tfrac{1}{2}e^{\frac{1}{4}R})$$

when z is large so that

$$I_2 = O(R)\exp(-\tfrac{1}{2}e^{\frac{1}{4}R}) = o(R^{-2}).$$

Thus
$$E(z) + \frac{1}{z} = O(z^{-2}),$$

as $z \to \infty$ in any manner.

Now let $E_1(z)$ represent the value of $E(z)$ for z inside A_0 and $E_2(z)$ the value of $E(z)$ outside A_0. Both $E_1(z)$, $E_2(z)$ can be analytically continued beyond L, since we can deform L without altering $E(z)$. For z near L,

$$E_2(z) - E_1(z) = \frac{1}{2\pi i} \int_C \frac{e e^\zeta\, d\zeta}{\zeta - z},$$

where C is a contour surrounding z once in the positive direction. Thus

$$E_2(z) - E_1(z) = e^{e^z},$$

and $E_1(z)$, $E_2(z)$ are both integral functions. In particular,

$$E_2(z) = E(z) = -\frac{1}{z} + \frac{O(1)}{z^2}, \quad \text{as } z \to \infty \text{ outside } A_0; \tag{4.7}$$

$$E_2(z) = E_1(z) + e^{e^z} = E(z) + e^{e^z} = e^{e^z} - \frac{1}{z} + \frac{O(1)}{z^2}, \quad \text{as } z \to \infty \text{ inside } A_0. \tag{4.8}$$

Also for ζ on L, and $|z - \zeta| \leqslant \frac{1}{4}\pi$, we have

$$e^{e^z} = O\{e^{-\frac{1}{2}e^x}\} = O(|z|^{-2}),$$

so that (4.7) and (4.8) remain valid uniformly in a disk of radius $\frac{1}{4}\pi$ and centre z. We set

$$E_0(z) = E_2'(z) = \frac{1}{2\pi} \int_0^{2\pi} E_2(z + \tfrac{1}{4}\pi e^{i\theta}) \frac{4}{\pi} e^{-i\theta}\, d\theta,$$

and using (4.7) and (4.8) we deduce Lemma 4.1.

Example. If $E_0(z)$ is the function of Lemma 4.1 prove that

$$\log M\{r, E_0(z)\} \sim e^r, \qquad T\{r, E_0(z)\} \sim \frac{e^r}{\pi r},$$

as $r \to \infty$. Hence show that Theorem 1.8 no longer holds when $K = 1$.

4.1.2. We now write A_n for the half-strip

$$A_n: x > 0, \quad (2n-1)\pi \leqslant y \leqslant (2n+1)\pi.$$

Let
$$E_n(z) = E_0(z-2n\pi i),$$

where $E_0(z)$ is defined as in Lemma 4.1. Then $E_n(z)$ has similar behaviour in A_n to that of $E_0(z)$ in A_0. Let b_n, c_n be complex numbers such that
$$b_{-n} = b_n, \quad c_{-n} = c_n \qquad (n = 0 \text{ to } \infty)$$

and
$$s = \sum_{n=-\infty}^{\infty} \frac{|b_n|+|c_n|}{1+n^2} < \infty. \tag{4.9}$$

Put
$$f(z) = \exp(-e^z-z) \sum_{n=-\infty}^{\infty} (c_n+b_n z)E_n(z). \tag{4.10}$$

We shall see that $f(z)$ has all required properties for suitable b_n and c_n.

LEMMA 4.2. *We have as $z = x+iy \to \infty$ in any manner*

$$f(z) = b_m z+c_m+O\{(1+|z|^3)\exp(-e^z-z)\},$$

where m is the integer defined by

$$(2m-1)\pi < y \leqslant (2m+1)\pi.$$

Let m be defined as in Lemma 4.2. If

$$|n| \geqslant 2|m|+1,$$

then
$$|y-2\pi n| \geqslant 2\pi|n|-2\pi|m|-\pi \geqslant 2\pi|n|-\pi|n| = \pi|n| \geqslant \pi,$$

so that, by Lemma 4.1,

$$|E_n(z)| = |E_0\{x+(y-2\pi n)i\}| < An^{-2},$$

where A is an absolute constant. Hence

$$\left| \sum_{|n| \geqslant 2|m|+1} (b_n z+c_n)E_n(z) \right| \leqslant \sum_{|n| \geqslant 2|m|+1} (|b_n|+|c_n|)(|z|+1)An^{-2}$$

$$\leqslant 2As(1+|z|),$$

where s is defined by (4.9). If

$$|n| < 2|m|+1 \quad (n \neq m),$$

then z lies outside A_n and therefore

$$E_n(z) = O(1),$$

$$\left| \sum_{\substack{|n| < 2|m|+1 \\ n \neq m}} (b_n z + c_n) E_n(z) \right| = O(1 + |z|) \sum_{|n| < 2|m|+1} (|b_n| + |c_n|)$$

$$= O\{(1 + |z|)(1 + m^2)\} \sum \frac{|b_n| + |c_n|}{1 + n^2}$$

$$= O\{s(1 + |z|)(1 + y^2)\} = O(1 + |z|^3).$$

Thus $\qquad \exp(e^z + z) f(z) = (b_m z + c_m) E_m(z) + O(1 + |z|^3).$

By Lemma 4.1, $\qquad E_m(z) = \exp(e^z + z) + O(1);$
also by (4.9),

$$|b_m z + c_m| \leqslant (1 + |z|)(1 + m^2) \frac{|b_m| + |c_m|}{1 + m^2} = O(1 + |z|^3).$$

Hence, finally,

$$f(z) = b_m z + c_m + O(1 + |z|^3) \exp(-e^z - z),$$

which is Lemma 4.2.

4.1.3. *Estimate of $T(r,f)$.* Our next result is

LEMMA 4.3. *Suppose that $\phi(y)$ is a bounded, non-negative and even function for real y and that*

$$\frac{1}{Y} \int_0^Y \phi(y) \, dy \to l \quad as \ Y \to \infty.$$

Then $\quad I(r) = \frac{1}{2\pi} \int_{-\pi}^{\pi} e^{r \cos \theta} \phi(r \sin \theta) \, d\theta = \frac{\{l + o(1)\} e^r}{(2\pi r)^{\frac{1}{2}}} \quad as \ r \to \infty.$

Let

$$\psi(y) = \int_0^y \phi(t) \, dt,$$

$$\chi(y) = \chi(y, r) = e^{\sqrt{(r^2 - y^2)}} / \sqrt{(r^2 - y^2)}.$$

Note that we have as $r \to \infty$ uniformly for $0 < y < \frac{1}{2} r \sqrt{3}$

$$\chi(y) = O(e^r / r),$$

$$0 < -\chi'(y) = O(e^r / r).$$

Set $r \sin \theta = y$. Then

$$I(r) = \frac{1}{\pi} \int_0^{\pi} e^{r \cos \theta} \phi(r \sin \theta) \, d\theta = \frac{1}{\pi} \int_0^{\frac{1}{3}\pi} e^{r \cos \theta} \phi(r \sin \theta) \, d\theta + O(e^{\frac{1}{2} r \sqrt{3}})$$

$$= \frac{1}{\pi} \int_0^{\frac{1}{2} r} \chi(y) \psi'(y) \, dy + o(e^r / r) = -\frac{1}{\pi} \int_0^{\frac{1}{2} r} \psi(y) \chi'(y) \, dy + o(e^r / r).$$

We split the range of integration into the intervals $(0, r^{1/6})$, $(r^{1/6}, \tfrac{1}{2}r)$. In the first interval

$$\psi(y)\chi'(y) = O(ye^r/r),$$

so that
$$\int_0^{r^{1/6}} \psi(y)\chi'(y)\, dy = O(r^{1/3}e^r/r) = o(e^r/r^{\frac{1}{2}}).$$

In the second interval uniformly

$$\psi(y) = \{l+o(1)\}y.$$

Hence

$$I(r) = -\frac{l}{\pi} \int_{r^{1/6}}^{\frac{1}{2}r} y\chi'(y)\, dy\, \{1+o(1)\}+o(e^r r^{-\frac{1}{2}})$$

$$= -\frac{l}{\pi} \int_0^{\frac{1}{2}r} y\chi'(y)\, dy\, \{1+o(1)\}+o(e^r r^{-\frac{1}{2}})$$

$$= \frac{l}{\pi}\{1+o(1)\} \int_0^{\frac{1}{2}r} \chi(y)\, dy+o(e^r r^{-\frac{1}{2}}). \qquad (4.11)$$

Let $\sqrt{(r^2-y^2)} = r-u;\ 1-\tfrac{1}{2}\sqrt{3} = \alpha$. Then

$$\int_0^{\frac{1}{2}r} \chi(y)\, dy = e^r \int_0^{\alpha r} e^{-u}(2ru-u^2)^{-\frac{1}{2}}\, du$$

$$= e^r \int_0^{r^{1/2}} e^{-u}u^{-\frac{1}{2}}(2r)^{-\frac{1}{2}}\{1+o(1)\}\, du+O(e^{r-r^{\frac{1}{2}}})$$

$$= e^r(2r)^{-\frac{1}{2}} \int_0^{\infty} e^{-u}u^{-\frac{1}{2}}\, du+o(e^r r^{-\frac{1}{2}})$$

$$= e^r(\pi/2r)^{\frac{1}{2}}+o(e^r r^{-\frac{1}{2}}). \qquad (4.12)$$

Now Lemma 4.3 follows on substitution from (4.12) into (4.11).

We deduce that if $f(z)$ is defined by (4.10), then

$$T(r,f) \leqslant e^r(2\pi^3 r)^{-\frac{1}{2}}\{1+o(1)\}. \qquad (4.13)$$

as $r \to \infty$.

We set
$$\phi(y) = \max(-\cos y, 0)$$

and note that

$$\lim_{Y \to \infty} \frac{1}{Y} \int_0^Y \phi(y)\, dy = \frac{1}{2\pi} \int_{\frac{1}{2}\pi}^{\frac{3}{2}\pi} (-\cos y)\, dy = \frac{1}{\pi}.$$

Also, if $z = x+iy$,

$$\log^+|e^{-e^z-z}| = \log^+(e^{-e^x\cos y-x}) \leqslant e^x\phi(y)+|z|.$$

Again, with the notation of Lemma 4.2, we have as $z \to \infty$,

$$\log^+ |f(z)| \leqslant \log^+ |b_m z + c_m| + 3 \log^+ |z| + \log^+ |e^{-e^z - z}| + O(1).$$

By (4.9),

$$|b_m z + c_m| < (1 + |z|)(1 + m^2) \frac{|b_m| + |c_m|}{1 + m^2} < s(1 + |z|)^3,$$

since $|m| \leqslant |z|/\pi$. Thus, for $z = x + iy$,

$$\log^+ |f(z)| \leqslant e^x \phi(y) + O(|z|),$$

$$T(r, f) = \frac{1}{2\pi} \int_{-\pi}^{\pi} \log^+ |f(re^{i\theta})| \, d\theta \leqslant \frac{1}{2\pi} \int_{-\pi}^{\pi} e^{r \cos \theta} \phi(r \sin \theta) \, d\theta + O(r).$$

Now (4.13) follows from Lemma 4.3 with $l = 1/\pi$.

4.1.4. *Densities of sets of integers.* Let S be a set of positive integers and let $t(n)$ be the number of integers from 1 to n which belong to S. The density of S is defined as

$$d(S) = \lim_{n \to \infty} t(n)/n,$$

provided this limit exists.

It is clear that if $S_1, S_2, ..., S_p$ are a finite number of mutually disjoint sets of positive integers having densities $d_1, d_2, ..., d_p$, then

$$S = \bigcup_{k=1}^{p} S_k \quad \text{has density} \quad \sum_{k=1}^{p} d_k.$$

In order to proceed we need

LEMMA 4.4. *Suppose that $1 \leqslant N \leqslant \infty$, and that δ_ν ($\nu = 1$ to N) are positive numbers such that*

$$\delta = \sum_{\nu=1}^{N} \delta_\nu \leqslant 1.$$

Set $\delta_0 = 1 - \delta$, so that $\sum_{\nu=0}^{N} \delta_\nu = 1$. Then it is possible to partition the positive integers into mutually disjoint sets S_ν of density δ_ν ($\nu = 0$ to N).

We proceed by induction. Suppose that S_0 to S_{n-1} have already been defined and let

$$\Sigma_n = \bigcup_{\nu=0}^{n-1} S_\nu.$$

Then Σ_n has density

$$d_n = \sum_{\nu=0}^{n-1} \delta_\nu.$$

Let $K_1, K_2, ..., K_p$ be the increasing sequence of integers in the complement C_n of Σ_n. Then C_n has density $1 - d_n$. Suppose that $n \leqslant N$, so that $d_n < 1$ and C_n is not empty. We define S_n to consist of all the integers $K_{[\alpha q]}$ $(q = 1, 2, ...)$, where

$$\alpha = (1-d_n)/\delta_n.$$

Since C_n has density $1-d_n$, it follows that

$$\frac{K_p}{p} \to \frac{1}{1-d_n} \quad \text{as } p \to \infty,$$

and so

$$\frac{K_{[\alpha q]}}{q} \to \frac{\alpha}{1-d_n} = \frac{1}{\delta_n} \quad \text{as } q \to \infty.$$

Thus S_n has density δ_n.

If $n = 0$ we proceed as above taking for C_0 the set of all integers. If N is finite the construction continues to be possible for $n = 1$ to N. Also S_N is equal to C_N, so we shall have used up all the positive integers. If $N = +\infty$, then $\delta_n < 1-d_n$ for every finite n and so C_n is never empty and S_n is defined for $n = 1$ to ∞. If C' is the set of integers not contained in any S_n, then C' has density at most $1-d_n$ and so C' has density zero. We add C' to S_0 and the new set S_0' has density $\delta_0+0 = \delta_0$. Thus we have achieved our partition also in this case. This proves Lemma 4.4.

We now take for δ_ν and a_ν the quantities of Theorem 4.1, and for S_ν the sets defined in Lemma 4.4. For $\nu \geqslant 1$ let S_ν' consist of all those integers n in S_ν for which

$$n > 2^\nu(1+|a_\nu|).$$

Since S_ν' is obtained from S_ν by subtracting a finite number of elements, S_ν' has the same density as S_ν, i.e. δ_ν. Furthermore, we define S_0' to consist of all non-negative integers not in any of the S_ν' $(\nu = 1$ to $N)$. Then S_0' contains S_0 and so has density at least δ_0. On the other hand, S_0' lies in the complement of S_1' to S_n' and so has density at most $1- \sum_{\nu=1}^{n} \delta_\nu$, for any finite $n \leqslant N$. Thus S_0' still has density δ_0.

We now set

$$\left. \begin{array}{ll} b_n = 0, & c_n = a_\nu \quad \text{if } |n| \in S_\nu' \ (1 \leqslant \nu \leqslant N) \\ b_n = 1, & c_n = 0 \quad \text{if } |n| \in S_0' \end{array} \right\} . \tag{4.14}$$

where the a_ν are the quantities of Theorem 4.1. This defines $f(z)$ uniquely in (4.10). We must only verify that (4.9) holds. Now

$$\sum_{|n| \in S_0'} \frac{|b_n|+|c_n|}{1+n^2} < 2 \sum_{n=0}^{\infty} \frac{1}{1+n^2} < \infty,$$

and for $1 \leqslant p \leqslant N$

$$\sum_{|n| \in S_p'} \frac{|b_n| + |c_n|}{1+n^2} < \sum_{n > 2^p(1+|a_p|)} \frac{2|a_p|}{1+n^2} < \frac{2|a_p|}{2^p |a_p|} = \frac{1}{2^{p-1}}.$$

Thus
$$s = \sum_{-\infty}^{+\infty} \frac{|b_n| + |c_n|}{1+n^2} = O\left(\sum_{p=1}^{\infty} 2^{-p}\right) < \infty,$$

which is (4.9).

4.1.5. *The lower bound for the deficiencies of $f(z)$.* We can now prove Lemma 4.5. *With the definitions* (4.14) *of b_n and c_n and with $f(z)$ given by* (4.10)

$$\delta(a_\nu, f) \geqslant \delta_\nu \quad (1 \leqslant \nu \leqslant N),$$

$$\delta(0, f(z) - z) \geqslant \delta_0.$$

Let
$$\phi_\nu(y) = \begin{cases} \cos y, & \text{if } (2n - \tfrac{1}{2})\pi < y < (2n + \tfrac{1}{2})\pi, \ |n| \in S_\nu', \\ 0, & \text{otherwise.} \end{cases}$$

Then
$$\lim_{Y \to \infty} \frac{1}{Y} \int_0^Y \phi_\nu(y)\, dy = \frac{1}{\pi} \delta_\nu. \tag{4.15}$$

Also, if $z = x + iy$ where $(2n - \tfrac{1}{2})\pi < y \leqslant (2n + \tfrac{1}{2})\pi$, $|n| \in S_\nu'$, then by (4.14) and Lemma 4.2,

$$f(z) - a_\nu = O(1 + |z|^3) |e^{-e^z - z}| \quad (\nu \geqslant 1),$$

$$f(z) - z = O(1 + |z|^3) |e^{-e^z - z}| \quad (\nu = 0).$$

Thus, for $\nu \geqslant 1$ and large z,

$$\log^+ \left| \frac{1}{f(z) - a_\nu} \right| \geqslant e^x \phi_\nu(y) - \log(1 + |z|^3) - |z| - O(1)$$
$$\geqslant e^x \phi_\nu(y) - O(z).$$

Using Lemma 4.3 and (4.15) we deduce that

$$m\left(r, \frac{1}{f(z) - a_\nu}\right) \geqslant \{\delta_\nu + o(1)\} e^r (2\pi^3 r)^{-\frac{1}{2}},$$

as $r \to \infty$.

Similarly,
$$m\left(r, \frac{1}{f(z) - z}\right) \geqslant \{\delta_0 + o(1)\} e^r (2\pi^3 r)^{-\frac{1}{2}}.$$

In view of (4.13) and the fact that

$$T(r, f(z) - z) \leqslant T(r, f) + T(r, z) + O(1) \leqslant e^r (2\pi^3 r)^{-\frac{1}{2}} \{1 + o(1)\},$$

we have Lemma 4.5.

4.1.6.† *Completion of proof of Theorem* 4.1. To prove Theorem 4.1 we shall establish that for any transcendental integral function $f(z)$

$$\sum_{a \neq \infty} \delta(a,f) + \delta(0, f(z) - z) \leqslant 1. \tag{4.16}$$

Since by Lemma 4.5 we have for our particular $f(z)$

$$\sum_{a \neq \infty} \delta(a,f) \geqslant \sum_{\nu=1}^{N} \delta_\nu = 1 - \delta_0, \qquad \delta(0, f(z) - z) \geqslant \delta_0,$$

the sign of equality must hold here and in (4.16), which is only possible if (i) $\delta(a,f) = 0$ for all values of a distinct from the a_ν and (ii) $\delta(a_\nu, f) = \delta_\nu$. These last two statements are the assertion of Theorem 4.1.

It remains to prove (4.16). Let $f(z)$ be a transcendental integral function and $a_1, a_2, ..., a_q$ distinct complex numbers. Set

$$F(z) = \sum_{\nu=1}^{q} \frac{1}{f(z) - a_\nu}.$$

Then it follows from (2.1) and Theorem 2.2 that

$$\sum_{\nu=1}^{q} m\left(r, \frac{1}{f(z) - a_\nu}\right) \leqslant m\{r, F(z)\} + O(1)$$

$$\leqslant m\left(r, \frac{1}{f'(z)}\right) + m\{r, f'(z) F(z)\} + O(1)$$

$$\leqslant m\left(r, \frac{1}{f'(z)}\right) + o\left[T\{r, f(z)\}\right] \tag{4.17}$$

outside a set of finite linear measure. By applying this result to $f(z) - z$ with $q = 1$, $a_1 = 0$ we deduce similarly that

$$m\left(r, \frac{1}{f(z) - z}\right) \leqslant m\left(r, \frac{1}{f'(z) - 1}\right) + o\left[T\{r, f(z) - z\}\right]$$

$$\leqslant m\left(r, \frac{1}{f'(z) - 1}\right) + o\{T(r, f)\}. \tag{4.18}$$

A further application shows that

$$m\left(r, \frac{1}{f'(z)}\right) + m\left(r, \frac{1}{f'(z) - 1}\right)$$

$$\leqslant m\left(r, \frac{1}{f''}\right) + o\{T(r, f')\} \leqslant m(r, f'') + o\{m(r, f')\}$$

$$\leqslant \{1 + o(1)\} m(r, f') + m\left(r, \frac{f''}{f'}\right) \leqslant \{1 + o(1)\} m(r, f) + m\left(r, \frac{f'}{f}\right)$$

$$\leqslant \{1 + o(1)\} m(r, f), \tag{4.19}$$

† The author is indebted to Dr. A. A. Gol'dberg for pointing out an error in an earlier version of this section.

outside a set of finite linear measure. On combining (4.17), (4.18), and (4.19) we deduce that outside a set of finite linear measure

$$\sum_{v=1}^{q} m\left(r, \frac{1}{f(z)-a_v}\right) + m\left(r, \frac{1}{f(z)-z}\right) \leqslant \{1+o(1)\}T(r,f(z)). \qquad (4.20)$$

We divide by $T(r,f(z))$ and take the lower limit of the left-hand side. We note also that

$$T(r,f(z)-z) = T(r,f)+O(\log r) \sim T(r,f).$$

Thus (4.20) yields

$$\sum_{v=1}^{q} \delta(a_v,f)+\delta(0,f(z)-z) \leqslant 1,$$

which gives (4.16) for any transcendental integral function $f(z)$. Thus the proof of Theorem 4.1 is complete.

Example. If $a = a(z)$ is a polynomial and $f(z)$ a transcendental integral function we define

$$\delta(a,f) = \varprojlim_{n\to\infty} \frac{m\left(r, \dfrac{1}{f(z)-a(z)}\right)}{T(r,f)}.$$

With this notation prove that

$$\sum_a \delta(a,f) \leqslant 1,$$

where the sum is taken over all distinct polynomials.

4.2. On the deficiencies of meromorphic functions of finite order

In this section we shall consider what can be said about the deficiencies $\delta(a,f)$ of meromorphic functions $f(z)$ of finite order beyond the inequality

$$\sum \delta(a,f) \leqslant 2.$$

We shall prove in particular†

THEOREM 4.2. *Suppose that $f(z)$ is meromorphic and of lower order λ in the plane, where $0 < \lambda < \infty$. Then for $\alpha > \frac{1}{3}$, we have*

$$\sum \delta(a,f)^\alpha < A(\alpha,\lambda),$$

where $A(\alpha,\lambda)$ depends on α and λ only.

The case $\alpha = \frac{1}{2}$ of the above result is due to Fuchs [1] who proved it with $A(\frac{1}{2},\lambda) = A(q \log q)^2$, where $q = \max(2,\lambda)$, and A is an absolute constant. We shall see that Theorem 4.2 fails for $\alpha < \frac{1}{3}$, while the case $\alpha = \frac{1}{3}$ remains in doubt. Our method yields

$$A(\alpha,\lambda) = A(1+\lambda^{3\alpha})/(3\alpha-1)^\alpha \quad (\tfrac{1}{3} < \alpha \leqslant \tfrac{1}{2}).$$

† Not previously published. In this section A denotes an absolute constant not necessarily the same each time it occurs.

4.2.1. Following Fuchs [1] our proof of Theorem 4.2 will be based upon the Poisson–Jensen formula applied to $f'(z)$. We need first, however, to introduce a type of variation or oscillation of a real function of a real variable defined in an interval I, which will enable us to deal with the various terms arising in our formulae.

Let I be an interval $\theta_1 \leqslant \theta \leqslant \theta_2$, θ_0 an interior point of I and $\psi(\theta)$ a function of θ defined on I. We define $|I| = \theta_2 - \theta_1$, and

$$v(I) = v(\theta_0, I, \psi(\theta)) = \frac{\theta_2-\theta_0}{\theta_2-\theta_1}\psi(\theta_1) + \frac{\theta_0-\theta_1}{\theta_2-\theta_1}\psi(\theta_2) - \psi(\theta_0). \qquad (4.21)$$

We note that for fixed θ_0 and I, $v(\theta_0, I, \psi)$ is a linear functional of ψ. Also if $\psi'(\theta)$ is continuous then

$$v(I) = \frac{\theta_0-\theta_1}{\theta_2-\theta_1}\int_{\theta_0}^{\theta_2}\psi'(\theta)\,d\theta - \frac{\theta_2-\theta_0}{\theta_2-\theta_1}\int_{\theta_1}^{\theta_0}\psi'(\theta)\,d\theta,$$

so that

$$|v(I)| \leqslant \int_{\theta_1}^{\theta_2}|\psi'(\theta)|\,d\theta. \qquad (4.22)$$

Also if $\psi''(\theta)$ is continuous we note that

$$v(I) = \frac{\theta_2-\theta_0}{\theta_2-\theta_1}\int_{\theta_1}^{\theta_0}(\theta-\theta_1)\psi''(\theta)\,d\theta + \frac{\theta_0-\theta_1}{\theta_2-\theta_1}\int_{\theta_0}^{\theta_2}(\theta_2-\theta)\psi''(\theta)\,d\theta,$$

so that

$$|v(I)| \leqslant (\theta_2-\theta_1)\int_{\theta_1}^{\theta_2}|\psi''(\theta)|\,d\theta = |I|\int_{\theta_1}^{\theta_2}|\psi''(\theta)|\,d\theta. \qquad (4.23)$$

The usefulness of our concept $v(I)$ will turn on the fact that the point θ_0 is completely at our disposal and that the inequalities (4.22) and (4.23) both hold so that we can use whichever is most convenient at the time.

We prove

LEMMA 4.6. *If with the above notation $r > 0$, a is complex, $|a| < 2r$, and $|a| \neq r$, further $\psi(\theta) = \log|re^{i\theta} - a|$, then we have for $\theta_1 < \theta_2 \leqslant \theta_1 + 2\pi$, and $1 \leqslant \beta \leqslant 2$,*

$$v(I) \leqslant 2|I|^{\beta-1}\int_{\theta_1}^{\theta_2}\left|\frac{r}{re^{i\theta}-a}\right|^{\beta}d\theta.$$

We set $\zeta = re^{i\theta}$, then

$$\psi'(\theta) = \mathscr{R}\frac{i\zeta}{\zeta-a}, \qquad \psi''(\theta) = \mathscr{R}\frac{a\zeta}{(\zeta-a)^2}.$$

Thus (4.22) and (4.23) give

$$v(I) \leqslant \int_{\theta_1}^{\theta_2} \frac{r \, d\theta}{|re^{i\theta}-a|}, \qquad v(I) \leqslant |I| \int_{\theta_1}^{\theta_2} \frac{r|a| \, d\theta}{|re^{i\theta}-a|^2}.$$

We distinguish between two cases. Suppose first that for some θ in I we have

$$|re^{i\theta}-a| \leqslant r|I|. \tag{4.24}$$

Then we have for every θ in I

$$|re^{i\theta}-a| \leqslant 2r|I|,$$

and so from (4.22) we have, since $\beta \geqslant 1$,

$$v(I) \leqslant \int_{\theta_1}^{\theta_2} \frac{r \, d\theta}{|re^{i\theta}-a|} \leqslant (2|I|)^{\beta-1} \int_{\theta_1}^{\theta_2} \left| \frac{r}{re^{i\theta}-a} \right|^\beta d\theta.$$

Since $\beta \leqslant 2$, Lemma 4.6 is proved in this case. Next suppose that (4.24) is false at every point of I. Then we obtain from (4.23), since $|a| < 2r$,

$$v(I) \leqslant |I| \int_{\theta_1}^{\theta_2} \frac{r|a| \, d\theta}{|re^{i\theta}-a|^2} \leqslant 2|I| \int_{\theta_1}^{\theta_2} \left| \frac{r}{re^{i\theta}-a} \right|^2 d\theta$$

$$\leqslant 2|I|^{\beta-1} \int_{\theta_1}^{\theta_2} \left| \frac{r}{re^{i\theta}-a} \right|^\beta d\theta \quad (\beta \leqslant 2).$$

This proves Lemma 4.6.

4.2.2. We can now prove a result which we state as a theorem since it appears to have some independent interest, apart from being a lemma for Theorem 4.2.

THEOREM 4.3. *Suppose that $g(z)$ is meromorphic and not constant in the plane and of finite lower order λ. Let $\{I_p\}$ be the mutually disjoint intervals $\theta_p < \theta < \theta_p'$ in which $|g(re^{i\theta})| < 1$, such that*

$$\theta_1 < \theta_1' \leqslant \theta_p < \theta_p' \leqslant \theta_1 + 2\pi.$$

Set $|I_p| = \theta_p' - \theta_p$, let $-m_p$ be the minimum of $\log|g(re^{i\theta})|$ in I_p and suppose that $1 \leqslant \beta < 2$. Then we have, for some arbitrarily large R,

$$\sum_p m_p |I_p|^{1-\beta} \leqslant \frac{A(1+\lambda^3)}{2-\beta} T(r, g)$$

for a set of r in the interval $(0, R)$ having linear measure at least $AR/(1+\lambda)$.

We set
$$k = R_0/\max(5, \lambda),$$

where R_0 is chosen so that

$$T(R_0, g) < \left(1 - \frac{3k}{R_0}\right)^{-(1+\lambda)} T(R_0 - 3k, g). \qquad (4.25)$$

There exist arbitrarily large such values R_0. For if not we can define R_1 sufficiently large and

$$R_n = R_1\{1 - 3/\max(5, \lambda)\}^{-n},$$

and deduce that for all $n \geqslant 2$

$$T(R_n, g) \geqslant \left(\frac{R_n}{R_{n-1}}\right)^{1+\lambda} T(R_{n-1}, g) \geqslant \cdots \geqslant R_n^{1+\lambda} \frac{T(R_1, g)}{R_1^{1+\lambda}} = C R_n^{1+\lambda},$$

where C is a constant. Also for $R_n \leqslant R \leqslant R_{n+1}$, we have $R \leqslant C' R_n$, and

$$T(R) \geqslant C R_n^{1+\lambda} \geqslant \frac{C}{(C')^{1+\lambda}} R^{1+\lambda} = C'' R^{1+\lambda}.$$

This inequality thus holds for all sufficiently large R contrary to our hypothesis that $f(z)$ has lower order λ. Suppose then that R_0 has been defined so that (4.25) holds. We set

$$R = R_0 - k, \quad R_1 = R_0 - 2k \quad \text{and} \quad R_2 = R_0 - 3k.$$

Let $a_1, a_2, \ldots$ be the zeros and $b_1, b_2, \ldots$ be the poles of $g(z)$ in $|z| < R$ and suppose that $R_2 < r < R_1$. Then we have for $z = re^{i\theta}$ by the Poisson–Jensen formula, Theorem 1.1,

$$\log|g(z)| = \left\{\frac{1}{2\pi} \int_0^{2\pi} \log|g(Re^{i\phi})| \frac{(R^2 - r^2)\, d\phi}{R^2 - 2Rr\cos(\theta - \phi) + r^2} + \right.$$
$$+ \sum_\mu \log\left|\frac{R}{R^2 - \bar{a}_\mu z}\right| - \sum_\nu \log\left|\frac{R}{R^2 - b_\nu z}\right|\right\} +$$
$$+ \left\{\sum_\mu \log|z - a_\mu| - \sum_\nu \log|z - b_\nu|\right\}$$
$$= \{\psi_1(\theta, r)\} - \{\psi_2(\theta, r)\},$$

say. For each fixed I_p occurring in Theorem 4.3 we choose a point θ_0 in I_p such that $\log|g(re^{i\theta_0})| = -m_p$. Also by our hypotheses

$$\log|g(re^{i\theta_p})| = \log|g(re^{i\theta'_p})| = 0.$$

Thus setting $\psi(\theta) = \log|g(re^{i\theta})|$, I_p instead of I in (4.21) we have

$$v(\theta_0, I_p, \psi) = m_p.$$

Since $v(\theta_0, I_p, \psi)$ is an additive functional in ψ we deduce that

$$m_p = v(I_p, \psi_1(\theta, r)) - v(I_p, \psi_2(\theta, r)). \qquad (4.26)$$

We note that

$$\psi_1''(\theta) = -\mathscr{R}\left(\frac{Rz}{\pi} \int_0^{2\pi} \log|g(Re^{i\phi})| \frac{e^{i\phi}(Re^{i\phi}+z)\,d\phi}{(Re^{i\phi}-z)^3} + \right.$$

$$\left. + \sum_\mu \frac{R^2\bar{a}_\mu z}{(R^2-\bar{a}_\mu z)^2} - \sum_\nu \frac{R^2\bar{b}_\nu z}{(R^2-\bar{b}_\nu z)^2} \right).$$

Also

$$|R^2-\bar{a}_\mu z| \geqslant R^2-Rr = R(R-r), \qquad |R^2-\bar{b}_\nu z| \geqslant R(R-r).$$

Thus

$$|\psi_1''(\theta)| \leqslant 4\left(\frac{R}{R-r}\right)^3 \left\{ m(R,g)+m\left(R,\frac{1}{g}\right) \right\} + \left\{ n(R,g)+n\left(R,\frac{1}{g}\right) \right\}\left(\frac{R}{R-r}\right)^2.$$

Also

$$N(R_0,g) \geqslant \int_R^{R_0} n(t,g)\frac{dt}{t} \geqslant \frac{R_0-R}{R_0}n(R,g) = \frac{k}{R_0}n(R,g), \qquad (4.27)$$

and $R-r \geqslant k$, $R \leqslant R_0$. Thus we deduce that

$$|\psi_1''(\theta)| \leqslant A\left(\frac{R_0}{k}\right)^3 \{T(R_0,g)+O(1)\} \quad (0 \leqslant \theta \leqslant 2\pi), \quad \text{as } R_0 \to \infty,$$

where A is an absolute constant. In view of (4.23) this gives

$$|v\{I_p,\psi_1(\theta)\}| \leqslant A|I_p|^2\left(\frac{R_0}{k}\right)^3 \{T(R_0,g)+O(1)\},$$

$$\sum_p v\{I_p,\psi_1(\theta)\}|I_p|^{1-\beta} \leqslant A\left(\frac{R_0}{k}\right)^3 \{T(R_0,g)+O(1)\} \sum_p |I_p|^{3-\beta}$$

$$\leqslant A\left(\frac{R_0}{k}\right)^3 \{T(R_0,g)+O(1)\}, \qquad (4.28)$$

since $3-\beta \geqslant 1$, and $\sum_p |I_p| \leqslant 2\pi$. Again, it follows from Lemma 4.6 that

$$|v(I_p, \log|re^{i\theta}-a_\mu|)| \leqslant 2|I_p|^{\beta-1} \int_{\theta_p}^{\theta_p'} \left|\frac{r}{re^{i\theta}-a_\mu}\right|^\beta d\theta.$$

Thus

$$\sum_p v\{I_p,\psi_2(\theta)\}|I_p|^{1-\beta} \leqslant 2\sum_p \int_{I_p} \left(\sum_\mu \left|\frac{r}{re^{i\theta}-a_\mu}\right|^\beta + \sum_\nu \left|\frac{r}{re^{i\theta}-b_\nu}\right|^\beta\right) d\theta$$

$$\leqslant 2\int_0^{2\pi} \left(\sum_\mu \left|\frac{r}{re^{i\theta}-a_\mu}\right|^\beta + \sum_\nu \left|\frac{r}{re^{i\theta}-b_\nu}\right|^\beta\right) d\theta.$$

We note that for $1 \leqslant \beta < 2$, $z = x+iy = a_\mu+\rho e^{i\theta}$,

$$\iint_{|z-a_\mu|<2R_0} \frac{dx\,dy}{|z-a_\mu|^\beta} = \int_0^{2\pi} d\theta \int_0^{2R_0} \rho^{1-\beta}\,d\rho = \frac{2\pi(2R_0)^{2-\beta}}{2-\beta}.$$

Thus

$$\int_{R_2}^{R_1} \Big[\sum_p v\{I_p, \psi_2(\theta, r)\} |I_p|^{1-\beta} \Big] r^{1-\beta} \, dr$$

$$\leqslant 2 \int_{R_2}^{R_1} r \, dr \int_0^{2\pi} d\theta \Big(\sum_\mu \Big| \frac{1}{re^{i\theta} - a_\mu} \Big|^\beta + \sum_\nu \Big| \frac{1}{re^{i\theta} - b_\nu} \Big|^\beta \Big)$$

$$\leqslant 2 \sum_\mu \iint_{|z-a_\mu| < 2R_0} \frac{dx\,dy}{|z-a_\mu|^\beta} + 2 \sum_\nu \iint_{|z-b_\nu| < 2R_0} \frac{dx\,dy}{|z-b_\nu|^\beta}$$

$$\leqslant \frac{8\pi R_0^{2-\beta}}{2-\beta} \Big\{ n(R, g) + n\Big(R, \frac{1}{g}\Big) \Big\} \leqslant \frac{16\pi R_0^{3-\beta}}{k(2-\beta)} \{T(R_0, g) + O(1)\}$$

by (4.27). It follows that we have for a set of r in the interval $R_2 \leqslant r \leqslant R_1$ having measure at least $\frac{1}{2}k = \frac{1}{2}(R_2 - R_1)$,

$$\sum_p |v\{I_p, \psi_2(\theta, r)\}| |I_p|^{1-\beta} r^{1-\beta} \leqslant \frac{32\pi R_0^{3-\beta}}{k^2(2-\beta)} \{T(R_0, g) + O(1)\}.$$

Also $r \leqslant R_0$. Thus we deduce for these values of r

$$\sum_p |v\{I_p, \psi_2(\theta, r)\}| |I_p|^{1-\beta} \leqslant \frac{A R_0^2}{k^2(2-\beta)} \{T(R_0, g) + O(1)\}$$

$$\leqslant \frac{A(1+\lambda^2)}{2-\beta} T(R_0, g),$$

if R_0 is sufficiently large. On combining this with (4.26) and (4.28) we deduce for such values of r

$$\sum_p m_p |I_p|^{1-\beta} \leqslant \frac{A(1+\lambda^3)}{2-\beta} T(R_0, g) \leqslant \frac{A(1+\lambda^3)}{2-\beta} T(r, g),$$

by (4.25), since $R_0 - 3k \leqslant r \leqslant R_0$. This is the inequality of Theorem 4.3. Also the set of r in the interval $R_2 \leqslant r \leqslant R_1$ in which it holds has measure at least $\frac{1}{2}k = \frac{1}{2}R_0/\max(5, \lambda) \geqslant R/(10+2\lambda)$, and $R_1 \leqslant R$. Thus the proof of Theorem 4.3 is complete.

4.2.3. *Completion of proof of Theorem* 4.2. Suppose now that $\{a_n\}$ constitutes a finite set of complex numbers satisfying

$$|a_m - a_n| \geqslant 2(\pi+1) \quad (1 \leqslant m < n \leqslant N). \tag{4.29}$$

Then we shall prove that for $\alpha > \frac{1}{3}$

$$\sum_{n=1}^N \delta(a_n, f)^\alpha < A(\alpha, \lambda). \tag{4.30}$$

Our result will follow from this. In fact if the a_n are distinct and do

not satisfy (4.29) it will follow that when K is a sufficiently large positive constant
$$K|a_m - a_n| \geqslant 2(\pi + 1) \quad (m \neq n).$$
Thus we may apply (4.30) to $Kf(z)$ and obtain
$$\sum_{n=1}^{N} \delta(Ka_n, Kf)^\alpha < A(\alpha, \lambda).$$
Since $\delta(Ka_n, Kf) = \delta(a_n, f)$, (4.30) follows for $f(z)$. Since N is arbitrary we may let $N \to \infty$ in (4.30) and obtain
$$\sum_{a \neq \infty} \delta(a, f)^\alpha < A(\alpha, \lambda),$$
and hence
$$\sum_{a} \delta(a, f)^\alpha < A(\alpha, \lambda) + 1.$$
Thus our proof will be complete when we have proved (4.30) with the hypotheses of Theorem 4.2 together with the hypothesis (4.29).

Let $\mathscr{E}_n(r)$ be the set of θ such that $0 \leqslant \theta \leqslant 2\pi$ and $|f(z) - a_n| < 1$, where $z = re^{i\theta}$. We may assume that $\delta(a_n, f) > 0$ in (4.30) for $n = 1$ to N so that $\mathscr{E}_n(r)$ is not empty for sufficiently large r. Suppose that θ_m, θ_n are points of $\mathscr{E}_m(r)$, $\mathscr{E}_n(r)$ respectively for $m \neq n$. Then we must have
$$|zf'(z)| \geqslant 1$$
at some point on each of the arcs of $|z| = r$ joining $re^{i\theta_m}$ to $re^{i\theta_n}$, since otherwise we should have
$$|a_m - a_n| - 2 < |f(re^{i\theta_m}) - f(re^{i\theta_n})| \leqslant 2\pi r \frac{1}{r},$$
which contradicts (4.29). Also we have, with $z = re^{i\theta}$,
$$\int_{\mathscr{E}_n(r)} \log^+ \left| \frac{1}{f(z) - a_n} \right| d\theta$$
$$\leqslant \int_{\mathscr{E}_n(r)} \log^+ \left| \frac{f'(z)}{f(z) - a_n} \right| d\theta + \int_{\mathscr{E}_n(r)} \log^+ |z| \, d\theta + \int_{\mathscr{E}_n(r)} \log^+ \left| \frac{1}{zf'(z)} \right| d\theta.$$
Thus we have, by Theorem 2.2,
$$\frac{1}{T(r,f)} m(a_n, r, f) \leqslant \frac{1}{2\pi T(r,f)} \int_{\mathscr{E}_n(r)} \log^+ \left| \frac{1}{rf'(re^{i\theta})} \right| d\theta + o(1),$$
as $r \to \infty$ outside a set of finite linear measure. We enclose the points of $\mathscr{E}_n(r)$ where $|zf'(z)| < 1$ in maximal intervals throughout which $|zf'(z)| < 1$. Since a_n is deficient there will be such points, and hence such intervals, for all sufficiently large r. The intervals corresponding to $\mathscr{E}_m(r)$ and $\mathscr{E}_n(r)$ for $m \neq n$ will be distinct, since as we saw they will be separated by points where $|zf'(z)| \geqslant 1$. If $J_{\nu,n}$ are the

intervals corresponding to $\mathscr{E}_n(r)$ for $\nu = 1$ to K_n then

$$\frac{1}{T(r,f)} m(a_n, r, f) \leqslant \frac{2+o(1)}{T(r, zf')} \sum_{\nu=1}^{K_n} \frac{1}{2\pi} \int\limits_{J_{\nu,n}} \log^+\left|\frac{1}{zf'(z)}\right| d\theta \qquad (4.31)$$

outside a set of finite linear measure, since we have

$$T(r, zf') \leqslant T(r, f') + O(\log r) \leqslant \{2+o(1)\} T(r, f)$$

outside such a set by Theorem 3.1.

We now note that the set of r for which the inequality of Theorem 4.3 holds has infinite linear measure. For if E is this set then the part E' of E in the interval $\{AR/2(1+\lambda), R\}$ satisfies

$$\int\limits_{E'} dr \geqslant \frac{AR}{2(1+\lambda)}.$$

Since R may be as large as we please, E must have infinite linear measure.

We now apply Theorem 4.3 to $g(z) = zf'(z)$. Then we can find a sequence of $r = r_k \to \infty$ for which the inequality of Theorem 4.3 and also (4.31) holds for $n = 1$ to N. We have then by (4.31)

$$\sum_{n=1}^{N} \delta(a_n, f)^\alpha \leqslant \lim_{k\to\infty} \frac{2^\alpha}{T(r_k, g)^\alpha} \sum_{n=1}^{N} \left(\sum_{\nu=1}^{K_n} \frac{1}{2\pi} \int\limits_{J_{\nu,n}} \log^+\left|\frac{1}{g(z)}\right| d\theta\right)^\alpha$$

$$\leqslant \lim_{k\to\infty} \frac{2^\alpha}{T(r_k, g)^\alpha} \sum_{n=1}^{N} \sum_{\nu=1}^{K_n} \left(\frac{1}{2\pi} \int\limits_{J_{\nu,n}} \log^+\left|\frac{1}{g(z)}\right| d\theta\right)^\alpha,$$

since† $\alpha < 1$. Thus we have *a fortiori*

$$\sum_{n=1}^{N} \delta(a_n, f)^\alpha \leqslant \lim_{k\to\infty} \frac{2^\alpha}{T(r_k, g)^\alpha} \sum_{p} \left(\frac{1}{2\pi} \int\limits_{I_p} \log^+\left|\frac{1}{g(z)}\right| d\theta\right)^\alpha,$$

where the sum is taken over all the separate intervals I_p of $\theta \pmod{2\pi}$ such that $|g(r_k e^{i\theta})| < 1$.

We note that with the notation of Theorem 4.3 we have

$$\int\limits_{I_p} \log^+\left|\frac{1}{g(z)}\right| d\theta \leqslant |I_p| m_p.$$

Thus we have, choosing $\beta = (1-\alpha)/\alpha$, so that $2-1/\alpha = 1-\beta$, in Theorem 4.3

$$\sum_{p} \left(\int\limits_{I_p} \log^+\left|\frac{1}{g(z)}\right| d\theta\right)^\alpha \leqslant \sum |I_p|^\alpha m_p^\alpha$$

$$\leqslant \left(\sum m_p |I_p|^{(2\alpha-1)/\alpha}\right)^\alpha \left(\sum |I_p|^{(1-\alpha)/(1-\alpha)}\right)^{1-\alpha}$$

† If $c_\nu \geqslant 0$ ($\nu = 1$ to K), then $(\sum c_\nu)^\alpha \leqslant \sum c_\nu^\alpha$. In fact if $\sum c_\nu = s$, then $c_\nu/s \leqslant 1$, so that $(c_\nu/s)^\alpha \geqslant c_\nu/s$, and hence $\sum (c_\nu/s)^\alpha \geqslant \sum (c_\nu/s) = 1$.

by Hölder's inequality. Also the choice of β is legitimate if $\frac{1}{3} < \alpha \leqslant \frac{1}{2}$, since this implies $1 \leqslant \beta < 2$. Now Theorem 4.3 yields

$$\sum_{n=1}^{N} \delta(a_n, f)^{\alpha} \leqslant 2^{\alpha} \lim_{r \to \infty} \left(\frac{A(1+\lambda^3)}{2-\beta}\right)^{\alpha} \frac{T(r,g)^{\alpha}}{T(r,g)^{\alpha}} \leqslant \frac{A(1+\lambda^{3\alpha})}{(3\alpha-1)^{\alpha}}.$$

This proves Theorem 4.2 if $\frac{1}{3} < \alpha \leqslant \frac{1}{2}$. Since the left-hand side decreases with increasing α the result remains valid for $\alpha > \frac{1}{2}$.

4.3. The examples of Gol'dberg type

We proceed to give some counter-examples to Theorem 4.2 which show in particular that Theorem 4.2 fails to hold when $\alpha < \frac{1}{3}$. These examples are a simplified version of those of Gol'dberg [2].† We shall prove the following:

THEOREM 4.4. *Suppose that $\{\eta_\nu\}$ is a sequence of positive numbers such that $\sum_{1}^{\infty} \eta_\nu = 1$, and let $\{a_n\}$ be an arbitrary sequence of distinct complex numbers. Then there exists a meromorphic function $f(z)$ of order 1 mean type in the plane such that*

$$\delta(a_n, f) > \tfrac{1}{6}\eta_n^3 \quad (n = 1 \text{ to } \infty).$$

By choosing $\eta_n = C/n\{\log(n+2)\}^2$, where C is a suitable constant, we deduce that $\sum \delta(a_n, f)^{\alpha}$ may diverge for every $\alpha < \frac{1}{3}$. More generally we see that $\delta(a_n, f)^{1/3}$ may be greater than a multiple of an arbitrary convergent series for $n = 1$ to ∞, so that if Theorem 4.2 remains true for $\alpha = \frac{1}{3}$ the resulting theorem would be best possible. Unfortunately our argument for Theorem 4.2 fails for $\alpha = \frac{1}{3}$.

We assume without loss in generality that η_n is decreasing since this may be achieved by relabelling the η_n and a_n simultaneously. We set $\eta_0 = \eta_1$, and define

$$\theta_0 = 0, \qquad \theta_n = \pi \sum_{\nu=0}^{n-1} \eta_\nu \quad (n = 1 \text{ to } \infty).$$

Thus θ_n is a strictly increasing sequence and

$$\theta_n \to \pi \sum_{\nu=0}^{\infty} \eta_\nu = \pi\eta_0 + \pi \sum_{1}^{\infty} \eta_\nu \leqslant 2\pi, \quad \text{as } n \to \infty.$$

We now choose a sequence c_n of positive numbers such that

$$S_1 = \sum_{n=1}^{\infty} c_n |a_n| < \infty, \qquad S_2 = \sum_{n=1}^{\infty} c_n < \infty,$$

---

† However, Theorem 4.4 appears to be new in its present form.

and define
$$\phi_1(z) = \sum_{n=1}^{\infty} c_n a_n \exp(ze^{-i\theta_n}), \qquad \phi_2(z) = \sum_{n=1}^{\infty} c_n \exp(ze^{-i\theta_n}),$$
$$f(z) = \phi_1(z)/\phi_2(z).$$

We note that for $|z| = r$,
$$|\phi_1(z)| < S_1 e^r, \qquad |\phi_2(z)| < S_2 e^r,$$
and so
$$T(r,f) = T\left(r, \frac{\phi_1}{\phi_2}\right) < T(r,\phi_1) + T(r,\phi_2) + O(1) < 2r + O(1). \quad (4.32)$$

Suppose next that $n \geqslant 1$ and that
$$\theta_n - \tfrac{1}{3}\pi\eta_n < \theta \leqslant \theta_n + \tfrac{1}{3}\pi\eta_n. \qquad (4.33)$$

Then we have for $\nu < n$
$$\theta - \theta_\nu \geqslant (\theta_n - \theta_{n-1}) - \tfrac{1}{3}\pi\eta_n = \pi(\eta_{n-1} - \tfrac{1}{3}\eta_n) \geqslant \tfrac{2}{3}\pi\eta_n,$$

and for $\nu > n$, we have
$$\theta_\nu - \theta \geqslant \theta_{n+1} - \theta_n - \tfrac{1}{3}\pi\eta_n = \tfrac{2}{3}\pi\eta_n.$$

Thus in all cases
$$|\theta_\nu - \theta_n| \geqslant \tfrac{2}{3}\pi\eta_n \pmod{2\pi} \quad (\nu \neq n),$$
and so
$$\cos(\theta_\nu - \theta) \leqslant \cos(\tfrac{2}{3}\pi\eta_n).$$

Thus if θ lies in the range (4.33) and $z = re^{i\theta}$ we have
$$|\phi_1(z) - c_n a_n \exp(ze^{-i\theta_n})| \leqslant \sum_{\nu \neq n} |c_\nu a_\nu \exp\{r\cos(\theta - \theta_\nu)\}|$$
$$\leqslant S_1 \exp(r\cos\tfrac{2}{3}\pi\eta_n).$$

Similarly we have in this range
$$|\phi_2(z) - c_n \exp(ze^{-i\theta_n})| \leqslant S_2 \exp(r\cos\tfrac{2}{3}\pi\eta_n),$$
so that
$$|\phi_2(z)| > c_n|\exp(ze^{-i\theta_n})| - S_2 \exp(r\cos\tfrac{2}{3}\pi\eta_n)$$
$$\geqslant c_n \exp(r\cos\tfrac{1}{3}\pi\eta_n) - S_2 \exp(r\cos\tfrac{2}{3}\pi\eta_n)$$
$$\geqslant \tfrac{1}{2}c_n \exp(r\cos\tfrac{1}{3}\pi\eta_n)$$

for all sufficiently large r. Thus
$$|f(z) - a_n| = \left|\frac{\phi_1(z) - a_n\phi_2(z)}{\phi_2(z)}\right| \leqslant \frac{\{S_1 + |a_n|S_2\}\exp(r\cos\tfrac{2}{3}\pi\eta_n)}{\tfrac{1}{2}c_n \exp(r\cos\tfrac{1}{3}\pi\eta_n)}.$$

We deduce that as $r \to \infty$, we have uniformly for $|\theta_n - \theta| \leqslant \tfrac{1}{3}\pi\eta_n$,
$$\log^+\left|\frac{1}{f(re^{i\theta}) - a_n}\right| \geqslant r(\cos\tfrac{1}{3}\pi\eta_n - \cos\tfrac{2}{3}\pi\eta_n) + O(1)$$
$$= 2r\sin\tfrac{1}{6}\pi\eta_n \sin\tfrac{1}{2}\pi\eta_n + O(1) \geqslant r\eta_n^2 + O(1).$$

Thus
$$m\left(r, \frac{1}{f - a_n}\right) \geqslant \frac{1}{2\pi} \int_{\theta_n - \frac{1}{3}\pi\eta_n}^{\theta_n + \frac{1}{3}\pi\eta_n} \log^+\left|\frac{1}{f(re^{i\theta}) - a_n}\right| d\theta \geqslant \tfrac{1}{3}\eta_n^3 r + O(1).$$

Thus in view of (4.32)

$$\delta(a_n, f) \geqslant \frac{1}{2r} \frac{\eta_n^3 r}{3} = \frac{\eta_n^3}{6}.$$

This proves Theorem 4.3.

4.3.1. The idea of the above construction goes back to Gol'dberg [2], though Gol'dberg used a more complicated meromorphic function instead of e^z. He [4] also constructed similar examples where $f(z)$ has arbitrary order ρ, subject to $0 < \rho < \infty$, and proved further that $f(z)$ has no deficient values other than the a_n. Such results may also be achieved by means of a construction similar to the above. In fact if

$$\psi_\rho(z) = \prod_{n=1}^{\infty} (1 + z/n^{-1/\rho}) \quad (0 < \rho < 1),$$

then it is classical that $\psi_\rho(z)$ is an integral function of order ρ and

$$\log \psi_\rho(re^{i\theta}) \sim \frac{\pi}{\sin \pi\rho} z^\rho, \quad \text{as } z \to \infty$$

uniformly for $|\arg z| < \pi - \delta$, and

$$\log |\psi_\rho(re^{i\theta})| < \left(\frac{\pi}{\sin \pi\rho} + o(1) \right) \cos \rho(\pi - \delta) r^\rho \quad (\pi - \delta < |\arg z| \leqslant \pi)$$

(see section 4.6.4). Thus if we set

$$f_\rho(z) = \frac{\displaystyle\sum_{n=1}^{\infty} c_n a_n \psi_\rho(ze^{-i\theta_n})}{\displaystyle\sum_{n=1}^{\infty} c_n \psi_\rho(ze^{-i\theta_n})}$$

we can prove just as in the above example that $f_\rho(z)$ has order ρ mean type and that

$$\delta(a_n, f) \geqslant \frac{\rho^2 \eta_n^3}{6} \quad (n = 1 \text{ to } \infty).$$

The reader should verify this. By considering $f_\rho(z^q)$ instead of $f_\rho(z)$, where q is an arbitrary integer, we obtain a function $f(z)$ with similar properties and order $q\rho$ which can be an arbitrary positive number. It is also possible to calculate the deficiencies $\delta(a_n, f)$ explicitly and to prove that the a_n are the only deficient values in examples similar to the above, but here the proofs are more complicated and we omit them.

4.4. Some results for functions of non-integral order

It was shown by R. Nevanlinna [1, p. 51] that a meromorphic function $f(z)$ of order ρ can only have two distinct values a, b, such that

$\delta(a,f) = \delta(b,f) = 1$ if ρ is a positive integer or if $\rho = +\infty$. The examples $f(z) = e^{g(z)}$, where $g(z) = z^q$ or $g(z) = e^z$, and

$$\delta(0,f) = \delta(\infty,f) = 1$$

shows that these cases are indeed exceptional. We proceed to prove Nevanlinna's

THEOREM 4.5. *Suppose that $f(z)$ is meromorphic in the plane and of finite order λ, where λ is not a positive integer. Then*

$$K(f) = \varlimsup_{r \to \infty} \frac{N(r,f) + N(r, 1/f)}{T(r,f)} \geqslant k(\lambda),$$

where $k(\lambda) \geqslant 1 - \lambda, \quad if \ 0 < \lambda < 1,$
and

$$k(\lambda) \geqslant (q+1-\lambda)(\lambda-q)/2\lambda(q+1)\{2+\log(q+1)\} \quad if \ \lambda > 1 \ and \ q = [\lambda].$$

To prove this result we need a lemma proved for sequences by Pólya† and in the present form by Shah [1, 2] and also used by Edrei and Fuchs [3].

LEMMA 4.7. *Suppose that $\phi(t)$ and $\psi(t)$ are continuous positive functions of t for $t \geqslant t_0$, that $\psi(t)$ is non-decreasing, and further*

$$\varlimsup_{t \to \infty} \phi(t) = +\infty, \tag{4.34}$$

$$\lim_{t \to \infty} \frac{\phi(t)}{\psi(t)} = 0. \tag{4.35}$$

Then there exist arbitrarily large values of r such that simultaneously

$$\phi(t) \leqslant \phi(r) \quad (t_0 \leqslant t < r) \tag{4.36}$$

and $$\frac{\phi(t)}{\psi(t)} \leqslant \frac{\phi(r)}{\psi(r)} \quad (r \leqslant t). \tag{4.37}$$

Values of r satisfying (4.36) and (4.37) are frequently called *Pólya peaks*. Suppose that $r_0 > t_0$. Then by (4.34) there exists $\nu_0 > r_0$, such that

$$\phi(\nu_0) = \sup_{t_0 \leqslant t \leqslant \nu_0} \phi(t).$$

By (4.35), and since $\phi(t)/\psi(t)$ is positive and continuous for $t \geqslant t_0'$, there exists $\nu_1 \geqslant \nu_0$ such that

$$\frac{\phi(\nu_1)}{\psi(\nu_1)} = \sup_{\nu_0 \leqslant t} \frac{\phi(t)}{\psi(t)}.$$

Since $\phi(t)$ is continuous there exists r, such that $\nu_0 \leqslant r \leqslant \nu_1$ and

$$\phi(r) = \sup_{\nu_0 \leqslant t \leqslant \nu_1} \phi(t) = \sup_{t_0 \leqslant t \leqslant \nu_1} \phi(t),$$

† Pólya and Szegö [1, p. 18].

which implies (4.37) since $\psi(t)$ is non-decreasing and for $t \geqslant \nu_0$ we have

$$\frac{\phi(t)}{\psi(t)} \leqslant \frac{\phi(\nu_1)}{\psi(\nu_1)} \leqslant \frac{\phi(r)}{\psi(r)}.$$

Thus (4.36) and (4.37) both hold for this value of r, and since $r \geqslant r_0$, and r_0 may be chosen as large as we please, we have Lemma 4.7.

4.4.1. We now suppose that $0 \leqslant \lambda < \infty$ and that λ is not a positive integer and set $q = [\lambda]$. If $f(z)$ is the function of Theorem 4.5, then it follows from Theorems 1.9 and 1.11 that

$$f(z) = z^p e^{P(z)} \frac{\displaystyle\prod_\mu E\left(\frac{z}{a_\mu}, q\right)}{\displaystyle\prod_\nu E\left(\frac{z}{b_\nu}, q\right)},$$

where $\qquad E(z, q) = (1-z)\exp\left(z + \tfrac{1}{2}z^2 + \ldots + \frac{1}{q}z^q\right),$

the products are formed with the zeros a_μ and poles b_ν of $f(z)$, $P(z)$ is a polynomial of degree at most q, and p is an integer. We deduce that

$$T(r, f) \leqslant T\left(r, \prod E\left(\frac{z}{a_\mu}, q\right)\right) + T\left(r, \prod E\left(\frac{z}{b_\nu}, q\right)\right) + O(r^q) + O(\log r).$$

In view of Theorem 1.11 applied with $q+1$ instead of q we have

$$T(r, f) \leqslant c_1(q)\left(r^q \int_0^r \frac{n(t)\,dt}{t^{q+1}} + r^{q+1} \int_r^\infty \frac{n(t)\,dt}{t^{q+2}}\right) + O(r^q) + O(\log r),$$

where $\qquad n(t) = n(t, f) + n(t, 1/f) - n(0, f) - n(0, 1/f).$

Here we use the fact that for an integral function $\Pi(z)$

$$T(r, \Pi) \leqslant \log \max_{|z|=r} |\Pi(z)|$$

together with (1.21). Also

$$c_1(q) = 1, \quad \text{if } q = 0,$$
$$c_1(q) = 2(q+1)\{2 + \log(q+1)\} \quad \text{if } q \geqslant 1.$$

We integrate by parts and deduce that

$$T(r, f) \leqslant c_1(q)\left(qr^q \int_0^r \frac{N(t)\,dt}{t^{q+1}} + (q+1)r^{q+1} \int_r^\infty \frac{N(t)\,dt}{t^{q+2}}\right) + O(r^q).$$

If $N(r)$ has order less than λ, we deduce immediately that $T(r)$ has order less than λ and so obtain a contradiction. Thus $N(r)$ has order λ

and we can apply Lemma 4.7 with $N(t)/t^{\lambda-\epsilon}$, and $t^{2\epsilon}$ instead of $\phi(t)$, $\psi(t)$ respectively, where ϵ is a small positive number. This gives

$$N(t) \leqslant \left(\frac{t}{r}\right)^{\lambda-\epsilon} N(r) \quad (1 \leqslant t \leqslant r),$$

$$N(t) \leqslant \left(\frac{t}{r}\right)^{\lambda+\epsilon} N(r) \quad (r \leqslant t \leqslant \infty).$$

If $\lambda < 1$, $q = 0$, so that $c_1(q) = 1$, and we deduce

$$T(r,f) \leqslant rN(r) \int\limits_{r}^{\infty} \left(\frac{t}{r}\right)^{\lambda+\epsilon-2} dt + O(1) = \frac{N(r)}{1-\epsilon-\lambda} + O(1).$$

Since ϵ may be chosen as small as we please this gives

$$\varlimsup_{r\to\infty} \frac{N(r)}{T(r,f)} = K(f) \geqslant 1-\lambda.$$

Suppose next that $q > 0$, so that $q < \lambda < q+1$. Then we obtain
$T(r,f) - O(r^q)$

$$\leqslant c_1(q)N(r)\left\{qr^q \int\limits_{0}^{r} \left(\frac{t}{r}\right)^{\lambda-\epsilon} \frac{dt}{t^{q+1}} + (q+1)r^{q+1} \int\limits_{r}^{\infty} \left(\frac{t}{r}\right)^{\lambda+\epsilon} \frac{dt}{t^{q+2}}\right\}$$

$$= N(r)c_1(q)\left\{\frac{q}{\lambda-q-\epsilon} + \frac{q+1}{q+1-\lambda-\epsilon}\right\} = \frac{N(r)c_1(q)\{\lambda-(2q+1)\epsilon\}}{(\lambda-q-\epsilon)(q+1-\lambda-\epsilon)}$$

for a sequence of $r \to \infty$. It is clear that for such values of r

$$\frac{N(r)}{r^{\lambda-\epsilon}} \geqslant C > 0, \quad \text{so that } r^q = o\{N(r)\}.$$

Also ϵ may be chosen as small as we please. Thus in this case

$$K(f) = \varlimsup_{r\to\infty} \frac{N(r)}{T(r,f)} \geqslant \frac{(q+1-\lambda)(\lambda-q)}{\lambda c_1(q)}.$$

This completes the proof of Theorem 4.5.

The bounds obtained for $k(\lambda)$ are not sharp. The inequality

$$k(\lambda) \geqslant 1-\lambda \quad (0 < \lambda < 1)$$

is due to S. M. Shah [3]. The best possible value of $k(\lambda)$ in this case is given by
$$k(\lambda) = 1 \quad (0 \leqslant \lambda \leqslant \tfrac{1}{2}),$$
$$k(\lambda) = \sin \pi\lambda \quad (\tfrac{1}{2} < \lambda < 1).$$

This result, due to Edrei and Fuchs [3], will be proved in Theorem 4.14. In case $\lambda > 1$ the best value of $k(\lambda)$ is not known. However, Edrei and

Fuchs [1, p. 294] have proved that the best value of $k(\lambda)$ satisfies the inequalities

$$\frac{|\sin(\pi\lambda)|}{2\cdot2\lambda+\frac{1}{2}|\sin(\pi\lambda)|} \leqslant k(\lambda) \leqslant \frac{|\sin(\pi\lambda)|}{q+|\sin(\pi\lambda)|},$$

where $q = [\lambda]$.

4.4.2. Before continuing we prove the following result of Wittich [1, p. 22]:

THEOREM 4.6. *If $f(z)$ is an integral function of finite order, then*

$$\sum_{a\neq\infty} \delta(a,f) \leqslant \delta(0,f').$$

In fact in this case it follows from Theorem 2.2 that (4.17) holds in a somewhat stronger form and without exception as $r \to \infty$, for any finite set of distinct numbers a_ν ($\nu = 1$ to q) , so that

$$\sum_{\nu=1}^{q} m\left(r, \frac{1}{f(z)-a_\nu}\right) \leqslant m\left(r, \frac{1}{f'}\right) + O(\log r),$$

as $r \to \infty$. Thus dividing by $T(r,f')$ we deduce that

$$\sum_{\nu=1}^{q} \lim_{r\to\infty} \frac{m(r, 1/\{f(z)-a_\nu\})}{T(r,f')} \leqslant \delta(0,f').$$

Further,

$$T(r,f') = m(r,f') \leqslant m(r,f) + m(r,f'/f) \leqslant T(r,f) + O(\log r).$$

Thus

$$\delta(a_\nu,f) = \lim_{r\to\infty} \frac{m(r, 1/\{f(z)-a_\nu\})}{T(r,f)} \leqslant \lim_{r\to\infty} \frac{m(r, 1/\{f(z)-a_\nu\})}{T(r,f')}.$$

Thus we deduce

$$\sum_{\nu=1}^{q} \delta(a_\nu,f) \leqslant \delta(0,f'),$$

which gives Theorem 4.6.

We deduce the following:

THEOREM 4.7. *If $f(z)$ is an integral function of finite order λ which is not a positive integer, we have*

$$\sum_{a\neq\infty} \delta(a,f) \leqslant 1 - k(\lambda),$$

where $k(\lambda)$ is the quantity of Theorem 4.5.

It is known that if $f(z)$ is any meromorphic function then $f(z)$ and $f'(z)$ have the same order.† For integral functions $f(z)$ we prove this very simply as follows. Let

$$M(r) = \max_{|z|=r}|f(z)|, \qquad M_1(r) = \max_{|z|=r}|f'(z)|.$$

---

† This result was announced by Valiron [1, p. 129], who proved that the order of $f'(z)$ does not exceed that of $f(z)$. Whittaker [1] proved that the two orders are actually the same.

Then
$$M(r) \leqslant rM_1(r) + O(1),$$
so that
$$\log M(r) \leqslant \log M_1(r) + O(\log r).$$

Thus the order of $f(z)$ (which may be defined in terms of $M(r)$ by Theorem 1.7) is not greater than that of $f'(z)$. Conversely we have by Theorem 2.2

$$T(r,f') \leqslant T(r,f) + m(r,f'/f) \leqslant T(r,f) + O(\log r),$$

so that the order of $f'(z)$ does not exceed that of $f(z)$. We deduce that in our case $f'(z)$ has order λ and so by Theorem 4.5 applied to $f'(z)$ we have, since $N(r,f') = 0$,

$$\delta(0,f') = 1 - \overline{\lim_{r \to \infty}} \frac{N(r, 1/f')}{T(r,f')} \leqslant 1 - k(\lambda).$$

On combining this with Theorem 4.6 we deduce Theorem 4.7.

4.4.3. We note in particular that if

$$\sum_{a \neq \infty} \delta(a,f) = 1$$

for an integral function of finite order λ, then λ is an integer q. This result is due to Pfluger [1]. However, much more than this is known. Pfluger himself proved that in this case all the deficiencies are integral multiples of $1/q$. Recently Edrei and Fuchs [1, 2] have notably extended Pfluger's result. They have shown that in this case $f(z)$ also has lower order q [1, Theorem 5] and all the deficient values a_ν of $f(z)$ are asymptotic values, i.e. $f(z) \to a_\nu$ as $z \to \infty$ along a suitable path Γ_ν [2, Theorem 2]. Further, if

$$f(z) = \sum_0^\infty f_n z^n$$

then the set of integers n for which $f_n \neq 0$ has a positive density δ which is also an integral multiple of $1/q$. Further results yielding this as a special case also hold whenever $K(f')$ is sufficiently small, depending on the order of $f(z)$, where $K(f)$ is the quantity occurring in Theorem 4.5.

Lack of space prevents us from giving proofs of the above results, which are far from simple, but the reader is referred to the original papers.

No analogue of Theorem 4.7 is known for meromorphic functions $f(z)$ but it is conjectured that such an analogue holds, namely that in this case

$$\sum \delta(a,f) = 2$$

implies that $f(z)$ has order $\frac{1}{2}q$, where q is a positive integer or $+\infty$. For examples of cases where the order is in fact an odd multiple of $\frac{1}{2}$ see F. Nevanlinna [1] and R. Nevanlinna [2].

4.5. Gol'dberg's theorems on the means of analytic functions

We now proceed to discuss some results of Gol'dberg [3] which have far-reaching effects on the problem of deficiencies of meromorphic functions of genus zero. We have

THEOREM 4.8. *Suppose that $\phi(y)$ is a convex function of $\log y$ for $0 < y < \infty$. Suppose further that, for $\nu = 1$ to n and real θ, the functions $y_\nu(\theta)$ are even, periodic with period 2π, monotonically increasing in the range $0 \leqslant \theta \leqslant \pi$, and satisfy $0 < m \leqslant y_\nu(\theta) \leqslant M$. Then if the θ_ν ($\nu = 1$ to n) are arbitrary real numbers, we have the inequality*

$$\int_{-\pi}^{\pi} \phi\left\{\prod_{\nu=1}^{n} y_\nu(\theta+\theta_\nu)\right\} d\theta \leqslant \int_{-\pi}^{\pi} \phi\left\{\prod_{\nu=1}^{n} y_\nu(\theta)\right\} d\theta.$$

We need the following

LEMMA 4.8. *If $\psi(t)$ is a convex function of t for all real t, then $\psi(t+h)+\psi(t-h)$ is an increasing function of h for a fixed t and $h \geqslant 0$.*

It follows from the definition of convexity that if $t_1 < t_2 < t_3$ we have

$$(t_3-t_1)\psi(t_2) \leqslant (t_2-t_1)\psi(t_3)+(t_3-t_2)\psi(t_1).$$

We set $t_1 = t-h_2$, $t_3 = t+h_2$, and $t_2 = t \mp h_1$ in turn, where

$$0 \leqslant h_1 < h_2.$$

This gives

$$2h_2\psi(t+h_1) \leqslant (h_1+h_2)\psi(t+h_2)+(h_2-h_1)\psi(t-h_2),$$
$$2h_2\psi(t-h_1) \leqslant (h_2-h_1)\psi(t+h_2)+(h_2+h_1)\psi(t-h_2).$$

Adding these inequalities we obtain

$$2h_2\{\psi(t+h_1)+\psi(t-h_1)\} \leqslant 2h_2\{\psi(t+h_2)+\psi(t-h_2)\},$$

which yields the lemma.

We deduce

LEMMA 4.9. *If $\phi(y)$ is a convex function of $\log y$ for $0 < y < \infty$ and if $0 < a \leqslant A < \infty$, $0 < b \leqslant B < \infty$, then we have*

$$\phi(Ab)+\phi(aB) \leqslant \phi(ab)+\phi(AB).$$

We set $a = e^{t_1-h_1}$, $A = e^{t_1+h_1}$, $b = e^{t_2-h_2}$, $B = e^{t_2+h_2}$, and $\psi(t) = \phi(e^t)$ so that $\psi(t)$ is a convex function of t for all real t. Then Lemma 4.7 gives

$$\psi(t_1+t_2+h_2-h_1)+\psi(t_1+t_2+h_1-h_2)$$
$$\leqslant \psi(t_1+t_2+h_1+h_2)+\psi(t_1+t_2-h_1-h_2)$$

which is Lemma 4.9.

4.5.1. We can now complete the proof of Theorem 4.8. Since the $y_\nu(\theta)$ are periodic of period 2π, we suppose, as we may do without loss in generality, that $0 \leqslant \theta_\nu < 2\pi$ ($\nu = 1$ to n). Suppose that $\theta_\mu > 0$. Then it follows again from the periodicity of the functions $y_\nu(\theta)$ that

$$\int_{-\pi}^{\pi} \phi\Big\{ \prod_{\nu=1}^{n} y_\nu(\theta+\theta_\nu) \Big\} \, d\theta = \int_{-\pi-\frac{1}{2}\theta_\mu}^{\pi-\frac{1}{2}\theta_\mu} \phi\Big\{ \prod_{\nu=1}^{n} y_\nu(\theta+\theta_\nu) \Big\} \, d\theta$$

$$= \int_{-\pi}^{\pi} \phi\Big\{ \prod_{\nu=1}^{n} y_\nu(\theta+k_\nu) \Big\} \, d\theta,$$

where

$$k_\nu \equiv \theta_\nu - \tfrac{1}{2}\theta_\mu \ (\mathrm{mod}\ 2\pi) \quad (0 \leqslant k_\nu < 2\pi, \ 1 \leqslant \nu \leqslant n).$$

We set

$$f_1(\theta) = \prod_{0 \leqslant k_\nu < \pi} y_\nu(\theta+k_\nu),$$

$$f_2(\theta) = \prod_{\pi \leqslant k_\nu < 2\pi} y_\nu(-\theta+k_\nu) = \prod_{\pi \leqslant k_\nu < 2\pi} y_\nu(\theta-k_\nu),$$

since the $y_\nu(\theta)$ are even. We note that if $0 \leqslant \theta \leqslant \pi$, we have

$$y_\nu(\theta-k_\nu) \leqslant y_\nu(\theta+k_\nu) \quad \text{if } 0 \leqslant k_\nu < \pi,$$

while

$$y_\nu(\theta+k_\nu) \leqslant y_\nu(\theta-k_\nu) \quad \text{if } \pi \leqslant k_\nu < 2\pi.$$

In fact

$$\cos(\theta-k_\nu) - \cos(\theta+k_\nu) = 2\sin\theta\sin k_\nu,$$

so that $\cos(\theta-k_\nu) \lessgtr \cos(\theta+k_\nu)$ according as $\pi \lessgtr k_\nu$. Since by hypothesis the functions $y_\nu(\theta)$ are decreasing functions of $\cos\theta$, our result follows. We deduce further that for $0 \leqslant \theta \leqslant \pi$

$$f_1(-\theta) \leqslant f_1(\theta), \qquad f_2(-\theta) \leqslant f_2(\theta).$$

Thus Lemma 4.9 yields

$$\int_{-\pi}^{\pi} \phi\Big\{ \prod_{\nu=1}^{n} y_\nu(\theta+\theta_\nu) \Big\} \, d\theta = \int_{-\pi}^{\pi} \phi\{ f_1(\theta) f_2(-\theta) \} \, d\theta$$

$$= \int_{0}^{\pi} [\phi\{ f_1(\theta) f_2(-\theta) \} + \phi\{ f_1(-\theta) f_2(\theta) \}] \, d\theta$$

$$\leqslant \int_{0}^{\pi} \phi\{ f_1(\theta) f_2(\theta) \} + \phi\{ f_1(-\theta) f_2(-\theta) \} \, d\theta$$

$$= \int_{-\pi}^{\pi} \phi\{ f_1(\theta) f_2(\theta) \} \, d\theta$$

$$= \int_{-\pi}^{\pi} \phi\Big\{ \prod_{0 \leqslant k_\nu < \pi} y_\nu(\theta+k_\nu) \prod_{\pi \leqslant k_\nu < 2\pi} y_\nu(\theta-k_\nu) \Big\} \, d\theta$$

$$= \int_{-\pi}^{\pi} \phi\Big\{ \prod_{\nu=1}^{n} y_\nu(\theta+\theta'_\nu) \Big\} \, d\theta,$$

where
$$\theta'_\nu \equiv k_\nu - \tfrac{1}{2}\theta_\mu \ (\mathrm{mod}\ 2\pi), \qquad 0 \leqslant \theta'_\nu < 2\pi, \quad \text{if } 0 \leqslant k_\nu < \pi;$$
$$\theta'_\nu \equiv -k_\nu - \tfrac{1}{2}\theta_\mu \ (\mathrm{mod}\ 2\pi), \qquad 0 \leqslant \theta'_\nu < 2\pi, \quad \text{if } \pi \leqslant k_\nu < 2\pi.$$
If $\theta_\nu = 0$ then $k_\nu = 2\pi - \tfrac{1}{2}\theta_\mu > \pi$, so that $\theta'_\nu = 0$. Further,
$$k_\mu = \tfrac{1}{2}\theta_\mu < \pi,$$
so that $\theta'_\mu = 0$. If one of the quantities θ'_ν is different from zero we proceed in this way again and obtain a new set θ''_ν which are zero whenever θ'_ν is zero and for one extra value of ν. After at most n steps we reach a position where all the θ_ν are zero. Since

$$\int_{-\pi}^{\pi} \phi\Big\{\prod_{\nu=1}^{n} y_\nu(\theta+\theta_\nu)\Big\}\, d\theta$$

is non-decreasing from stage to stage, Theorem 4.8 follows.

4.5.2. Gol'dberg's inequality in Theorem 4.8 has many applications to function theory. The most important one from our point of view is the following due to Gol'dberg [3] himself.

THEOREM 4.9. *Suppose that $f(z)$ is a meromorphic function of genus 0,*

$$f(z) = Cz^q \prod_{\mu=1}^{M}\Big(1-\frac{z}{a_\mu}\Big)\Big/\prod_{\nu=1}^{N}\Big(1-\frac{z}{b_\nu}\Big), \tag{4.38}$$

and set
$$\hat{f}(z) = |C|z^q \prod_{\mu=1}^{M}\Big(1-\frac{z}{|a_\mu|}\Big)\Big/\prod_{\nu=1}^{N}\Big(1+\frac{z}{|b_\nu|}\Big). \tag{4.39}$$

Then if $\phi(y)$ is a convex function of $\log y$ for $y > 0$ we have

$$\int_0^{2\pi} \phi(|f(re^{i\theta})|)\, d\theta \leqslant \int_0^{2\pi} \phi(|\hat{f}(re^{i\theta})|)\, d\theta, \tag{4.40}$$

provided that $r \neq |a_\mu|,\ r \neq |b_\nu|$ for any μ or ν. In particular
$$m(r,f) \leqslant m(r,\hat{f}), \quad m(r,1/f) \leqslant m(r,1/\hat{f}) \qquad (0 < r < \infty),$$
and hence $\qquad \delta(0,f) \leqslant \delta(0,\hat{f}), \qquad \delta(\infty,f) \leqslant \delta(\infty,\hat{f}).$

To prove (4.40) suppose first that the products in (4.38), (4.39) are finite. Then (4.40) follows from Theorem 4.8 on setting

$$a_\mu = |a_\mu|e^{i\alpha_\mu} \quad (\mu = 1 \text{ to } M), \qquad b_\nu = |b_\nu|e^{i\beta_\nu} \quad (\nu = 1 \text{ to } N);$$

$$y_\nu(\theta) = \Big|1-\frac{r}{|a_\nu|}e^{i\theta}\Big|, \qquad \theta_\nu = -\alpha_\nu \quad (\nu = 1 \text{ to } M);$$

$$y_\nu(\theta) = \Big|1+\frac{r}{|b_{\nu-M}|}e^{i\theta}\Big|^{-1}, \qquad \theta_\nu = \pi - \beta_{\nu-M} \quad (\nu = M{+}1 \text{ to } M{+}N);$$

$$y_\nu(\theta) = |C|r^q \quad (\nu = M{+}N{+}1).$$

It is clear that the hypotheses of Theorem 4.8 are satisfied and (4.40) follows in this case. Also the general case of (4.40) follows at once since, on a circle $|z| = r$ containing no zero or pole of $f(z)$ and $\hat{f}(z)$, $f(z)$ and $\hat{f}(z)$ can be uniformly approximated by ratios of partial products $P(z)$ and $\hat{P}(z)$ of the infinite products occurring in (4.38) and (4.39). Since $\phi(y)$ is continuous for positive and finite values of y and so uniformly continuous on the ranges of $P(z)$ and $\hat{P}(z)$ the inequality (4.40) follows from the corresponding result for $P(z)$ and $\hat{P}(z)$.

By choosing $\phi(y) = \log^+ y = \max(\log y, 0)$, which is clearly a convex function of $\log y$, we obtain

$$m(r,f) \leqslant m(r,\hat{f})$$

and by taking $\phi(y) = \log^+(1/y) = \max(-\log y, 0)$, we deduce

$$m\left(r, \frac{1}{f}\right) \leqslant m\left(r, \frac{1}{\hat{f}}\right).$$

This inequality holds in the first instance for $r \neq |a_\mu|$ or $|b_\nu|$, but remains true by continuity for all positive values of r.

Finally, we evidently have $N(r,f) = N(r,\hat{f})$. Thus

$$\delta(0,f) = \lim_{r\to\infty} \frac{m(r,f)}{m(r,f)+N(r,f)} \leqslant \lim_{r\to\infty} \frac{m(r,\hat{f})}{m(r,\hat{f})+N(r,\hat{f})} = \delta(0,\hat{f})$$

and similarly $\delta(\infty,f) \leqslant \delta(\infty,\hat{f}).$

This completes the proof of Theorem 4.9.

4.6. Deficiencies of functions of genus zero

In this section we consider the following problem. Suppose that $f(z)$ is a meromorphic function of order ρ, where $0 \leqslant \rho \leqslant 1$, and that

$$\delta_a = \delta(a,f), \qquad \delta_b = \delta(b,f), \tag{4.41}$$

where a, b are distinct complex numbers, one of which may be infinite. What can we say about the possible values of the pair of numbers δ_a, δ_b? The complete answer to this question was found by Edrei and Fuchs [3] in the following striking

THEOREM 4.10. *With the above hypotheses set $u = 1-\delta_a$, $v = 1-\delta_b$. Then in addition to the trivial inequalities $0 \leqslant u \leqslant 1$, $0 \leqslant v \leqslant 1$, u, v satisfy the inequalities*

$$u^2+v^2-2uv\cos\pi\rho \geqslant \sin^2\pi\rho. \tag{4.42}$$

Further,

$$\text{if } u < \cos\pi\rho, \text{ then } v = 1 \quad \text{and} \quad \text{if } v < \cos\pi\rho, \text{ then } u = 1. \tag{4.43}$$

Edrei and Fuchs also showed that if δ_a, δ_b is any pair of numbers satisfying the conditions of Theorem 4.10 then a meromorphic function $f(z)$ of order ρ exists satisfying (4.41), but we shall prove this only when equality holds in (4.42) or when (4.43) holds. The inequality (4.42) represents the outside of an ellipse touching the lines $u = \mp 1$, $v = \mp 1$. If $\rho = 1$, Theorem 4.10 becomes trivial. If $\frac{1}{2} < \rho < 1$, the theorem asserts that (u, v) must be confined to those parts of the square $S: 0 \leqslant u \leqslant 1, 0 \leqslant v \leqslant 1$ which lie outside or on the ellipse

$$E:\ u^2 + v^2 - 2uv \cos \pi\rho = \sin^2 \pi\rho,$$

which in this case touches $u = 1$ and $v = 1$ at points exterior to the boundary of S. If $0 < \rho \leqslant \frac{1}{2}$ the ellipse E touches $u = 1$, $v = 1$ at the points $(1, \cos \pi\rho)$, $(\cos \pi\rho, 1)$ respectively. In this case (u, v) lies either on one of the lines $u = 1$ or $v = 1$, or in the corner of the square S, containing the point $(1, 1)$ on its boundary, which is cut off from S by the smaller arc of E which joins $(1, \cos \pi\rho)$ to $(\cos \pi\rho, 1)$. Finally, if $\rho = 0$, Theorem 4.10 asserts that $u = 1$ or $v = 1$, so that in this case $f(z)$ can have at most one deficient value. This result is due to Valiron [2].

4.6.1. To prove Theorem 4.10 we may confine ourselves to the case $0 \leqslant \rho < 1$, since the result is trivial for $\rho = 1$. Also we may suppose without loss in generality that $a = 0$, $b = \infty$. For if a, b are both finite we may set

$$\phi(z) = \frac{f(z) - a}{f(z) - b}$$

and then $\phi(z)$ has the same order as $f(z)$, and

$$\delta(0, \phi) = \delta(a, f), \qquad \delta(\infty, \phi) = \delta(b, f).$$

If a is finite and $b = \infty$, we consider similarly $\phi(z) = f(z) - a$. Next we may assume that $f(0) = 1$, since otherwise $f(z) = cz^p g(z)$, where $g(0) = 1$ and $f(z)$, $g(z)$ have the same deficiencies at 0, ∞, except in the trivial case when $f(z)$ is rational, which we ignore. Thus

$$f(z) = \frac{\displaystyle\prod_{n=1}^{\infty} (1 - z/a_n)}{\displaystyle\prod_{n=1}^{\infty} (1 - z/b_n)},$$

where a_n, b_n are the zeros and poles of $f(z)$. It follows from Gol'dberg's Theorem 4.9 that if

$$\hat{f}(z) = \frac{\displaystyle\prod_{n=1}^{\infty} (1 + z/|a_n|)}{\displaystyle\prod_{n=1}^{\infty} (1 - z/|b_n|)} \tag{4.44}$$

then $\delta(0,f) \leqslant \delta(0,\hat{f})$ and $\delta(\infty,f) \leqslant \delta(\infty,\hat{f})$. Also by Theorems 1.9, 1.10, and 1.11 the orders of $f(z)$ and $\hat{f}(z)$ are the same, being given in each case by the larger of the orders of $N(r,0)$ and $N(r,\infty)$. Thus if Theorem 4.10 holds for $\hat{f}(z)$ it holds also for $f(z)$. Hence we may confine ourselves to the case when $f(z)$ has all its zeros on the negative real axis and all its poles on the positive real axis so that $f(z) = \hat{f}(z)$ is given by (4.44).

In this case we have, except when z is real,

$$\log f(z) = \int\limits_0^\infty \log(1+z/t)\,dn(t,0) - \int\limits_0^\infty \log(1-z/t)\,dn(t,\infty).$$

Integrating by parts twice we obtain

$$\log f(z) = z \int\limits_0^\infty N(t,0)\frac{dt}{(t+z)^2} + z \int\limits_0^\infty N(t,\infty)\frac{dt}{(t-z)^2}.$$

Theorem 4.10 is trivial if either $u = 1$, or $v = 1$, i.e. unless $\delta(0,f) > 0$ and $\delta(\infty,f) > 0$. Thus we may suppose that for all sufficiently large r we have

$$m(r,f) > 0 \quad \text{and} \quad m(r,1/f) > 0. \tag{4.45}$$

It is easy to see that $|f(re^{i\theta})|$ is an even function of θ, which decreases as θ increases from 0 to π. Thus in view of (4.45) we have

$$\log|f(r)| > 0 > \log|f(-r)|.$$

Also there exists a uniquely determined number $\beta = \beta(r)$ such that

$$0 < \beta(r) < \pi, \qquad \log|f(re^{i\beta})| = 0, \tag{4.46}$$

and

$$m(r,f) = \frac{1}{\pi} \int\limits_0^\beta \log|f(re^{i\theta})|\,d\theta = \frac{1}{\pi}\lim_{\delta\to0} \int\limits_\delta^\beta \log|f(re^{i\theta})|\,d\theta$$

$$= \frac{1}{\pi}\lim_{\delta\to0}\left\{ \mathscr{I} \int\limits_0^\infty N(t,0)\,dt \int\limits_{re^{i\delta}}^{re^{i\beta}} \frac{dz}{(z+t)^2} + \mathscr{I} \int\limits_0^\infty N(t,\infty)\,dt \int\limits_{re^{i\delta}}^{re^{i\beta}} \frac{dz}{(z-t)^2} \right\}.$$

This gives

$$m(r,f) = \frac{1}{\pi} \int\limits_0^\infty N(t,0)\frac{r\sin\beta\,dt}{t^2+2tr\cos\beta+r^2} + \frac{1}{\pi} \int\limits_0^\infty N(t,\infty)\frac{r\sin\beta\,dt}{t^2-2tr\cos\beta+r^2} -$$

$$-\lim_{\delta\to0}\frac{1}{\pi} \int\limits_0^\infty N(t,0)\frac{r\sin\delta\,dt}{t^2+2tr\cos\delta+r^2} - \lim_{\delta\to0}\frac{1}{\pi} \int\limits_0^\infty N(t,\infty)\frac{r\sin\delta\,dt}{t^2-2tr\cos\delta+r^2}.$$

Here the first limit on the right-hand side is clearly zero. Also as $\delta \to 0$,

$$\frac{r \sin \delta}{t^2 - 2tr \cos \delta + r^2} = \frac{O(\delta)}{t^2 + 1}$$

for a fixed r, uniformly in t outside a range $r - \eta < t < r + \eta$ for any fixed positive η. Also since $N(t, \infty)$ is continuous, $N(t, \infty)$ is nearly equal to $N(r, \infty)$ in this range if η is small. Using these facts we deduce that as $\delta \to 0$,

$$\frac{1}{\pi} \int_0^\infty N(t, \infty) \frac{r \sin \delta \, dt}{t^2 - 2tr \cos \delta + r^2} = \frac{N(r, \infty)}{\pi} \int_{r-\eta}^{r+\eta} \frac{r \sin \delta \, dt}{t^2 - 2tr \cos \delta + r^2} + o(1)$$

$$= \frac{N(r, \infty)}{\pi} \int_0^\infty \frac{r \sin \delta \, dt}{t^2 - 2tr \cos \delta + r^2} + o(1)$$

$$= \frac{N(r, \infty)}{\pi} \left[\tan^{-1} \left(\frac{t - r \cos \delta}{r \sin \delta} \right) \right]_0^\infty + o(1) = N(r, \infty) + o(1).$$

Thus we deduce finally that

$$T(r, f) = m(r, \infty) + N(r, \infty)$$

$$= \frac{1}{\pi} \int_0^\infty N(t, 0) \frac{r \sin \beta \, dt}{t^2 + 2tr \cos \beta + r^2} + \frac{1}{\pi} \int_0^\infty N(t, \infty) \frac{r \sin \beta \, dt}{t^2 - 2tr \cos \beta + r^2}. \quad (4.47)$$

4.6.2. *Proof of Theorem 4.10.* We now set

$$P(t, r, \gamma) = \frac{1}{\pi} \frac{r \sin \gamma}{t^2 + 2tr \cos \gamma + r^2} \quad (0 < \gamma < \pi),$$

so that (4.47) may be written as

$$T(r, f) = \int_0^\infty N(t, 0) P(t, r, \beta) \, dt + \int_0^\infty N(t, \infty) P(t, r, \pi - \beta) \, dt. \quad (4.48)$$

By hypothesis this equation is valid for all sufficiently large r and some $\beta = \beta(r)$ satisfying (4.46). We now apply Lemma 4.7, choosing

$$\phi(t) = \frac{T(t)}{t^{\lambda - 2\epsilon}}, \qquad \psi(t) = t^{2\epsilon},$$

where ϵ is a fixed positive number, and $\lambda = \rho + \epsilon$. We also assume that

$$0 < \lambda < 1.$$

Then by Lemma 4.7 we can find a fixed positive t_0 and some arbitrarily large values of r such that

$$\left. \begin{aligned} \frac{T(t)}{t^{\lambda - 2\epsilon}} &\leqslant \frac{T(r)}{r^{\lambda - 2\epsilon}} \quad (t_0 \leqslant t \leqslant r) \\ \frac{T(t)}{t^\lambda} &\leqslant \frac{T(r)}{r^\lambda} \quad (r \leqslant t) \end{aligned} \right\} . \qquad (4.49)$$

We choose
$$U > u = 1 - \delta(0, f), \qquad V > v = 1 - \delta(\infty, f), \qquad (4.50)$$
so that we have for all sufficiently large t
$$N(t, 0) < UT(t, f), \qquad N(t, \infty) < VT(t, f).$$
Thus (4.48) and (4.49) yield for some arbitrarily large values of r,

$$T(r, f) \leqslant UT(r, f)\left\{ \int_0^r P(t, r, \beta)(t/r)^{\lambda - 2\epsilon}\, dt + \int_r^\infty (t/r)^\lambda P(t, r, \beta)\, dt \right\} +$$

$$+ VT(r, f)\left\{ \int_0^r P(t, r, \pi - \beta)(t/r)^{\lambda - 2\epsilon}\, dt + \int_r^\infty (t/r)^\lambda P(t, r, \pi - \beta)\, dt \right\} + \eta(r),$$
$$(4.51)$$

where
$$\eta(r) \leqslant N(t_0, 0) \int_0^{t_0} P(t, r, \beta)\, dt + N(t_0, \infty) \int_0^{t_0} P(t, r, \pi - \beta)\, dt = \frac{O(1)}{r}.$$

Since we may replace U or V by a slightly larger quantity, and $T(r, f) \to \infty$, as $r \to \infty$, the inequality (4.51) holds for some arbitrarily large r with $\eta(r) = 0$, whenever U, V satisfy (4.50). We set $t = rs$ in (4.51) and deduce that

$$\int_0^r (t/r)^{\lambda - 2\epsilon} P(t, r, \gamma)\, dt + \int_r^\infty (t/r)^\lambda P(t, r, \gamma)\, dt$$

$$= \int_0^1 s^{\lambda - 2\epsilon} P(s, 1, \gamma)\, ds + \int_1^\infty s^\lambda P(s, 1, \gamma)\, ds$$

$$= \int_0^\infty s^\lambda P(s, 1, \gamma)\, ds + \int_0^1 (s^{\lambda - 2\epsilon} - s^\lambda) P(s, 1, \gamma)\, ds.$$

An elementary contour integration shows that, for $0 < \lambda < 1$,

$$\int_0^\infty s^\lambda P(s, 1, \gamma)\, ds = \frac{1}{\pi} \int_0^\infty \frac{s^\lambda \sin \gamma\, ds}{s^2 + 2s \cos \gamma + 1}$$

$$= \frac{2i}{1 - e^{2\pi i \lambda}} \left(\sum \text{residues of } \frac{s^\lambda \sin \gamma}{s^2 + 2s \cos \gamma + 1} \text{ at } z = e^{i(\pi \mp \gamma)} \right)$$

$$= \frac{\sin(\gamma \lambda)}{\sin(\pi \lambda)}.$$

Also since $\lambda > 0$, we have, if $0 < \epsilon < \frac{1}{5}$,

$$\int_0^1 (s^{\lambda - 2\epsilon} - s^\lambda) P(s, 1, \gamma)\, ds \leqslant \left\{ \max_{0 \leqslant s \leqslant 1} (s^{\frac{1}{2} - 2\epsilon} - s^{\frac{1}{2}}) \right\} \int_0^1 s^{-\frac{1}{2}} P(s, 1, \gamma)\, ds$$

$$\leqslant A\epsilon,$$

where A is an absolute constant. Thus we deduce from (4.51) that we have for some arbitrarily large values of r

$$1 \leqslant \max_{0 \leqslant \beta \leqslant \pi} \frac{U\sin(\beta\lambda) + V\sin(\pi-\beta)\lambda}{\sin \pi\lambda} + A\epsilon,$$

when ϵ is a sufficiently small positive quantity, e.g. if $0 < \epsilon < \frac{1}{5}$. Suppose that γ is so chosen that $0 \leqslant \gamma \leqslant \pi$, and

$$U\sin\gamma\lambda + V\sin(\pi-\gamma)\lambda$$

is maximal. Then we have for this value of γ

$$(1-A\epsilon)\sin \pi\lambda \leqslant U\sin\gamma\lambda + V\sin(\pi-\gamma)\lambda$$

$$= (U - V\cos \pi\lambda)\sin\gamma\lambda + V\sin \pi\lambda\cos\gamma\lambda. \qquad (4.52)$$

Hence, by Schwarz's inequality,

$$(1-A\epsilon)^2 \sin^2\pi\lambda \leqslant \{(U - V\cos \pi\lambda)^2 + V^2 \sin^2\pi\lambda\}(\sin^2\gamma\lambda + \cos^2\gamma\lambda)$$

$$= U^2 + V^2 - 2UV\cos \pi\lambda.$$

In this inequality we first make $\epsilon \to 0$, and then let $U \to u$ and $V \to v$. This yields (4.42) as required.

It remains to prove (4.43). Suppose, for example, that $u < \cos \pi\rho$, $v < 1$. We may then choose ϵ so small that $u < \cos \pi\lambda = \cos \pi(\rho+\epsilon)$ and further choose V such that $v < V < 1$ and $u < V\cos \pi\lambda$ and set $U = V\cos \pi\lambda$. Then (4.52) yields

$$(1-A\epsilon)\sin \pi\lambda \leqslant V\sin \pi\lambda\cos\gamma\lambda \leqslant V\sin \pi\lambda.$$

In this inequality we can let V decrease until either $V \to v$, or $V\cos \pi\lambda \to u$. Thus we deduce that either $v \geqslant 1-A\epsilon$, or $u\sec \pi\lambda \geqslant 1-A\epsilon$. We now let $\epsilon \to 0$, so that $\lambda \to \rho$, and obtain a contradiction. This completes the proof of Theorem 4.10.

4.6.3. *Consequences of Theorem* 4.10. We can deduce immediately some striking corollaries from Theorem 4.10. We have first

THEOREM 4.11. *If $f(z)$ is a meromorphic function of order ρ, where $0 \leqslant \rho < \frac{1}{2}$, and $\delta(a,f) > 0$ when $\rho = 0$ or $\delta(a,f) \geqslant 1-\cos \pi\rho$ when $\rho > 0$, then a is the only deficient value of $f(z)$. In particular a meromorphic function of order zero can have at most one deficient value.*

If $\delta(a,f) > 1-\cos \pi\rho$, this result follows at once from (4.43). If $0 < \rho \leqslant \frac{1}{2}$ and $\delta(a,f) = 1-\cos \pi\rho$, so that $u = \cos \pi\rho$ in Theorem 4.10, then (4.42) yields $v = 1$ or $v \leqslant \cos 2\pi\rho$. In the latter case (4.43) implies $u = 1$, since $\cos 2\pi\rho < \cos \pi\rho$, for $0 < \rho \leqslant \frac{1}{2}$, giving a contradiction. Thus we must have $v = 1$.

Theorem 4.11 was proved by Teichmüller [1] for functions with positive poles and negative zeros and in the general case by Gol'dberg by means of his Theorem 4.9. The case $\rho = 0$ is due to Valiron [2].

We have next

THEOREM 4.12. *If $f(z)$ is a meromorphic function of order ρ, where $0 \leqslant \rho < 1$, having zeros a_ν and poles b_ν, such that*

$$|a_\nu| = |b_\nu| \quad (\nu = 1, 2, 3, \ldots),$$

then

$$\delta(0, f) = \delta(\infty, f) \leqslant 1 - \cos \tfrac{1}{2}\pi\rho.$$

We have clearly in this case

$$N(r, f) = N(r, 1/f) \quad \text{and hence} \quad \delta(0, f) = \delta(\infty, f).$$

Hence by Theorem 4.11 we may assume $\rho > 0$. We apply Theorem 4.9 with $u = v = 1 - \delta(0, f) = 1 - \delta(\infty, f)$. Then (4.42) yields

$$2u^2(1 - \cos \pi\rho) \geqslant \sin^2 \pi\rho, \qquad u^2 \geqslant \cos^2 \tfrac{1}{2}\pi\rho,$$

which gives the desired conclusion. This result is due to Teichmüller [1] for functions with negative zeros and positive poles and to Gol'dberg [3] in the general case.

We have also two results due to Edrei and Fuchs [3].

THEOREM 4.13. *If $f(z)$ is an integral function of order ρ, then*

$$\sum_{a \neq \infty} \delta(a, f) \begin{cases} = 0 & (0 \leqslant \rho \leqslant \tfrac{1}{2}), \\ \leqslant 1 - \sin \pi\rho & (\tfrac{1}{2} \leqslant \rho \leqslant 1). \end{cases}$$

We have by Theorem 4.6

$$\sum_{a \neq \infty} \delta(a, f) \leqslant \delta(0, f');$$

also $f'(z)$ has the same order as $f(z)$, and setting $u = 1 - \delta(\infty, f') = 0$, $v = 1 - \delta(0, f')$, we obtain from (4.42)

$$v \geqslant \sin \pi\rho,$$

which gives the required result for $\tfrac{1}{2} \leqslant \rho \leqslant 1$, and for $0 \leqslant \rho < \tfrac{1}{2}$ we have $v = 1$ from (4.43). This proves Theorem 4.13.

For $\rho < \tfrac{1}{2}$ Theorem 4.13 follows at once from a classical theorem of Wiman [1] that there exists a sequence $r_n \to \infty$, such that as $n \to \infty$,

$$|f(r_n e^{i\theta})| \to +\infty, \quad \text{uniformly in } \theta.$$

Thus $m\{r_n, (f-a)^{-1}\} = 0$ for any finite a and all large n, and so $\delta(a, f) = 0$. The case $\tfrac{1}{2} \leqslant \rho < 1$, however, represents a sharp form of Theorem 4.7 for functions of order less than 1.

Finally we have

THEOREM 4.14. *If $f(z)$ is meromorphic of order ρ, then*

$$K(f) = \varlimsup_{r \to \infty} \frac{N(r,0) + N(r,\infty)}{T(r,f)} \geqslant k(\rho),$$

where $k(\rho) = 1$ if $0 \leqslant \rho < \frac{1}{2}$, $k(\rho) = \sin \pi\rho$, if $\frac{1}{2} \leqslant \rho < 1$.

This result represents a sharp form of Theorem 4.5 for functions of order less than 1. We cannot deduce Theorem 4.14 at once from Theorem 4.10. In fact that theorem would only yield the weaker inequality $\delta(0,f) + \delta(\infty,f) \leqslant 2 - k(\rho)$. However, we can proceed as follows. If $\rho = 0$, $f(z)$ has at most one deficient value by Theorem 4.11 and hence either $\delta(0,f) = 0$ or $\delta(\infty,f) = 0$. If, for example, $\delta(0,f) = 0$, we have

$$K(f) \geqslant \varlimsup_{r \to \infty} \frac{N(r,0)}{T(r,f)} = 1 - \delta(0,f) = 1,$$

so that Theorem 4.14 follows in this case.

Suppose next that $0 < \rho < 1$. We assume again that $\delta(0,f) > 0$, $\delta(\infty,f) > 0$, since otherwise Theorem 4.14 is trivial. Then (4.48) yields

$$T(r,f) \leqslant \int\limits_0^\infty \{N(t,0) + N(t,\infty)\} P(t,r,\tau) \, dt,$$

where $\tau = \tau(r) = \max\{\beta(r),\ \pi - \beta(r)\}$, so that

$$P(t,r,\tau) = \max\{P(t,r,\beta),\ P(t,r,\pi - \beta)\}.$$

For $K > K(f)$, we have

$$N(t,0) + N(t,\infty) < KT(t)$$

for all large t. Proceeding as in section 4.6.2 we are led to

$$T(r) \leqslant KT(r)\left\{ \int\limits_0^r P(t,r,\tau)(t/r)^{\lambda - 2\epsilon} \, dt + \int\limits_r^\infty P(t,r,\tau)(t/r)^\lambda \, dt \right\} + O(1)/r$$

for some arbitrarily large r, where $\lambda = \rho + \epsilon$, and hence to

$$(1 - A\epsilon)\sin \pi\lambda \leqslant K \max_{0 \leqslant \tau \leqslant \pi} \sin \tau\lambda, \qquad (4.53)$$

instead of (4.52). This yields in any case $K \geqslant (1 - A\epsilon)\sin \pi\lambda$, and hence $K(f) \geqslant \sin \pi\rho$ on letting $\epsilon \to 0$, $K \to K(f)$. If $0 < \rho < \frac{1}{2}$, we may choose $\lambda < \frac{1}{2}$, and so $\sin \tau\lambda \leqslant \sin \pi\lambda$, for $0 \leqslant \tau \leqslant \pi$. Then (4.53) yields $K(f) \geqslant 1$ as required.

4.6.4. *Some counter-examples.* We proceed to give some examples to show that the conclusions of Theorems 4.10 to 4.14 are best possible. Suppose that $f(z)$ is an integral function of genus zero, that $f(z)$ has real negative zeros and $f(0) = 1$. Then we have

$$\log f(z) = z \int\limits_0^\infty \frac{n(t,0)\,dt}{t(z+t)}.$$

Suppose that $n(t,0) = [\alpha t^\rho]$, where $\alpha \geqslant 0$ and $0 < \rho < 1$. Then we deduce that for the corresponding function $f(z) = f(z, \alpha, \rho)$ we have

$$\log f(z) = z \int\limits_0^\infty \frac{\alpha t^{\rho-1}\,dt}{z+t} + z \int\limits_0^\infty \frac{O(1)\,dt}{(1+t)|z+t|} = I_1 + I_2, \quad \text{say}.$$

If $z = re^{i\theta}$, where $1 \leqslant r < \infty$, $0 \leqslant |\theta| < \pi$, the second integral is easily seen to satisfy

$$|I_2| < A\left\{\log\left(\frac{2\pi}{\pi-|\theta|}\right) + \log r\right\},$$

where A is an absolute constant. Also by means of a complex substitution $t = zx$, the first integral becomes

$$I_1 = \alpha z^\rho \int\limits_0^\infty \frac{x^{\rho-1}\,dx}{1+x} = \frac{\alpha\pi r^\rho(\cos\rho\theta + i\sin\rho\theta)}{\sin\pi\rho}.$$

Thus we have for $z = re^{i\theta}$, $0 < |\theta| < \pi$, $1 < r < \infty$,

$$\log|f(z,\alpha,\rho)| = \frac{\alpha\pi}{\sin\pi\rho} r^\rho \cos\rho\theta + O\left(\log r + \log\frac{2\pi}{\pi-|\theta|}\right).$$

We can set
$$f(z) = \frac{f(z,\alpha,\rho)}{f(-z,\beta,\rho)},$$

where $0 < \rho < 1$, and $\alpha \geqslant \beta \geqslant 0$. We deduce that for $z = re^{i\theta}$, $0 < |\theta| < \pi$, we have as $r \to \infty$, uniformly in θ,

$$\log|f(z)| = \frac{\pi r^\rho}{\sin\pi\rho}(\alpha\cos\rho\theta - \beta\cos\{\rho(\pi-|\theta|)\}) + O\{\log(r\,|\mathrm{cosec}\,\theta|)\}.$$

The function $\alpha\cos\rho\theta - \beta\cos\rho(\pi-\theta)$ decreases steadily with θ, for $0 \leqslant \theta \leqslant \pi$ from $\alpha - \beta\cos\rho\pi$ to $\alpha\cos\rho\pi - \beta$. We now distinguish two cases.

(i) If $\alpha\cos\rho\pi \geqslant \beta$, then as $r \to \infty$, we have

$$m(r,f) = \frac{\pi r^\rho}{\sin\pi\rho}\frac{1}{\pi}\int\limits_0^\pi \{\alpha\cos\rho\theta - \beta\cos\rho(\pi-\theta)\}\,d\theta + O(\log r)$$

$$= \frac{\alpha-\beta}{\rho}r^\rho + O(\log r),$$

$$N(r,f) = \int\limits_0^r \frac{n(t,f)\,dt}{t} = \frac{\beta}{\rho}r^\rho + O(\log r),$$

$$m(r,1/f) = O(\log r).$$

Thus
$$T(r,f) \sim \frac{\alpha r^\rho}{\rho},$$

and
$$\delta(0,f) = 0, \qquad \delta(\infty,f) = \frac{\alpha-\beta}{\alpha}.$$

Thus $\delta = \delta(\infty,f)$ may take any value satisfying $1-\cos\rho\pi \leqslant \delta \leqslant 1$, while $\delta(0,f) = 0$. Thus we see that any pair of values (u,v) or the line segments (4.43) can actually occur for a meromorphic function of order ρ $(0 < \rho < 1)$.

(ii) Suppose next that $\alpha\cos\rho\pi < \beta \leqslant \alpha$. Let θ_0 satisfy
$$\alpha\cos\rho\theta_0 = \beta\cos\rho(\pi-\theta_0), \quad \text{so that} \quad \tan\rho\theta_0 = \frac{\alpha-\beta\cos\rho\pi}{\beta\sin\rho\pi}.$$
Then we have as $r \to \infty$

$$m(r,f) = \frac{\pi r^\rho}{\sin\pi\rho}\frac{1}{\pi}\int_0^{\theta_0}\{\alpha\cos\rho\theta-\beta\cos\rho(\pi-\theta)\}\,d\theta+O(\log r)$$

$$= \frac{r^\rho}{\rho\sin\pi\rho}\{\alpha\sin\rho\theta_0+\beta\sin\rho(\pi-\theta_0)-\beta\sin\pi\rho\}+O(\log r),$$

and similarly

$$m\left(r,\frac{1}{f}\right) = \frac{-r^\rho}{\rho\sin\pi\rho}\{\alpha\sin\pi\rho-\alpha\sin\rho\theta_0-\beta\sin\rho(\pi-\theta_0)\}+O(\log r).$$

Further,

$$N(r,f) = \int_0^r \frac{\beta t^\rho\,dt}{t} + O(\log r) = \frac{\beta}{\rho}r^\rho+O(\log r);$$

$$N\left(r,\frac{1}{f}\right) = \frac{\alpha}{\rho}r^\rho+O(\log r).$$

Thus

$$T(r,f) = \frac{r^\rho}{\rho\sin\pi\rho}\{\alpha\sin\rho\theta_0+\beta\sin\rho(\pi-\theta_0)\}+O(\log r),$$

$$u = 1-\delta(\infty,f) = \frac{\beta\sin\pi\rho}{\alpha\sin\rho\theta_0+\beta\sin\rho(\pi-\theta_0)}$$

$$= \frac{\sin\pi\rho\cos\rho\theta_0}{\sin\rho\theta_0\cos\rho(\pi-\theta_0)+\sin\rho(\pi-\theta_0)\cos\rho\theta_0} = \cos\rho\theta_0,$$

$$v = 1-\delta(0,f) = \frac{\alpha\sin\pi\rho}{\alpha\sin\rho\theta_0+\beta\sin\rho(\pi-\theta_0)} = \cos\rho(\pi-\theta_0).$$

Thus (u,v) lies on the ellipse
$$u^2+v^2-2uv\cos\pi\rho = \sin^2\pi\rho, \tag{4.54}$$
so that equality is possible in (4.42).

If $0 < \rho < \frac{1}{2}$, β may vary from $\alpha \cos \rho \pi$ to α, and then θ_0 varies from π to $\frac{1}{2}\pi$, and (u, v) describes the smaller arc of (4.54) from $(\cos \rho \pi, 1)$ to $(\cos \frac{1}{2}\rho \pi, \cos \frac{1}{2}\rho \pi)$. The case $\alpha = \beta$ shows that the inequality of Theorem 4.12 is sharp. Also by taking θ_0 just less than π, so that $\delta(\infty, f)$ is just less than $1 - \cos \pi \rho$ while $\delta(0, f) = 1 - \cos \rho(\pi - \theta_0) > 0$, we see that Theorem 4.11 cannot be sharpened.

If $\frac{1}{2} \leqslant \rho < 1$, then β may vary between 0 and α, and if $\beta = 0$, so that $\theta_0 = \pi/(2\rho)$, $f(z)$ becomes an integral function. In general θ_0 varies from $\pi/(2\rho)$ to $\frac{1}{2}\pi$, and (u, v) describes the arc of the ellipse (4.54) from $(0, \cos \pi(\rho - \frac{1}{2}))$ to $(\cos \frac{1}{2}\pi \rho, \cos \frac{1}{2}\pi \rho)$, i.e. from $(0, \sin \pi \rho)$ to $(\cos \frac{1}{2}\pi \rho, \cos \frac{1}{2}\pi \rho)$. Thus again any points on the ellipse (4.54) which lie in the first quadrant can actually occur. Also the point $(0, \sin \pi \rho)$ corresponds to $\beta = 0$ so that $f(z)$ becomes an integral function. Thus the inequalities of Theorems 4.13, 4.14 are also sharp.

For examples in the cases where strict inequality holds in (4.42) we refer the reader to Edrei and Fuchs [3].

4.7. Extension of a theorem of Wiman

We conclude the chapter by proving

THEOREM 4.15. *Suppose that $f(z)$ is a meromorphic function of order ρ, where $0 \leqslant \rho < \frac{1}{2}$, and that $\delta(a, f) > 1 - \cos \pi \rho$. Then there exists a sequence $r_n \to +\infty$, such that*

$$f(r_n e^{i\theta}) \to a, \quad \text{as } n \to \infty, \quad \text{uniformly for } 0 \leqslant \theta \leqslant 2\pi.$$
(4.55)

This theorem represents a striking extension of (4.43), for it is evident that a function $f(z)$ satisfying (4.55) cannot have any deficient values other than a. For integral functions of order $\rho < \frac{1}{2}$ the theorem states that the minimum modulus

$$\mu(r, f) = \min_{|z| = r} |f(z)|$$

is unbounded as $r \to \infty$. This is an old theorem of Wiman [1].

Theorem 4.15 was proved by Teichmüller [1] for functions $f(z)$ with negative zeros and positive poles and $a = \infty$. The general result was then deduced by Gol'dberg [2, 3] from Theorem 4.9. In fact suppose that

$$\delta(\infty, f) > 1 - \cos \pi \rho$$

and that $\hat{f}(z)$ is defined as in Theorem 4.9. Then by that theorem $\hat{f}(z)$ has order ρ and satisfies

$$\delta(\infty, \hat{f}) > 1 - \cos \pi \rho.$$

If we assume that Theorem 4.15 has been proved for $\hat{f}(z)$ we deduce that $\mu(r,\hat{f}(z))$ is unbounded as $r \to \infty$, and hence so is $\mu(r,f)$ since evidently $\mu(r,f) \geqslant \mu(r,\hat{f})$. Thus Theorem 4.15 holds for general $f(z)$ with $a = \infty$ if it holds for the functions $\hat{f}(z)$ with $a = \infty$. The case of finite a can be reduced to the above case by considering $\{f(z)-a\}^{-1}$ instead of $f(z)$. Thus to prove Theorem 4.15 it is enough to assume that $f(z)$ has positive poles and negative zeros and that $a = \infty$. In this case $f(z)$ attains its minimum modulus on the negative real axis. We shall assume that $|f(-r)| < 1$, $0 < r < \infty$, and shall derive a contradiction from this and the assumption $\delta(\infty,f) > 1 - \cos \pi\rho$. Our proof follows that of Teichmüller.

4.7.1. We need some preliminary results.

LEMMA 4.10. *Suppose that $f(z)$ is a meromorphic function of order $\rho < \tfrac{1}{2}$, that $f(z)$ has positive poles $z = b_n$, $0 < n < \infty$, and that $|f(-r)| < 1$, $0 < r < \infty$. Then*

$$\log|f(z)| \leqslant \sum_{n=1}^{\infty} g(z,b_n),$$

where
$$g(z,b) = \log\left|\frac{z^{\frac{1}{2}}+b^{\frac{1}{2}}}{z^{\frac{1}{2}}-b^{\frac{1}{2}}}\right|.$$

Clearly $g(z,b)$ vanishes continuously as z approaches the negative real axis for fixed b. Also for $|z| < \tfrac{1}{2}|b|$

$$0 < g(z,b) < \left|\frac{z}{b}\right|^{\frac{1}{2}}\left(1+\frac{1}{3}\left|\frac{z}{b}\right|+\frac{1}{5}\left|\frac{z}{b}\right|^2+\dots\right) < 2\left|\frac{z}{b}\right|^{\frac{1}{2}}.$$

Thus the series $\sum g(z,b_n)$ converges since $f(z)$ has order less than $\tfrac{1}{2}$, and so

$$u(z) = \log|f(z)| - \sum_{n=1}^{\infty} g(z,b_n)$$

is harmonic in the plane cut along the negative real axis, and $u(z) \leqslant 0$ near the negative real axis.

Again if $|z| = r = \tfrac{1}{2}R$, the Poisson–Jensen formula shows that

$$\log|f(z)| \leqslant \frac{R+r}{R-r}m(R,f) + \sum \log^+\left|\frac{R^2-b_n z}{R(z-b_n)}\right|.$$

Thus

$$u(z) \leqslant 3m(R,f) + \sum_{b_n < R} \log\left|\frac{R^2-b_n z}{R(z-b_n)}\right|\left|\frac{z^{\frac{1}{2}}-b_n^{\frac{1}{2}}}{z^{\frac{1}{2}}+b_n^{\frac{1}{2}}}\right|$$

$$\leqslant 3m(R,f) + \sum_{b_n < R} \log\frac{|R^2+b_n z|}{R|z^{\frac{1}{2}}+b_n^{\frac{1}{2}}|^2}.$$

Now $|z^{\frac{1}{2}}+b_n^{\frac{1}{2}}| \geqslant b_n^{\frac{1}{2}}$, and $|b_n z| < R^2$. Thus we obtain for $|z| = r$

$$u(z) \leqslant 3m(R,f) + \sum \log^+ \frac{2R}{b_n} \leqslant 4T(2R,f) = 4T(4r,f) = o(r^\lambda)$$

as $r \to \infty$, where λ is any number such that $\rho < \lambda < \frac{1}{2}$. We now apply the usual Phragmén–Lindelöf argument. Consider for $z = re^{i\theta}$, $0 \leqslant |\theta| < \pi$,

$$u_1(z) = u(z) - \epsilon r^\lambda \cos \lambda\theta,$$

where $\epsilon > 0$, and $\rho < \lambda < \frac{1}{2}$. Then $u_1(z)$ is harmonic in the plane cut along the negative real axis and $u_1(z) \leqslant 0$ near the negative real axis. Also on $|z| = r$

$$u_1(z) \leqslant o(r^\lambda) - \epsilon r^\lambda \cos \lambda\pi \to -\infty, \quad \text{as } r \to -\infty,$$

so that $u_1(z) \leqslant 0$ on $|z| = r$ for large r. Hence by the maximum modulus principle applied to the disk $|z| \leqslant r$, cut along the negative axis, we see that $u_1(z) \leqslant 0$ for $|z| < r$, and so for all z, since r may be chosen as large as we please. Thus

$$u(z) \leqslant \epsilon r^\lambda \cos \lambda\theta.$$

Since ϵ is arbitrary $u(z) \leqslant 0$, and Lemma 4.10 is proved.

We now write

$$\chi(x) = \frac{2}{\pi} \int_0^x \tan^{-1} t \, \frac{dt}{t}$$

and note that for positive b and r

$$\frac{1}{2\pi} \int_{-\pi}^{\pi} g(re^{i\theta}, b) \, d\theta = \mathscr{R} \frac{1}{2\pi} \int_{-\pi}^{\pi} \log\left(\frac{1 + (re^{i\theta}/b)^{\frac{1}{2}}}{1 - (re^{i\theta}/b)^{\frac{1}{2}}}\right) d\theta = \begin{cases} 2\chi\{(r/b)^{\frac{1}{2}}\} & (r < b), \\ 2\chi\{(b/r)^{\frac{1}{2}}\} & (r > b). \end{cases}$$

We can see this by expanding the logarithm in a power series and integrating term by term. Also since $\tan^{-1} x + \tan^{-1} 1/x = \frac{1}{2}\pi$ we easily deduce that $\chi(1/t) = \chi(t) - \log t$ $(t > 1)$. Thus

$$\frac{1}{2\pi} \int_{-\pi}^{\pi} g(re^{i\theta}, b) \, d\theta = 2\chi\left\{\left(\frac{r}{b}\right)^{\frac{1}{2}}\right\} - 2\log^+\left(\frac{r}{b}\right)^{\frac{1}{2}},$$

if $b \neq r$, and the result continues to hold by continuity if $b = r$. In view of Lemma 4.10 and the fact that $g(re^{i\theta}, b) > 0$ for $\theta < \pi$, we deduce that

$$m(r,f) \leqslant 2 \sum_{n=1}^{\infty} \chi\left\{\left(\frac{r}{b_n}\right)^{\frac{1}{2}}\right\} - \sum_{n=1}^{\infty} \log^+ \frac{r}{b_n} = 2 \sum_{n=1}^{\infty} \chi\left\{\left(\frac{r}{b_n}\right)^{\frac{1}{2}}\right\} - N(r,f).$$

Thus
$$T(r,f) \leqslant 2 \sum_{n=1}^{'\infty} \chi\left\{\left(\frac{r}{b_n}\right)^{\frac{1}{2}}\right\}. \tag{4.56}$$

4.7.2. To complete the proof we now need

LEMMA 4.11. *We have for every positive a and $0 < \lambda < 1$*

$$\int_a^\infty \frac{\chi(x)\,dx}{x^{1+\lambda}} < \sec(\tfrac{1}{2}\pi\lambda) \int_a^\infty \frac{\log^+ x\,dx}{x^{1+\lambda}}.$$

We have
$$\int_0^\infty \frac{\log^+ x\,dx}{x^{1+\lambda}} = \int_1^\infty \frac{\log x\,dx}{x^{1+\lambda}} = \frac{1}{\lambda}\int_1^\infty \frac{dx}{x^{1+\lambda}} = \frac{1}{\lambda^2}.$$

Again on integrating by parts twice and then setting $x^2 = y$ we obtain

$$\int_0^\infty \frac{\chi(x)\,dx}{x^{1+\lambda}} = \frac{1}{\lambda}\int_0^\infty \frac{\chi'(x)\,dx}{x^\lambda} = \frac{2}{\pi\lambda}\int_0^\infty \frac{\tan^{-1}x\,dx}{x^{1+\lambda}}$$

$$= \frac{2}{\pi\lambda^2}\int_0^\infty \frac{dx}{x^\lambda(1+x^2)} = \frac{1}{\pi\lambda^2}\int_0^\infty \frac{y^{-\frac{1}{2}-\frac{1}{2}\lambda}\,dy}{1+y} = \frac{1}{\pi\lambda^2}\,\pi\,\mathrm{cosec}\,\pi(\tfrac{1}{2}-\tfrac{1}{2}\lambda)$$

by a well-known contour integration. Thus

$$\int_0^\infty \frac{\{\chi(x)-\sec(\tfrac{1}{2}\pi\lambda)\log^+ x\}\,dx}{x^{1+\lambda}} = 0.$$

Here the integrand is clearly positive for $x \leqslant 1$. Also for $x > 1$

$$\chi'(x)-\sec(\tfrac{1}{2}\pi\lambda)\,\frac{1}{x} = \frac{1}{x}\Big(\frac{2}{\pi}\tan^{-1}x-\sec\tfrac{1}{2}\pi\lambda\Big).$$

The right-hand side is negative and so $\chi(x)-\sec(\tfrac{1}{2}\pi\lambda)\log^+ x$ steadily decreases for $x > 1$. Thus there exists $A > 1$, such that

$$\chi(x)-\sec(\tfrac{1}{2}\pi\lambda)\log^+ x > 0 \quad (0 < x < A),$$
$$\chi(x)-\sec(\tfrac{1}{2}\pi\lambda)\log^+ x < 0 \quad (A < x < \infty).$$

Thus
$$I(a) = \int_a^\infty \frac{\{\chi(x)-\sec(\tfrac{1}{2}\pi\lambda)\log^+(x)\}\,dx}{x^{1+\lambda}}$$

is zero for $a = 0$, decreases to a negative minimum for $a = A$, and then increases again to zero for $a = \infty$. In particular $I(a) < 0$ for all positive a. This proves Lemma 4.11.

4.7.3. *Proof of Theorem* 4.15. To conclude our proof we now note that by (4.56)

$$T(r,f) \leqslant 2\sum_{n=1}^\infty \chi\Big\{\Big(\frac{r}{b_n}\Big)^{\frac{1}{2}}\Big\}, \quad \text{while} \quad N(r,f) = \sum_{n=1}^\infty \log^+\Big(\frac{r}{b_n}\Big),$$

where b_n are the poles of $f(z)$ which are assumed to be real and positive.

Also for $\rho < \lambda < \frac{1}{2}$,

$$J(a) = \int_a^\infty \frac{\{T(r,f) - \sec(\pi\lambda)N(r,f)\}\,dr}{r^{1+\lambda}}$$

converges absolutely, since $f(z)$ has order less than λ and we may write

$$J(a) \leqslant \sum_{n=1}^\infty \int_a^\infty \left[2\chi\left\{\left(\frac{r}{b_n}\right)^{\frac{1}{2}}\right\} - \sec(\pi\lambda)\log^+\left(\frac{r}{b_n}\right) \right] \frac{dr}{r^{1+\lambda}}.$$

The change in the order of integration and summation is justified by the absolute convergence of the two series of integrals of positive functions. Again, setting $(r/b_n)^{\frac{1}{2}} = t$, we see that

$$\int_a^\infty \left[2\chi\left\{\left(\frac{r}{b_n}\right)^{\frac{1}{2}}\right\} - \sec(\pi\lambda)\log^+(r/b_n) \right] \frac{dr}{r^{1+\lambda}}$$

$$= \int_{(a/b_n)^{\frac{1}{2}}}^\infty \{\chi(t) - \sec(\pi\lambda)\log^+ t\} \frac{4(b_n)^{-\lambda}\,dt}{t^{1+2\lambda}} \leqslant 0,$$

by Lemma 4.11 applied with 2λ instead of λ. Thus $J(a) \leqslant 0$, and so for any positive a there exists $r > a$ such that

$$T(r,f) \leqslant \sec(\pi\lambda)N(r,f),$$
$$N(r,f) \geqslant \cos(\pi\lambda)T(r,f),$$
$$m(r,f) \leqslant \{1 - \cos(\pi\lambda)\}T(r,f) + O(1),$$

and so $\qquad\qquad\qquad \delta(\infty,f) \leqslant 1 - \cos(\pi\lambda)$.

Since λ is arbitrary subject to $\rho < \lambda < \frac{1}{2}$, we deduce that

$$\delta(\infty,f) \leqslant 1 - \cos(\pi\rho),$$

giving a contradiction.

It follows that if $f(z)$ is meromorphic of order $\rho < \frac{1}{2}$, and

$$\delta(\infty,f) > 1 - \cos\pi\rho,$$

then we cannot have $\mu(r,f) \leqslant 1$ $(0 < r < \infty)$. By applying this result to $f(z)/c$, we see that we cannot have $\mu(r,f) \leqslant c$ $(0 < r < \infty)$, so that $\mu(r,f)$ must be unbounded. If $f(0) \neq \infty$, so that $\mu(r,f)$ is bounded in any finite range, we deduce that we must have

$$\varlimsup_{r \to \infty} \mu(r,f) = +\infty.$$

Suppose finally that $f(0) = \infty$. If $f(z)$ is rational our hypotheses imply that $f(\infty) = \infty$, so that

$$f(z) \to \infty \quad \text{as } z \to \infty,$$

and Theorem 4.15 is trivial. Otherwise it follows from Theorem 4.11 that $\delta(0,f) = 0$, so that $f(z)$ has infinitely many zeros. In this case suppose that $f(z)$ has a pole of order p at the origin and let $a_1, a_2,..., a_p$ be distinct zeros of $f(z)$. Then we apply our result to

$$\phi(z) = \frac{z^p f(z)}{(z-a_1)(z-a_2)...(z-a_p)}.$$

Then $\phi(z)$ also has order ρ and $\delta(\infty,\phi) = \delta(\infty,f) > 1-\cos(\pi\rho)$. Also $\phi(0)$ is finite. Thus

$$\overline{\lim_{r\to\infty}} \mu(r,f) = \overline{\lim_{r\to\infty}} \mu(r,\phi) = +\infty,$$

and Theorem 4.15 is proved in all cases.

4.8. Conclusion

The results in this chapter represent a selection of the many interesting theorems that have been proved recently concerning the deficiencies of meromorphic functions. We have seen that a meromorphic function $f(z)$ of positive order ρ may possess a completely arbitrary countable set of deficient values (Theorems 4.1, 4.4). For $\rho = 0$ it follows from Theorem 4.11 that $f(z)$ may possess at most one deficient value. One of the most interesting open problems concerns the question of whether an integral function $f(z)$ of finite order ρ may possess infinitely many deficient values.† If $\rho \leqslant \frac{1}{2}$, it follows from Theorem 4.11 that such a function cannot have any finite deficient values, but nothing is known in general for $\rho > \frac{1}{2}$.

In certain special cases we have some information. Thus Edrei and Fuchs [4] have shown that if $f(z)$ has all its zeros on a finite number of straight lines then it can have at most a finite number of deficient values. Edrei, Fuchs, and Hellerstein [1] also showed that in this case zero is certainly a deficient value of $f(z)$ provided that the order is sufficiently large, depending on the configuration of the lines. Another interesting general question concerns the possibility of replacing the order by the lower order in some of the theorems of this chapter.‡ Thus Edrei and Fuchs [1, Theorem 4] have shown that if $f(z)$ is a meromorphic function with two distinct deficient values then $f(z)$ must have positive lower order. We have already mentioned their extension of Theorem 4.7 and the conjectured extension to meromorphic functions. The interested reader is encouraged to study some of the above papers whose contents the author omitted from this chapter with regret.

† A positive answer to this question has now been given by Arakeljan [1].
‡ A. Edrei and I. V. Ostrovskii have informed me independently that they have now done this.

5

AHLFORS'S THEORY OF COVERING
SURFACES

5.0. Introduction

IN this chapter we develop a theory due to L. Ahlfors† which is in
many ways parallel to that of Nevanlinna. The basic formulae are
comparable to differentiated versions of the first and second fundamental theorems of Nevanlinna. However, in Ahlfors's theory the role
of points is taken by domains and we ask for the number of times that
the image of a disk $|z| < R$ by a function $f(z)$ covers completely such
a domain.

Ahlfors's theory, unlike that of Nevanlinna, is very geometrical in
character and the methods extend to quasi-conformal mappings. However, we shall confine ourselves here to the simplest cases since the
extensions give rise to more complications without demanding essentially new ideas. Even the simpler applications, however, bring out
a rather startling and unsuspected link between results in the theory
of functions of a complex variable such as, for instance, Picard's
theorem and the topology and differential geometry of surfaces. Thus
the two exceptional values that are permitted in Picard's theorem are
related to the number 2 that appears in the Euler–Poincaré formula
for the characteristic of a surface.

5.1. Geometric preliminaries

We shall be concerned with the metric properties of sets of points
on the Riemann sphere of diameter 1. Lengths of curves will be defined
in the usual way. The distance between two points P_1, P_2 on a sphere
is the lower bound of lengths of curves joining them and will be denoted
by $P_1 P_2$; it is thus the smaller of the two great circle arcs joining the
two points. The *diameter* of a set E is the upper bound of the distances
between pairs of points in E. It will be denoted by $\delta(E)$. The closure
of a set E will be denoted by $\bar{E}$.

According to Jordan's theorem any closed Jordan curve γ divides
the sphere into two domains. Suppose that the diameter of γ is less

† Ahlfors [3]. See also R. Nevanlinna [3, chapter 13] and Valiron [3, chapter 5].

than $\frac{1}{4}\pi$ and let P_0 be a point of γ. The set of points distant at least $\frac{1}{4}\pi$ from P_0 constitutes a hemisphere which does not intersect γ and so lies entirely in one of the complementary domains of γ. This domain will be called the outside of γ and the other domain the inside. If the diameter of γ is greater than or equal to $\frac{1}{4}\pi$ the terms inside and outside of γ will not be defined.

Let D_0 be the inside domain of a Jordan curve γ. Then $\delta(\bar{D}_0) = \delta(\gamma)$. In fact since $\bar{D}_0$ is compact and distance is continuous there exist points P_1, P_2 in $\bar{D}_0$ whose distance apart is $\delta(\bar{D}_0)$. These points cannot be diametrically opposite, since $\bar{D}_0$ lies entirely in one hemisphere. If P_1 were an interior point of D_0 we could increase the distance $P_1 P_2$ slightly by moving P_1 away from P_2 along a great circle, thus contradicting the hypothesis that $P_1 P_2$ is maximal. Thus P_1 and P_2 must both lie on γ, so that $\delta(\bar{D}_0) = P_1 P_2 \leqslant \delta(\gamma)$. We note further that if γ is a set consisting of a finite number of mutually exclusive Jordan curves γ_1 to γ_n having interiors D_1 to D_n and if $\delta(\gamma) < \frac{1}{4}\pi$, the same argument shows that

$$\delta\left(\bigcup_{\nu=1}^{n} D_\nu \right) = \delta(\gamma).$$

The Riemann sphere can be made into a Riemann surface in the usual way (see section 1.5.1) and the term *analytic arc* is defined. If z is a local parameter near a point P_0 on such an arc γ, then the points of γ near P_0 have parameters $z = \alpha(t)$, $a \leqslant t \leqslant b$, where, if P_0 corresponds to $t = t_0$, we have $a < t_0 < b$ if P_0 is an interior point, and $t_0 = a$ or b otherwise. We also specify that $\alpha'(t_0) \neq 0$ so that $\alpha(t)$ is locally univalent.

By a *sectionally analytic* (s.a.) arc γ we shall mean the union of a finite number of analytic arcs $P_1 P_2$, $P_2 P_3$,..., $P_n P_{n+1}$, where we assume that at all points of γ through which more than one analytic arc, or branch of γ, passes, i.e. at the P_ν ($\nu = 2$ to n), and at multiple points of γ, no two such branches touch. An arc without multiple points will be called a Jordan arc.

A domain on the sphere whose boundary consists of a finite number of mutually disjoint s.a. Jordan curves is an *s.a. domain*. We shall denote by h, h_0, h_1, etc., constants depending on certain fixed domains or curves on the sphere, not necessarily the same each time. We shall specify what h depends on, unless this is clear from the context.

5.1.1. We have

LEMMA 5.1. *If γ is an s.a. Jordan arc or Jordan curve on the sphere, there exists a constant h, depending only on γ, such that if E is any set of points on γ, there exists an arc of γ containing E and of length at most $h\delta(E)$.*

Suppose first that γ is a Jordan arc, parametrized in terms of arc length s. Thus points on γ will be denoted by $P(s)$ $(a \leqslant s \leqslant b)$. Let $\delta(s_1, s_2)$ be the distance from $P(s_1)$ to $P(s_2)$. Consider the ratio

$$f(s_1, s_2) = \frac{\delta(s_1, s_2)}{s_2 - s_1} \quad (a \leqslant s_1 < s_2 \leqslant b).$$

We show that this ratio is bounded below. For if not there are sequences of points s_n, s_n' such that

$$f(s_n, s_n') \to 0. \tag{5.1}$$

This certainly implies that $\delta(s_n, s_n') \to 0$. By choosing a subsequence if necessary we may assume that $s_n \to s_0$ and $s_n' \to s_0$, where $a \leqslant s_0 \leqslant b$. If s_0 is not a 'corner' of γ so that γ locally approximates to its tangent, we deduce that

$$f(s_n, s_n') = \frac{\delta(s_n, s_n')}{|s_n - s_n'|} \to 1,$$

giving a contradiction. The same condition holds if $P(s_0)$ is one of the points P_ν and $P(s_n)$, $P(s_n')$ either both lie on $P_{\nu-1}P_\nu$ or on $P_\nu P_{\nu+1}$. Let α be the angle between these two arcs, so that $0 \leqslant \alpha < 2\pi$ $(\alpha \neq \pi)$. We have $s_n < s_0 < s_n'$. Then the distance of $P(s_n)$ from the arc $P_\nu P_{\nu+1}$ is asymptotic to $\eta(s_0 - s_n)$, where $\eta = |\sin \alpha|$ for $\frac{1}{2}\pi < \alpha < \frac{3}{2}\pi$ and $\eta = 1$ otherwise. Similarly the distance of $P(s_n')$ from $P_{\nu-1}P_\nu$ is asymptotic to $\eta(s_n' - s_0)$. Thus for large n

$$\delta(s_n, s_n') \geqslant (1 - \tfrac{1}{3})\eta \max\{(s_0 - s_n), (s_n' - s_0)\}$$
$$\geqslant \tfrac{1}{3}\eta|s_n' - s_n|,$$

again contradicting (5.1). This proves the lemma in the case when γ has different endpoints.

Suppose next that γ is a closed curve and let P_1, P_2, P_3, P_4 be four points in order along γ. Then the arcs $P_1 P_2$, $P_3 P_4$ are at a positive distance h_1, say, from each other. Let E be any set on γ and suppose $\delta(E) < h_1$. Then E cannot contain points on both $P_1 P_2$ and $P_3 P_4$. Suppose, for example, that E contains no points on $P_3 P_4$. Then E lies on the s.a. Jordan arc $P_4 P_1 P_2 P_3$ and by the previous result we can find a subarc of length less than $h_2 \delta(E)$ containing E. We argue similarly if E contains no point of $P_1 P_2$. Thus in either case an arc of length at most $h_2 \delta(E)$ contains E, provided $\delta(E) < h_1$.

On the other hand if $\delta(E) \geqslant h_1$, then E lies on γ whose length is l, say, and $l = (l/h_1)h_1 \leqslant (l/h_1)\delta(E) = h_4 \delta(E)$, say. Thus the lemma is proved in all cases.

5.1.2. We have next

LEMMA 5.2. *Let F_0 be an s.a. domain on the sphere. Then there exists a positive constant h depending only on F_0 such that if γ_1 to γ_p are a finite number of disjoint continua, then $F_0-\gamma_1-\gamma_2-...-\gamma_p$ is the union of sets G_0, G_1,..., G_p, such that G_0 is connected and*

$$\sum_1^p \delta(G_\nu) \leqslant h \sum_1^p \delta(\gamma_\nu).$$

Let β_1, β_2,..., β_q be the boundary curves of F_0 and suppose that the mutual distance of any two of them is at least η. Let I_0 be the area of F_0 and let h_0 be a positive constant such that any set E on one of the curves β_ν lies on an arc of β_ν of length at most $h_0\delta(E)$. This constant exists by Lemma 5.1.

Set

$$d = \sum_{\nu=1}^p \delta(\gamma_\nu)$$

and

$$d_0 = \min\left(\tfrac{1}{2}\eta, \frac{I_0}{\pi^2(h_0+2)^2}\right)$$

so that

$$(h_0+1)d_0 \leqslant \frac{1}{4\pi} < \tfrac{1}{4}\pi.$$

We shall suppose

$$d < d_0. \qquad (5.2)$$

If this condition is not satisfied we take for G_0, G_1,..., G_{p-1} the empty set and for G_p the set $F_0-\gamma_1-\gamma_2-...-\gamma_p$. Then

$$\sum_{\nu=1}^p \delta(G_\nu) = \delta(G_p) \leqslant \pi \leqslant \frac{\pi}{d_0}d,$$

so that Lemma 5.2 is trivial in this case.

Since $\delta(\gamma_\nu) \leqslant d < \eta$, none of the γ_ν can meet more than one of the boundary curves β_μ. We next choose ϵ less than half the mutual distance between any of the γ_ν and between any γ_ν and those β_μ which γ_ν does not meet, and such that $2\epsilon < \delta(\gamma_\nu)$ ($\nu = 1$ to p), and $d+2\epsilon < \tfrac{1}{4}\pi$. We surround each point of all the γ_ν by disks of radius ϵ. Since the γ_ν are compact, a finite subset of these disks cover the γ_ν. We can decrease the radii of some of the circles bounding these disks slightly if necessary, so that no three of them pass through the same point, none pass through any corner of the boundary curves β_μ, and none of the circles touch each other or any of the β_μ. The union of the new disks containing points of γ_ν forms a domain which we denote by D'_ν. The boundary of D'_ν consists of a finite number of arcs of circles. Either γ_ν lies inside a single one of these circles or at each endpoint of a boundary arc there is exactly one other boundary arc. Thus the boundary of D'_ν consists of one or more s.a. Jordan curves. The union of these Jordan curves has diameter at most $\delta(\gamma_\nu)+2\epsilon < \tfrac{1}{4}\pi$, and so has D'_ν. Hence D'_ν cannot lie entirely outside all these Jordan curves. Thus D'_ν lies entirely inside one of these Jordan curves, which we denote by Γ_ν. The interior of Γ_ν is denoted by D_ν and contains γ_ν. By construction we have

$$\delta(\Gamma_\nu) = \delta(D_\nu) \leqslant \delta(\gamma_\nu) + 2\epsilon < 2\delta(\gamma_\nu) < \tfrac{1}{2}\pi.$$

By construction the D_ν are s.a. Jordan domains whose closures are disjoint. The area of the set of all points distant at most $(h_0+1)\delta(\Gamma_\nu)$ from a point of some D_ν is at most

$$\pi(h_0+2)^2 \sum \delta(\Gamma_\nu)^2 \leqslant \tfrac{1}{2}\pi^2(h_0+2)^2 \sum \delta(\Gamma_\nu) \leqslant \pi^2(h_0+2)^2 \sum \delta(\gamma_\nu)$$
$$< \pi^2(h_0+2)^2 d_0 \leqslant I_0$$

by (5.2). Thus there exists a point P_0 in F_0 distant at least $(h_0+1)\delta(\Gamma_\nu)$ from each D_ν. We denote by G_0 the component of $F_0 - \sum\limits_{\nu=1}^{p} \Gamma_\nu$, which contains P_0.

The boundary of G_0 then consists of certain arcs of the β_μ, or complete curves β_μ and certain arcs of the Γ_ν, or complete curves Γ_ν.

No such pair of arcs of Γ_ν can separate each other from P_0 and so they occur in order along β_μ. Let Γ be such an arc of Γ_ν having end-points P_1, P_2 on β_μ. By Lemma 5.1 the smaller arc $P_1 P_2$ of β_μ has diameter at most $h_0\delta(P_1, P_2) \leqslant h_0\delta(\Gamma)$. Thus the Jordan curve consisting of Γ and this arc has diameter at most

$$(h_0+1)\delta(\Gamma) < \tfrac{1}{4}\pi,$$

and so the interior of this Jordan curve exists and has diameter at most $(h_0+1)\delta(\Gamma)$, and so lies within a distance $(h_0+1)\delta(\Gamma)$ of the point P_1 of Γ. If G_ν is the union of all the domains associated with arcs Γ of Γ_ν in this way, then any point of G_ν lies within a distance

$$(h_0+1)\delta(\Gamma) \leqslant (h_0+1)\delta(\Gamma_\nu)$$

of some point of Γ_ν and so P_0 is outside G_ν. Also the diameter of G_ν is at most

$$(h_0+1)\delta(\Gamma_\nu) + \delta(\Gamma_\nu) + (h_0+1)\delta(\Gamma_\nu) \leqslant (2h_0+3)\delta(\Gamma_\nu)$$
$$\leqslant (4h_0+6)\delta(\gamma_\nu).$$

By construction each Γ_ν meets at most one β_μ. If Γ_ν meets no β_μ and so lies entirely in F_0, we take for G_ν the interior of Γ_ν. Then G_0 consists of all points of F_0 not in any of the G_ν and is connected and

$$\sum_{\nu=1}^{p} \delta(G_\nu) \leqslant (4h_0+6) \sum_{\nu=1}^{p} \delta(\gamma_\nu).$$

This proves Lemma 5.2.

5.2. Covering surfaces

Suppose that D_0 is an s.a. domain on the Riemann z-sphere and that $w = f(z)$ is meromorphic in $\bar{D}_0$. Let γ denote the frontier of D_0 and Γ the image of γ by $w = f(z)$. Then Γ divides the w-sphere into a finite number of domains, Δ_1 to Δ_ν, say. For w_1, w_2 not on Γ the number $n(w)$ of roots of the equation $f(z) = w$ in D_0 satisfies

$$n(w_1) - n(w_2) = \frac{1}{2\pi i} \int_\gamma \frac{f'(z)\,dz}{f(z) - w_1} - \frac{1}{2\pi i} \int_\gamma \frac{f'(z)\,dz}{f(z) - w_2} \qquad (5.3)$$

by Cauchy's Theorem of Residues.

Clearly the left-hand side of (5.3) is an integer and the right-hand side is continuous in w_1, w_2, provided that w_1 and w_2 each stay in a component of the complement of Γ. Thus in this case both sides are constant, and so $n(w)$ is constant in each such component. This constant value is called the *multiplicity* of the component.

Since Γ is sectionally analytic, we can split it into a finite number of simple Jordan arcs Γ_ν, two of which are either identical or have at most one endpoint in common. With each arc Γ_ν is associated a definite, *signed multiplicity* p_ν, being the number of times the arc is described as z describes γ once. We now write (5.3) as

$$n(w_1) - n(w_2) = \sum_\nu \frac{1}{2\pi} p_\nu \operatorname{var}_{\Gamma_\nu} \arg\left(\frac{w - w_1}{w - w_2}\right).$$

As w_1 crosses from one component Δ_1 of the complement of Γ to another Δ_2 across an arc Γ_ν of Γ, we see that

$$\operatorname{var}_{\Gamma_\mu} \arg\left(\frac{w - w_1}{w - w_2}\right)$$

remains continuous for $\mu \neq \nu$, and changes by $\mp 2\pi$ for $\mu = \nu$. Thus the change $n(w_1) - n(w_2)$ is $\mp 2\pi p_\nu$. We deduce

LEMMA 5.3. *If in the above analysis Δ_1 and Δ_2 are adjacent components of the complement of Γ, which are separated by an arc Γ' of Γ, and if n_1, n_2 are the multiplicities of Δ_1, Δ_2, then w describes Γ' at least $|n_2 - n_1|$ times as z describes the boundary of D_0.*

In fact p_ν, being the signed multiplicity of Γ', is not less than the total number of times that Γ is described, and the result follows.

We now suppose that, still with the above hypotheses, the values of $w = f(z)$ for z in D_0 all remain in a fixed s.a. domain F_0, henceforth called the *base domain*, on the w Riemann sphere. We say that the mapping from D_0 into F_0 constitutes a *covering surface* over F_0. In this case Γ will lie inside or on the boundary of F_0. We shall call the union of those arcs of Γ which lie interior to F_0 the *relative boundary* Γ_0 of our mapping or covering surface. The relative boundary divides F_0 into domains Δ_ν of given multiplicity and we denote by F_ν the closure of the union of those domains which have multiplicity at least ν. We suppose that F_ν is null for $\nu > n$. For any subset Δ of F_0 we denote by $L(\Delta)$ the length of the relative boundary of Δ, i.e. that part of the boundary of Δ which lies interior to F_0. We write

$$L_\nu = L(F_\nu) \quad (\nu = 1 \text{ to } n),$$

and denote by L the total length of the arcs of the relative boundary Γ_0, when each arc is counted as often as it is described when z describes the boundary of D_0. With this notation we have

$$\sum_{\nu=1}^{n} L_\nu \leqslant L. \tag{5.4}$$

In fact the relative boundary of F_ν consists of certain arcs of the relative boundary Γ_0. If such an arc Γ' of length L' lies between components Δ_1, Δ_2 of the complement of Γ_0, having multiplicities n_1, n_2 respectively, where $n_1 > n_2$, then Γ' belongs to the boundary of F_ν, precisely for $n_2 < \nu \leqslant n_1$, and so Γ' contributes precisely $(n_2-n_1)L'$ to the left-hand side of (5.4). On the other hand, by Lemma 5.3, Γ' contributes at least $(n_2-n_1)L'$ to the right-hand side of (5.4). Thus we deduce (5.4) by addition.

5.3. The first fundamental theorem

In the applications the quantity L will in general play the role of a rather unimportant error term, similar to the S which occurs in the second fundamental theorem of Nevanlinna. We show first as an analogue to the first fundamental theorem that if L is small compared with the area of the image of D_0 by $f(z)$, then the mapping covers different domains or arcs with roughly the same multiplicity.

THEOREM 5.1. *There exist positive integers* N ($s_1 = 1 < s_2 < ... < s_{n+1}$) *and sets* Δ_s ($s = 1$ *to* $s_{n+1}-1$), *such that*

(i) $F_0 \subset F_\nu \cup \sum_{s=s_\nu}^{s_{\nu+1}-1} \Delta_s \quad (1 \leqslant \nu \leqslant N),$

(ii) $F_\nu \subset \sum_{s=s_\nu}^{s_{\nu+1}-1} \Delta_s \quad\quad (N < \nu \leqslant n),$

and (iii) $\sum_{s=1}^{s_{n+1}-1} \delta(\Delta_s) \leqslant hL,$

where h *is a constant depending only on the base domain* F_0.

5.3.1. The relative boundary Γ_ν of F_ν consists of a finite number of s.a. Jordan arcs of total length L_ν. Suppose that these arcs are formed into a set of continua γ_1 to γ_p. Each continuum will have diameter not greater than the sum of the lengths of the arcs comprising it. It follows that F_ν consists of some of the components into which γ_1 to γ_p split F_0. By Lemma 5.2 there exists one such component G_0, such that the others can be included in sets G_1 to G_p such that

$$\sum_{t=1}^{p} \delta(G_t) \leqslant h \sum_{t=1}^{p} \delta(\gamma_t) \leqslant hL_\nu. \tag{5.5}$$

Let N be the largest integer ν for which the area of F_ν is greater than $\frac{1}{2}$ that of F_0. Suppose that $\nu \leqslant N$. Then if F_ν contains the component G_0, the complement of F_ν with respect to F_0 lies in the union of the G_1 to G_p, which we label Δ_s ($s_\nu \leqslant s < s_{\nu+1}$), where $s_1 = 1$ and $s_{\nu+1} = s_\nu + p$. Also, by (5.5),

$$\sum_{s=s_\nu}^{s_{\nu+1}-1} \delta(\Delta_s) \leqslant hL_\nu. \tag{5.6}$$

Suppose alternatively that F_ν lies entirely in the union of the sets G_1 to G_p. Each set G_t lies in a circle of radius $\delta(G_t)$ and so has area at most $\pi\delta(G_t)^2 \leqslant \pi^2\delta(G_t)$. Thus in this case, if I_0 is the area of F_0, the area of F_ν and so of $\bigcup_{t=1}^{p} G_t$ is at least $\frac{1}{2}I_0$ and

$$\tfrac{1}{2}I_0 \leqslant \pi^2 \sum_{t=1}^{p} \delta(G_t) \leqslant hL_\nu.$$

Hence in this case the complement of F_ν with respect to F_0, considered as a single set Δ_s, has a diameter which satisfies

$$\delta(\Delta_s) \leqslant \pi \leqslant \frac{2\pi h}{I_0} L_\nu.$$

Thus in any case we have (5.6), possibly with a different constant h.

Suppose next that $\nu > N$ so that the area of F_ν is less than $\frac{1}{2}I_0$. Then either F_ν is contained in $\bigcup_{t=1}^{p} G_t$, in which case we have again (5.6) as required, on labelling

$$\Delta_s = G_{s-s_\nu+1} \quad \text{for} \quad s_\nu \leqslant s \leqslant s_{\nu+1}-1 = s_\nu+p-1,$$

or F_ν contains the whole domain G_0. In this case the area of G_0 is at most $\frac{1}{2}I_0$, and so that of $\bigcup_{t=1}^{p} G_t$ is at least $\frac{1}{2}I_0$, so that again

$$\tfrac{1}{2}I_0 \leqslant \pi^2 \sum_{t=1}^{p} \delta(G_t) \leqslant hL_\nu$$

and $L_\nu \geqslant I_0/(2h)$. In this case we set $\Delta_{s_\nu} = F_\nu$ and have

$$\delta(\Delta_{s_\nu}) \leqslant \pi \leqslant \frac{2\pi h}{I_0} L_\nu.$$

Thus in any case for $\nu \leqslant N$, the complement of F_ν lies in Δ_s satisfying (5.6) and for $\nu > N$, F_ν itself lies in Δ_s satisfying (5.6) and we have

$$\sum_{s=1}^{s_{n+1}-1} \delta(\Delta_s) \leqslant h \sum_{\nu=1}^{n} L_\nu \leqslant hL$$

by (5.4). This proves Theorem 5.1.

5.3.2. We now introduce some new notation. If D is any subdomain of F_0, let $I(D)$ be the area of D and define

$$I_\nu(D) = I(D \cap F_\nu) \quad (\nu = 0 \text{ to } n).$$

We define the *covering number* $S(D)$ of D by

$$S(D) = \sum_{\nu=1}^{n} \frac{I_\nu(D)}{I_0(D)}.$$

In particular the *mean covering number* S of the mapping is defined by

$$S = \sum_{\nu=1}^{n} \frac{I_\nu}{I_0},$$

where I_ν is the area of F_ν. Similarly, if β is any sectionally analytic arc of $\overline{F}_0$ we define $L_\nu(\beta)$ as the length of $\overline{F}_\nu \cap \beta$, and define the covering number $S(\beta)$ of β by

$$S(\beta) = \sum_{\nu=1}^{n} \frac{L_\nu(\beta)}{L_0(\beta)}.$$

We then have the following analogue of Nevanlinna's first fundamental theorem.

THEOREM 5.2. *If N is the integer defined in Theorem 5.1 and D is any domain in F_0, we have*

$$|S(D) - N| \leqslant \frac{hL}{I_0(D)},$$

and in particular $\qquad |S - N| \leqslant \dfrac{hL}{I_0},$ $\qquad\qquad$ (5.7)

where h depends only on F_0.

Further, if β is any s.a. curve, there exists a constant h_β depending only on β and the base domain F_0, such that

$$|S(\beta) - N| \leqslant h_\beta L. \qquad\qquad (5.8)$$

5.3.3. *Proof of Theorem* 5.2. The area A_s of each domain Δ_s which occurs in Theorem 5.1 is at most $\pi^2\delta(\Delta_s)$. Hence

$$\sum_{s=s_1}^{s_{n+1}-1} A_s \leqslant \pi^2 hL,$$

by that theorem. Thus the part of D which does not lie in F_ν for $\nu = 1$ to N has area at most

$$\sum_{s_\nu}^{s_{\nu+1}-1} A_s,$$

and hence $\qquad I_\nu(D) \geqslant I_0(D) - \sum_{s_\nu}^{s_{\nu+1}-1} A_s \quad (\nu = 1 \text{ to } N),$

$$\sum_{\nu=1}^{N} I_\nu(D) \geqslant N I_0(D) - \sum_{s_1}^{s_{N+1}-1} A_s \geqslant N I_0(D) - \pi^2 hL.$$

Thus $\qquad\qquad S(D) \geqslant N - \dfrac{\pi^2 hL}{I_0(D)}.$

Similarly the part of D which lies in F_ν for $\nu > N$ has area at most

$$\sum_{s_\nu}^{s_{\nu+1}-1} A_s,$$

so that $\qquad \sum_{\nu=1}^{n} I_\nu(D) \leqslant N I_0(D) + \sum_{s=s_{N+1}}^{s_{n+1}-1} A_s \leqslant N I_0(D) + \pi^2 hL.$

This proves the first inequality of Theorem 5.2 and hence (5.7).

Next if β is any s.a. curve, the part of β in Δ_ν has by Lemma 5.1 length at most $h_\beta\delta(\Delta_\nu)$. Hence the total length of all the arcs of β_ν in Δ_ν for all ν is at most

$$h_\beta \sum_{s=1}^{s_{n+1}-1} \delta(\Delta_s) \leqslant h\, h_\beta\, L = h'_\beta\, L.$$

Thus the lengths $\lambda_\nu(\beta)$ of the arcs of β in F_ν for $\nu = 1$ to n satisfy

$$N\lambda - h'_\beta\, L \leqslant \sum_{\nu=1}^{n} \lambda_\nu(\beta) \leqslant N\lambda + h'_\beta\, L,$$

where λ is the length of β, and the proof of Theorem 5.2 is complete.

5.4. The topology of surfaces

In Theorem 5.2 we have obtained a result which tells us that if a Riemann surface R, which is the image over F_0 of a domain Δ_0, has a short relative boundary, then this image covers every subdomain of F_0 and every s.a. arc in F_0 or on the boundary of F_0 with nearly equal multiplicity. In the case of s.a. arcs in the interior of F_0 we note that the result of Theorem 5.2 is unaffected if we confine ourselves to the covering of γ by the interior instead of the closure of our surface, since by (5.4) the total length of the cover of γ by the boundary of R is at most equal to the relative boundary of R and so contributes at most L to the left-hand side of (5.8). For arcs lying on the boundary of F_0 we must, of course, consider the covering effected by the closure of R.

In order to carry our theory farther we wish to investigate not only the multiplicity of coverings effected by our surface R but also the way in which R covers particular domains. We shall be able to show that if F_0 is the whole sphere, then the bulk of the covering of a domain D in F_0 arises generally from a number of single islands over D, i.e. (1–1) topological maps of subdomains Δ_0 onto D. This result represents the crowning achievement of Ahlfors's theory. In order to prove it we shall require a more detailed analysis of the topology of our Riemann surface R or, what is the same thing, of the domain Δ_0 of which R is the 1–1 topological image. For this we shall require apart from Theorem 5.2 the notion of the Euler–Poincaré characteristic of a domain on the sphere.

5.4.1. We define a (finite) *triangulated surface* as a set R of points with the following properties. R is the union of a finite number of its subsets $\Delta_1, \Delta_2, ..., \Delta_r$ called 'triangles'. These will satisfy the following conditions.

(i) *With each 'triangle' is associated a (1, 1) map onto an equilateral triangle in a Euclidean plane. In this way* sides *and* vertices *are defined.*

(ii) *Two distinct 'triangles' have either nothing or a vertex or a side in common. In the latter case the correspondence between the sides of the two associated Euclidean triangles is assumed to be (1, 1) and continuous. No side belongs to more than two triangles.*

(iii a) *If each side of a 'triangle' belongs to exactly one other 'triangle', the surface is called* closed.

(iii b) *If some sides of a 'triangle' belong to no other triangle then such sides are called 'frontier' sides. We assume that each vertex belongs to no more than two frontier sides. Thus the frontier sides split up into a finite number p of closed curves $\gamma_1, ..., \gamma_p$, no two of which will have common points. In this case R is called non-closed and the set of curves γ_t is called the* frontier *of R.*

(iv) *The surface is* connected, *i.e. each vertex can be joined to every other vertex by a chain of sides $s_1, s_2, ..., s_t$, such that $s_\nu, s_{\nu+1}$ have a common vertex for $\nu = 1$ to $t-1$.*

In this connexion we shall assume as known the following two facts from algebraic topology.†

---

† For proofs of these results and related material see, e.g., Ahlfors and Sario [1 chapter 1].

(v) *If Δ_0 is an s.a. domain on the sphere or if Δ_0 is the whole sphere, then Δ_0 can be triangulated, i.e. transformed into a triangulated surface satisfying the above requirements.*

(vi) *If the whole sphere is triangulated and p, q, r denote the total number of vertices, sides, and 'triangles' respectively, then*

$$\rho = -p+q-r = -2.$$

The latter result goes back essentially to Euler and, for any surface, ρ is called the *Euler–Poincaré characteristic*.

Suppose now that Δ_0 is an s.a. domain on the sphere bounded by the s.a. Jordan curves γ_1 to γ_l. Then γ_t bounds a Jordan domain Δ_t not containing Δ_0. We choose a point P_t in Δ_t and join P_t in Δ_t to each of the vertices of the triangulation of Δ_0 which lie on γ_t, by Jordan arcs having no common points other than P_t. If there are ν such vertices on γ_t we obtain a triangulation of Δ_t having ν triangles, 2ν sides, and $\nu+1$ vertices, including those on γ_t. If we do this for each Jordan curve γ_t and the corresponding domains Δ_t we obtain a triangulation of the sphere having total characteristic

$$\rho = -p+q-r = -2$$

by (vi). The contribution to ρ of the sides, vertices, and triangles in each Δ_t and γ_t for $t = 1$ to l is just $-\nu+2\nu-(\nu+1) = -1$. Thus the contribution of the sides, vertices, and triangles interior to Δ_0 must be $l-2$. We deduce

LEMMA 5.4. *If Δ_0 is an s.a. domain on the sphere bounded by l Jordan curves γ_1 to γ_l then Δ_0 can be triangulated. Further, if in any such triangulation p, q, r denote the number of vertices, sides, and triangles which do not lie entirely on the boundary of Δ_0, we have*

$$\rho(\Delta_0) = -p+q-r = l-2.$$

We accordingly define the characteristic of Δ_0 to be $l-2$.

Suppose next that Δ_0 is an s.a. domain on the sphere which is divided into N s.a. subdomains Δ_1 to Δ_N by n s.a. *cross-cuts* (i.e. Jordan arcs lying except for their endpoints in Δ_0) C_1 to C_n and s s.a. Jordan curves C_{n+1} to C_{n+s} lying in Δ_0, no two of which have common points. Since Δ_1 to Δ_N are s.a. domains they can be triangulated. Let Δ_μ, Δ_ν have a curve C_λ in common. The vertices on C_λ due to the triangulations of Δ_μ, Δ_ν will in general be different. However, if a vertex V of the triangulation of Δ_μ lies on a side of a triangle T of the triangulation of Δ_ν, we can join V in T to the opposite vertex of V, thus splitting T into two triangles each of which has V as a vertex. By doing this consistently for all the vertices on C_λ of the triangulations of each of Δ_μ, Δ_ν which are not vertices of the other, and doing the same for each C_λ we obtain finally a triangulation of Δ_0 made up of the triangulations of Δ_1 to Δ_N.

Using this we can prove

LEMMA 5.5. *If an s.a. domain Δ_0 is divided into s.a. domains Δ_1 to Δ_N by $n \geqslant 1$ s.a. cross-cuts and s closed s.a. Jordan curves in Δ_0, then*

$$\rho(\Delta_0) = \sum_{\nu=1}^{N} \rho(\Delta_\nu) + n \geqslant n - N.$$

In fact we construct a triangulation of Δ_1 to Δ_N which gives rise to a triangulation of Δ_0. Then on each closed Jordan curve there is an equal number of vertices and sides, so that these curves contribute nothing to the characteristic of Δ_0. However, each cross-cut C is bounded by two vertices which are on the boundary of Δ_0, and so do not count towards the characteristic of Δ_0, and sides alternate with vertices along C. Thus C contains one more side than vertex in the interior of Δ_0 and so contributes $+1$ to the characteristic of Δ_0. Finally the remaining sides, vertices, and triangles of Δ_0 are the interior sides, vertices, and triangles of some Δ_ν. Since there are n cross-cuts we deduce

$$\rho(\Delta_0) = \sum_{\nu=1}^{N} \rho(\Delta_\nu) + n$$

as required. Again by Lemma 5.4 $\rho(\Delta_\nu) \geqslant -1$, since no Δ_ν can include the whole sphere, and so we deduce Lemma 5.5.

5.5. A lower bound for the characteristic of a covering surface

We can now state and prove our next basic result.

THEOREM 5.3. *Suppose that $w = f(z)$ is meromorphic on the closure of an s.a. domain Δ_0 of characteristic ρ_0 on the z-sphere, that on the boundary of Δ_0, $f'(z) \neq 0$ and $f(z)$ has only simple poles and that, for $z \in \Delta_0$, $f(z)$ has values lying in an s.a. domain F_0 on the w-sphere having characteristic $\rho \geqslant 1$. Let L be the length of the relative boundary on the w-sphere of the map of Δ_0 into F_0 and S the mean covering number of the mapping. Then*

$$\rho_0^+ \geqslant \rho S - hL, \tag{5.9}$$

where $\rho_0^+ = \max(\rho_0, 0)$, and h is a constant depending only on the particular domain F_0.

What Theorem 5.3 asserts is that if S is large and large compared with L, then ρ_0 must be large, so that Δ_0 must have large connectivity and so be limited by a large number of boundary curves.

In order to prove Theorem 5.3, set $q = \rho + 2$, so that F_0 is bounded by $q \geqslant 3$ s.a. Jordan curves γ_1 to γ_q. We join γ_ν to $\gamma_{\nu+1}$ for $\nu = 1$ to $q-1$ and γ_q to γ_1 by q s.a. cross-cuts β_ν ($\nu = 1$ to q), no two of which have common points. The β_ν will be fixed once and for all so as to depend only on the base domain. However, it is convenient to assume that none of the images of the points where $f'(z) = 0$ lie on the β_ν. Otherwise we may effect a slight change of the β_ν, which will affect all the constants involved by an arbitrarily small amount. We shall denote by h any constant depending only on F_0 and the β_ν, not necessarily the same each time.

With these assumptions each β_ν will correspond to a finite number of s.a. cross-cuts in Δ_0, two of which have at most one endpoint in common on the boundary of Δ_0. Cross-cuts corresponding to different β_ν have no common points. We shall assume that there are n such cross-cuts σ and that they divide Δ_0 into N domains Δ. We note that the cross-cuts β_1 to β_q divide F_0 into two Jordan domains F_0' and F_0'' of characteristic -1. The function $f(z)$ will map each domain Δ into either F_0' or F_0''. In fact the image of any Jordan arc in a domain Δ by $w = f(z)$ cannot cross the boundary of F_0' or F_0'', since Δ contains no interior points of any σ. Our conditions also imply that each Δ is an s.a. domain.

We shall use the inequality of Lemma 5.5 and proceed to estimate $n - N$. The basic idea is the following. If Δ_ν is one of the domains Δ, S_ν the mean covering number, and L_ν the length of the relative boundary of the mapping given by $w = f(z)$ from Δ_ν into either F_0' or F_0'', then by Theorem 5.2, if S_ν is sufficiently large compared with L_ν, the mapping must partly cover every one of the β_ν, and so the domain Δ_ν must have at least q cross-cuts σ on its boundary. Thus the N domains should give rise to nearly $\frac{1}{2}qN$ cross-cuts, since each cross-cut bounds two domains. Thus $n - N$ is not much less than $\frac{1}{2}N(q-2)$.

If the domains Δ each give rise to simple coverings, then since each domain covers only about half of F_0, they will contribute about $\frac{1}{2}N$ to the covering number of the map from Δ_0 into F_0, so that S is about $\frac{1}{2}N$. Thus we obtain about $S(q-2)$, i.e. $S\rho$, as a lower bound for ρ_0, as required.

Unfortunately, the above is only a rough sketch and a much more refined analysis is needed for the full proof which will now be given.

5.5.1. Since each cross-cut σ bounds two domains Δ, a situation is theoretically possible in which we have less cross-cuts than domains Δ

so that $n-N$ could actually be negative. We first eliminate this possibility in general.

Suppose that there exists at least one domain Δ whose boundary contains exactly one cross-cut σ. We take such a domain and label it Δ_1, and the corresponding cross-cut on its boundary will be defined to be σ_1. Suppose that Δ_1 to Δ_ν and corresponding cross-cuts σ_1 to σ_ν have already been defined. If there exists a domain Δ whose boundary contains, except possibly for some of the cross-cuts σ_1 to σ_ν, exactly one other cross-cut σ we define such a domain as $\Delta_{\nu+1}$ and the corresponding cross-cut as $\sigma_{\nu+1}$. Since the total number of domains Δ is finite, this process must cease after a certain stage (or it may not even start). There are now two possibilities. Either there is a domain Δ', whose boundary contains no cross-cuts σ, apart possibly from σ_1 to σ_ν, or all the remaining domains Δ, other than Δ_1 to Δ_ν, each contain at least two cross-cuts σ, other than σ_1 to σ_ν, on their boundary.

In the first case we note that Δ_1 to Δ_ν and Δ' together exhaust the whole domain Δ_0. In fact, suppose that σ_μ is a cross-cut on the boundary of Δ', where $\mu \leqslant \nu$. Then σ_μ lies on the boundary of Δ_μ, which has no common points with Δ', so that on crossing σ_μ from Δ' we enter Δ_μ. The cross-cuts σ on the boundary of Δ_μ consist apart from σ_μ of cross-cuts $\sigma_{\mu'}$, with $\mu' < \mu$. On crossing $\sigma_{\mu'}$ we enter the domain $\Delta_{\mu'}$, whose boundary contains apart from $\sigma_{\mu'}$ only cross-cuts $\sigma_{\mu''}$ with $\mu'' < \mu'$, etc. Now since Δ_0 is connected we can join any point of Δ' to any point of Δ_0 by an s.a. path in Δ_0. The above argument shows that such a path cannot meet any cross-cuts σ apart from the σ_μ with $\mu \leqslant \nu$ and cannot enter any domain Δ apart from the Δ_μ with $1 \leqslant \mu \leqslant \nu$. Thus any point of Δ_0 must lie inside or on the boundary of one of the domains Δ_μ ($\mu = 1$ to ν) and Δ'. The domains Δ_μ ($\mu = 1$ to ν) are called *domains of the first type*.

If there are any domains Δ whose boundary contains at least q cross-cuts σ apart from σ_1 to σ_ν, such domains will be called domains of the *third type*. The remaining domains Δ will be called domains of the *second type*. The domains of the second type may reduce to a single domain Δ', whose boundary contains no cross-cut σ apart possibly from some of σ_1 to σ_ν. In this case there are no domains of the third type. In all other cases the domains of the second type, if any, all have at least two and at most $q-1$ cross-cuts on their boundaries, apart from σ_1 to σ_ν.

5.5.2. *Discussion of the domains of the first type.* We shall see that the domains of the first and second types play in general a relatively unimportant role in the inequality of Theorem 5.3. We consider the map by $w = f(z)$ of a domain $\Delta = \Delta^1$ into either F_0' or F_0'' and define the mean covering number of this map by $S^1 = S$. Let L^1 be the length of the relative boundary of the map and $S^1(\beta_n)$ the covering number of this map over the boundary arc β_n for $n = 1$ to q. Then Theorem 5.2 yields

$$|S^1(\beta_n) - S^1| \leqslant hL^1 \quad (n = 1 \text{ to } q). \tag{5.10}$$

We apply (5.10) in particular to each domain Δ_μ of the first type. If S_μ is the corresponding mean covering number, L_μ the length of the relative boundary and $S_\mu(\beta_n)$ the covering number over the arc β_n we have

$$S_\mu(\beta_n) \geqslant S_\mu - hL_\mu,$$

and hence

$$\sum_{n=1}^{q} S_\mu(\beta_n) \geqslant qS_\mu - qhL_\mu,$$

and hence adding for all the domains of the first type we deduce

$$\sum_{n=1}^{q} \sum_{\mu=1}^{\nu} S_\mu(\beta_n) \geqslant qS^{(1)} - qhL^{(1)}, \tag{5.11}$$

where

$$S^{(1)} = \sum_{\mu=1}^{\nu} S_\mu, \quad L^{(1)} = \sum_{\mu=1}^{\nu} L_\mu.$$

The left-hand side of (5.11) can be regarded as made up of terms arising from the individual boundary arcs σ_μ ($\mu = 1$ to ν) which lie on the boundary of the domains Δ_μ. The arc σ_μ lies on the boundary of Δ_μ and its image lies over a boundary arc β_n, say. If $\lambda(\sigma_\mu)$ is the mean covering number of the map of σ_μ over this arc we have from (5.10)

$$\lambda(\sigma_\mu) \leqslant S_\mu + hL_\mu,$$

and hence by addition

$$\sum_{\mu=1}^{\nu} \lambda(\sigma_\mu) \leqslant S^{(1)} + hL^{(1)}. \tag{5.12}$$

Now each arc σ_μ occurs on the boundary of Δ_μ and at most one other domain $\Delta_{\mu'}$, and hence contributes at most $2\lambda(\sigma_\mu)$ to the left-hand side of (5.11). Thus (5.11) and (5.12) give

$$qS^{(1)} - qhL^{(1)} \leqslant \sum_{n=1}^{q} \sum_{\mu=1}^{\nu} S_\mu(\beta_n) \leqslant 2\sum_{\mu=1}^{\nu} \lambda(\sigma_\mu) \leqslant 2S^{(1)} + hL^{(1)}.$$

Thus we deduce that

$$(q-2)S^{(1)} \leqslant hL^{(1)}, \tag{5.13}$$

and hence we also have from (5.12)

$$S^{(1)}(\beta) = \sum_{\mu=1}^{\nu} \lambda(\sigma_\mu) \leqslant hL^{(1)}. \tag{5.14}$$

5.5.3. *Discussion of the domains of the second type.* Let us denote the domains of the second type, if any, by $\Delta_{\nu+1}, \Delta_{\nu+2}, ..., \Delta_\tau$. Each of these domains contains at most $q-1$ cross-cuts σ on its boundary apart from the cross-cuts σ_μ. Hence if $\nu < \mu \leq \tau$, there exists at least one n such that none of the cross-cuts on the boundary of Δ_μ corresponds to β_n, except perhaps for certain cross-cuts $\sigma_{\mu'}$, with $\mu' \leq \nu$. Hence for this n we have

$$S_\mu(\beta_n) = \Sigma_\mu \lambda(\sigma_{\mu'}),$$

where the sum Σ_μ is taken over some of the cross-cuts $\sigma_{\mu'}$, with $\mu' \leq \nu$ which lie on the boundary of Δ_μ. Using (5.10) we deduce, if S_μ is again the mean covering number of the map of Δ_μ, and L_μ the length of the relative boundary of the map, that

$$S_\mu \leq \Sigma_{\mu'} \lambda(\sigma_{\mu'}) + hL_\mu.$$

Adding for $\mu = \nu+1$ to τ, we deduce

$$S^{(2)} = \sum_{\mu=\nu+1}^\tau S_\mu \leq \sum_{\mu=\nu+1}^\tau \Sigma_{\mu'} \lambda(\sigma_{\mu'}) + hL^{(2)},$$

where $L^{(2)}$ is the total length of the relative boundaries of all the maps of the Δ_μ ($\mu = \nu+1$ to τ). Also since each $\sigma_{\mu'}$ with $\mu' \leq \nu$ can be on the boundary of at most one domain Δ_μ for $\mu > \nu$, we deduce that

$$\sum_{\mu=\nu+1}^\tau S_\mu \leq \sum_{\mu'=1}^\nu \lambda(\sigma_{\mu'}) + hL^{(2)},$$

or
$$S^{(2)} \leq h(L^{(1)} + L^{(2)}) \qquad (5.15)$$

by (5.14). Also we have by Theorem 5.2

$$S_\mu(\beta_n) \leq S_\mu + hL_\mu \quad (\mu = \nu+1 \text{ to } \tau, \ n = 1 \text{ to } q),$$

and hence

$$\sum_{\mu=\nu+1}^\tau \sum_{n=1}^q S_\mu(\beta_n) \leq q \sum_{\mu=\nu+1}^\tau (S_\mu + hL_\mu) \leq qS^{(2)} + hL^{(2)}.$$

Here the left-hand side arises as the sum of the contributions of the various cross-cuts σ on the boundary of domains of the second type. Each such σ contributes a term $\lambda(\sigma)$, and some cross-cuts σ may lie on the boundary of two domains and so contribute two terms. Thus, using (5.15), we deduce
$$\Sigma_2 \lambda(\sigma) \leq h(L^{(1)} + L^{(2)}), \qquad (5.16)$$

where the sum Σ_2 is taken over all cross-cuts σ, other than the σ_μ, which lie on the boundary of at least one domain of the second type.

5.5.4. *Completion of the proof of Theorem* 5.3. We now consider the map of the domain Δ_0 into the domain F_0 as a whole. Let S' and S'' be the covering number of this image over F_0' and over F_0'', and S that of the mapping as a whole. Then Theorem 5.2 gives

$$|S'-S| \leqslant hL, \qquad |S''-S| \leqslant hL.$$

Thus
$$S'+S'' \geqslant 2S-hL.$$

If $\Delta_{\tau+1}$, $\Delta_{\tau+2},\ldots$, Δ_N are the domains of the third type, if any, and S_μ is the mean covering of Δ_μ over F_0' or F_0'' and L_μ the length of the relative boundary of the corresponding map of Δ_μ, then

$$\sum_{\mu=1}^{N} S_\mu = S'+S'' \geqslant 2S-hL.$$

Also $L^{(1)} \leqslant L$ and $L^{(2)} \leqslant L$. Thus using (5.13) and (5.15) we deduce

$$\sum_{\mu=\tau+1}^{N} S_\mu \geqslant 2S-hL.$$

Next, if $S_\mu(\beta_n)$ denotes the covering number of the map of Δ_μ over β_n, we have
$$S_\mu(\beta_n) > S_\mu-hL_\mu,$$

and hence
$$\sum_{n=1}^{q} \sum_{\mu=\tau+1}^{N} S_\mu(\beta_n) \geqslant 2qS-hL. \tag{5.17}$$

Here the left-hand side arises from the contributions of all boundary arcs σ of the domains of the third type. Each σ which is on the boundary of two domains of the third type gives rise to two terms $\lambda(\sigma)$ in the sum (5.17). The remaining boundary arcs σ are also boundaries of a domain of the first or second type. Using (5.14) and (5.16) we see that their contribution is at most hL. Thus we deduce from (5.17) that

$$2\Sigma_3 \lambda(\sigma) \geqslant 2qS-hL, \tag{5.18}$$

where the sum Σ_3 is taken over all the arcs σ which are on the boundary of two domains of the third type. We shall call such arcs σ_{33} and suppose that their total number is n_{33}.

We have two cases. Suppose first that there are no domains of the third type. In this case the left-hand side of (5.17) is zero and we have $S \leqslant hL$. Hence in this case we can choose h so large in Theorem 5.3 that the right-hand side becomes negative. Thus in this case Theorem 5.3 is trivially satisfied, since $\rho_0^+ \geqslant 0$.

Next, if there is at least one domain of the third type then each domain of the second type has on its boundary at least two arcs σ other than σ_1 to σ_ν.

We divide these arcs into two classes σ_{22} and σ_{23} and suppose that there are n_{22} arcs σ_{22} which separate two domains of the second type and n_{23} arcs σ_{23} which separate one domain of the second type and one domain of the third type. Each domain of the second type has at least two arcs of one of these two types on its boundary and arcs σ_{22} occur twice while arcs σ_{23} occur only once. Since there are $\tau-\nu$ domains of the second type we deduce that

$$2n_{22}+n_{23} \geqslant 2(\tau-\nu). \tag{5.19}$$

Consider finally the domains of the third type. These are bounded either by arcs of type σ_{23} or σ_{33}. Each domain of the third type contains at least q such arcs, and an arc σ_{23} appears once while an arc σ_{33} appears twice on the boundary of such domains. Thus

$$n_{23}+2n_{33} \geqslant q(N-\tau). \tag{5.20}$$

The total number n of arcs σ is $n = \nu+n_{22}+n_{23}+n_{33}$, while the total number of domains Δ is N. We have

$$\begin{aligned}
n-N &= \nu+(n_{22}+n_{23}+n_{33})-N \\
&= \nu+n_{22}+\tfrac{1}{2}n_{23}+\tfrac{1}{2}n_{23}+n_{33}-N \\
&\geqslant \tfrac{1}{2}n_{23}+n_{33}-(N-\tau)
\end{aligned}$$

by (5.19). Using (5.20) we deduce finally that

$$\begin{aligned}
n-N &\geqslant \left(\frac{1}{2}-\frac{1}{q}\right)(n_{23}+2n_{33}) \\
&\geqslant \frac{q-2}{q}n_{33}.
\end{aligned}$$

We now use (5.18). It is clear that each term on the left-hand side of (5.18) is at most 1. The number of such terms is precisely n_{33}. Thus we deduce that with the notation of Theorem 5.3

$$\rho_0 \geqslant n-N \geqslant \frac{q-2}{q}n_{33} \geqslant \frac{q-2}{q}(qS-hL) \geqslant (q-2)S-hL,$$

as required. This completes the proof of Theorem 5.3.

5.6. Application to functions meromorphic in a disk

We now consider a function $w = f(z)$ meromorphic in $|z| < R$, where $0 < R \leqslant \infty$. This function maps each disk $|z| < r$ $(0 < r < R)$ into the Riemann w-sphere. We denote by $L(r)$ the length of the relative boundary and by $S(r)$ the mean covering number of the mapping. This quantity was denoted by $A(r)$ in section 1.5. If $|dz|$ is an element of length in the z-plane, then the corresponding elements of length in the w-plane and on the w-sphere are given by

$$|dw| = |f'(z)|\,|dz| \quad \text{and} \quad ds = \frac{|dw|}{1+|w|^2} = \frac{|f'(z)|\,|dz|}{1+|f(z)|^2},$$

respectively. Thus the length of the relative boundary and the mean covering number $S(r)$ of the mapping of the disk $|z| < r$ into the Riemann sphere are given for $0 < r < R$ by

$$L(r) = \int\limits_{|z|=r} \left|\frac{ds}{dz}\right| |dz| = \int\limits_0^{2\pi} \frac{|f'(re^{i\theta})| r \, d\theta}{1+|f(re^{i\theta})|^2} \tag{5.21}$$

and

$$S(r) = \frac{1}{\pi} \int\limits_{|z|<r} \left|\frac{ds}{dz}\right|^2 |dz|^2 = \frac{1}{\pi} \int\limits_0^r \rho \, d\rho \int\limits_0^{2\pi} \frac{|f'(\rho e^{i\theta})|^2 \, d\theta}{\{1+|f(\rho e^{i\theta})|^2\}^2}. \tag{5.22}$$

Let us suppose that we have

$$S(r) \leqslant h L(r) \quad (r_0 \leqslant r < R), \tag{5.23}$$

where h is a certain constant. We have by Cauchy's inequality

$$L^2(r) \leqslant \int\limits_0^{2\pi} r \, d\theta \int\limits_0^{2\pi} \frac{|f'(re^{i\theta})|^2 r \, d\theta}{\{1+|f(re^{i\theta})|^2\}^2} = 2\pi^2 r S'(r).$$

On combining this with (5.23) we deduce that

$$S^2(r) \leqslant 2\pi^2 h^2 r S'(r) \quad (r_0 < r < R),$$

and hence that for $r_0 < r < R$,

$$\frac{1}{S(r_0)} - \frac{1}{S(r)} = \int\limits_{r_0}^r \frac{S'(t)}{S(t)^2} \, dt \geqslant \frac{1}{2h^2\pi^2} \int\limits_{r_0}^r \frac{dt}{t},$$

so that

$$\frac{1}{S(r_0)} \geqslant \frac{1}{2h^2\pi^2} \log\frac{r}{r_0}, \qquad S(r_0) \leqslant \frac{2h^2\pi^2}{\log(r/r_0)}.$$

If $R = +\infty$, we may make $r \to \infty$ and deduce that $S(r_0) = 0$, which is only possible if $f(z)$ is constant. If $R < \infty$, then we may let $r \to R$ in the above and note that r_0 may be replaced by any number ρ, such that $r_0 \leqslant \rho < R$, without invalidating (5.23). Thus we deduce that in this case

$$S(\rho) \leqslant \frac{2h^2\pi^2}{\log(R/\rho)} \leqslant \frac{2h^2\pi^2 R}{R-\rho} \quad (r \leqslant \rho < R). \tag{5.24}$$

Further we obtain for the Ahlfors–Shimizu characteristic (see section 1.5 with $A(\rho)$ instead of $S(\rho)$) the inequality

$$T_0(r) = \int\limits_0^r \frac{S(\rho)}{\rho} \, d\rho = T_0(r_0) + \int\limits_{r_0}^r \frac{S(\rho)}{\rho} \, d\rho$$

$$\leqslant T_0(r_0) + 2h^2\pi^2 \log\frac{R^2}{r_0(R-r)} \quad (r_0 \leqslant r < R).$$

We deduce

THEOREM 5.4. *If $f(z)$ is meromorphic and not constant in $|z| < R \leqslant \infty$, then there exists an increasing sequence $r_n \to R$, such that*

$$\frac{L(r_n)}{S(r_n)} \to 0 \quad (n \to \infty) \tag{5.25}$$

provided that if $R < +\infty$, we have either

$$\varlimsup_{r \to R} (R-r)S(r,f) = +\infty,$$

or
$$\varlimsup_{r \to R} \frac{T_0(r,f)}{\log\{R/(R-r)\}} = +\infty.$$

For if (5.25) is false (5.23) must hold for suitable constants r_0 and h, and as we have just seen, this leads to a contradiction if the hypotheses of Theorem 5.4 are satisfied.

If a sequence r_n satisfying (5.25) exists, we say that the Riemann surface of $f(z)$ is *regularly exhaustible* (*regulär ausschöpfbar*). In such cases the Ahlfors theory can be effectively applied, since then $L(r_n)$ plays the role of a relatively unimportant remainder compared with $S(r_n)$.

5.6.1. While noting that our results will mainly be applied to the fairly wide class of functions satisfying the hypotheses and hence conclusions of Theorem 5.4, we assume for the time being only that $f(z)$ is meromorphic and not constant in $|z| < R$.

We consider $q \geqslant 3$ simply connected s.a. domains D_ν on the w-Riemann sphere, whose closures are non-intersecting. We also assume that the boundaries of the D_ν and the arcs β_ν joining them as in the previous section do not pass through any of the countable number of points $w_0 = f(z_0)$, such that z_0 is a zero of $f'(z)$ or a pole of $f(z)$ in $|z| < R$. This can always be achieved by expanding the D_ν and shifting the β_ν slightly. We take a value of r $(0 < r \leqslant R)$ such that the image of the circle $|z| = r$ does not touch the boundaries of the D_ν or the arcs β_ν or go through any of the corners of these s.a. curves. This can always be achieved by increasing r slightly.

Consider the mutually exclusive sets G_ν in $|z| < r$ which correspond to the D_ν by $w = f(z)$. The G_ν will have a finite number of components which will be of two types. A component G of G_ν will be called a *tongue* over D_ν if its closure meets $|z| = r$. Otherwise G will be called an *island*.

We remove in turn from $|z| < r$ all the tongues G_ν^t over all the domains D_ν. There remain certain simply connected domains G'. We next remove from the G' all the islands G_ν^i over the domains D_ν and are left with certain domains $\bar{G}$. The $\bar{G}$ are mapped by $w = f(z)$ into the domain F_0 on the w-sphere complementary to all the D_ν. If L is the length of the relative boundary, and S the mean covering number, of the map of $\bar{G}$ into F_0 and ρ is the characteristic of $\bar{G}$, we have, by Theorem 5.3,
$$\max(\rho, 0) \geqslant (q-2)S - hL.$$

In particular we see that if $\bar{G}$ does not meet $|z| = r$, so that $L = 0$, then $\rho > 0$, so that $\bar{G}$ is at least triply connected. If $\bar{G}$ is simply or doubly connected we deduce that
$$(q-2)S \leqslant hL.$$

Thus if S_0 denotes the total of the mean covering numbers of all the domains $\bar{G}$ which are simply or doubly connected we deduce that
$$S_0 \leqslant \frac{hL(r)}{(q-2)}, \tag{5.26}$$

where $L(r)$ is the length of the relative boundary of the map of $|z| < r$ into the Riemann w-sphere.

Consider now a domain G'. It is divided into islands G_ν^i and domains $\bar{G}$ by Jordan curves in the interior of G'. Only one such domain $\bar{G}$ meets the boundary of G', which is connected since G' is simply connected. If this domain $\bar{G}$ is simply connected, $\bar{G}$ must coincide with G', and G' contains no islands. We ignore such domains $\bar{G} = G'$. In all other cases all the residual domains $\bar{G}$ lying in G' are multiply connected. These domains give rise to a covering of the domain F_0, with mean covering number $S(\bar{G})$ and relative boundary $L(\bar{G})$ say. Since $\bar{G}$ is not simply connected we have, by Theorem 5.3,
$$\rho(\bar{G}) \geqslant (q-2)S(\bar{G}) - hL(\bar{G}).$$

Adding over all the domains $\bar{G}$ which are not simply connected,
$$\sum \rho(\bar{G}) \geqslant (q-2)S_1(F_0) - hL(r), \tag{5.27}$$

where $S_1(F_0)$ is the total covering number of F_0 due to all these domains $\bar{G}$. Now the mean covering number $S(F_0)$ of F_0 due to the map of $|z| < r$ into the Riemann sphere arises from the multiply connected domains $\bar{G}$ and the simply connected domains $\bar{G}$. The contribution of the latter is at most $hL(r)$ by (5.26). Thus
$$S(F_0) \leqslant S_1(F_0) + hL(r).$$

Again, by Theorem 5.2, we have

$$S(r) \leqslant S(F_0) + \frac{h}{I(F_0)} L(r),$$

and so (5.27) gives finally

$$\sum \rho(\bar{G}) \geqslant (q-2)S(r) - h_1 L(r), \tag{5.28}$$

where h_1 depends only on the geometry of the islands D_ν, and the sum on the left-hand side is taken over all the regions $\bar{G}$ which are multiply connected.

The regions G' which contain islands are divided into these islands and multiply connected domains $\bar{G}$ by closed Jordan curves. Thus, by Lemma 5.5,

$$-1 = \rho(G') = \sum \rho(G_\nu^i) + \sum \rho(\bar{G}),$$

where the sums are taken over all the islands G_ν^i and domains $\bar{G}$ in G'. Adding over all the domains G' which contain at least one island and all the multiply connected domains $\bar{G}$ and using (5.28) we obtain

$$- \sum\sum \rho(G_\nu^i) = \sum\left(\sum\rho(\bar{G})+1\right) = \sum\sum\rho(\bar{G})+N$$

$$\geqslant (q-2)S(r) - h_1 L(r) + N, \tag{5.29}$$

where N is the number of distinct domains G' which contain at least one island.

Now each island G_ν^i yields a map onto the domain D_ν with zero relative boundary, and so each point in D_ν is covered equally often by the map. Let $n(G_\nu^i)$ be this multiplicity, and write

$$n(G_\nu^i) + \rho(G_\nu^i) = n_1(G_\nu^i).$$

Writing $n_1 = (n-1)+(\rho+1)$, we see that n_1 is equal to the excess of the multiplicity of the map of the island over 1 plus the excess of the connectivity of the island over 1. If $n = 1$, the map is $(1, 1)$ and the island necessarily simply connected so that $n_1 = 0$. Otherwise $n_1 > 0$. We shall call n_1 the *excess* of the island.

Let $n(D_\nu) = \sum n(G_\nu^i)$, $n_1(D_\nu) = \sum n_1(G_\nu^i)$ for a fixed ν. Then

$$- \sum_{\nu=1}^{q} \sum \rho(G_\nu^i) = \sum_{\nu=1}^{q} n(D_\nu) - \sum_{\nu=1}^{q} n_1(D_\nu).$$

Thus (5.29) yields, since $N \geqslant 0$,

$$\sum_{\nu=1}^{q} n(D_\nu) - \sum_{\nu=1}^{q} n_1(D_\nu) \geqslant (q-2)S - hL.$$

5.7. The principal results of the theory

The last inequality may be stated as follows:

THEOREM 5.5. *If* $w = f(z)$ *yields a map of a disk* $|z| \leqslant r$ *into the Riemann sphere of mean covering number* $S(r)$ *and relative boundary length* $L(r)$, *then given* $q \geqslant 3$ *s.a. simply connected Jordan domains on the w-sphere,* $D_1, \ldots, D_q$, *whose closures have no common points, there exists a constant h depending only on the domains* D_ν, *such that*

$$\sum_{\nu=1}^{q} \{S(r) - n(D_\nu) + n_1(D_\nu)\} \leqslant 2S(r) + hL(r). \tag{5.30}$$

Here $n(D_\nu)$ *denotes the total multiplicity of all of the islands over* D_ν, *and* $n_1(D_\nu)$ *the total excess of all these islands.*

We deduce immediately Ahlfors's second theorem.

THEOREM 5.6. *Suppose that* $f(z)$ *is meromorphic in* $|z| < R$ *and has a Riemann surface which is regularly exhaustible. Suppose also that the* D_ν *for* $\nu = 1$ *to* q *are* $q \geqslant 3$ *simply connected domains whose closures have no common points, and that there are no islands over* D_ν *with multiplicity less than* μ_ν. *Then we have*

$$\sum_{\nu=1}^{q} \left(1 - \frac{1}{\mu_\nu}\right) \leqslant 2.$$

COROLLARY 1. *Unless* $R = \infty$ *and* $f(z)$ *is rational it is enough to suppose there are* $o\{S(r)\}$ *islands of multiplicity less than* μ_ν *in* $|z| < r$.

COROLLARY 2. *A non-constant meromorphic function in* $|z| < R$, *which satisfies the hypotheses of Theorem 5.6 possesses an island over at least one of 3 mutually exclusive domains on the Riemann sphere and a simply connected island over at least one of 5 such domains. Unless* $R = \infty$ *and* $f(z)$ *is rational there will be infinitely many such islands. If* $f(z)$ *is regular and the domains are bounded, the numbers 3, 5 may be replaced by 2, 3 respectively.*

5.7.1. *Proof of Theorem 5.6 and its corollaries.* Suppose that $r \to R$ through a sequence of values such that

$$\frac{L(r)}{S(r)} \to 0,$$

and that the other side conditions are satisfied. Suppose further that there are at most $o\{S(r)\}$ islands in $|z| < r$ having multiplicity less than μ_ν. These contribute only $o\{S(r)\}$ to the total number $n(D_\nu)$. Hence if in (5.30) we calculate the indices $n(D_\nu)$ and $n_1(D_\nu)$ with respect to all the remaining islands, we still obtain

$$\sum_{\nu=1}^{q} \{S(r)-n(D_\nu)+n_1(D_\nu)\} \leqslant \{2+o(1)\}S(r) \qquad (5.31)$$

as $r \to R$ through our sequence of values. Now if an island has multiplicity $\mu \geqslant \mu_\nu$, then the excess of that island is at least $\mu-1$, i.e. at least

$$\frac{\mu-1}{\mu}\mu \geqslant \frac{\mu_\nu-1}{\mu_\nu}\mu.$$

Thus in this case

$$n_1(D_\nu) \geqslant \frac{\mu_\nu-1}{\mu_\nu}n(D_\nu),$$

$$n(D_\nu)-n_1(D_\nu) \leqslant \frac{1}{\mu_\nu}n(D_\nu) \leqslant \frac{1}{\mu_\nu}\{1+o(1)\}S(r)$$

by Theorem 5.2.

Thus in this case (5.31) gives

$$\sum_{\nu=1}^{q} \left(1-\frac{1}{\mu_\nu}\right)S(r) \leqslant \{2+o(1)\}S(r),$$

so that Theorem 5.6 and Corollary 1 follow. The conclusion holds in all cases if there are no islands of multiplicity less than μ_ν over the domains D_ν. If $R < +\infty$, the hypotheses of Theorem 5.6 imply that $S(r) \to \infty$ as $r \to R$. If $R = +\infty$, this conclusion holds unless $T_0(r) = O\{\log r\}$, i.e. unless $f(z)$ is rational. Thus Corollary 1 gives a significantly stronger result than the main theorem and shows in particular that it is enough to assume that there are only a finite number of the islands of multiplicity less than μ_ν.

To prove Corollary 2 take $q = 5$, $\mu_\nu = 2$ in the main theorem. Then we obtain a contradiction. Thus for a sequence of $r \to R$ and at least one ν, $f(z)$ has at least $cS(r)$ simply connected islands over D_ν in $|z| < r$, where c is a positive constant. If $q = 3$, we may take $\mu_\nu = 4$ ($\nu = 1$ to 3) and obtain the conclusion that $f(z)$ has islands of multiplicity at most 3 over at least one of the domains D_ν. If $f(z)$ is regular and the D_ν are bounded, we may adjoin a domain over the point at ∞. Over this $f(z)$ will have no islands and so we can take $\mu_q = +\infty$ in Theorem 5.6 and obtain

$$\sum_{\nu=1}^{q-1} \left(1-\frac{1}{\mu_\nu}\right) \leqslant 1$$

for the remaining islands. Thus we obtain a contradiction if $q-1 = 2$, and $\mu_1 = 2$, $\mu_2 = 3$, or if $q-1 = 3$, $\mu_1 = \mu_2 = \mu_3 = 2$, in the main theorem. This proves Corollary 2.

5.8. Conclusion

Theorems 5.2 and 5.5 may be regarded as analogues of the first and second fundamental theorems in Nevanlinna's theory. The role of points in the latter theory is played by domains in Ahlfors's theory. The terms in Ahlfors's theory $S(r)$, $n(D)$, $n(D)-n_1(D)$, etc., correspond to the logarithmic derivatives of $T_0(r,f)$, $N(r,a)$, and $\overline{N}(r,a)$ in Nevanlinna's theory. By Theorem 5.2 we note that if $L(r) = o\{S(r)\}$, for a sequence of r, then for any domain D the mean covering number $S(r,D)$ of D satisfies

$$S(r,D) \sim S(r)$$

for such r. The contribution to $S(r,D)$ arises from islands and from tongues over D, corresponding to the terms m, N in the first fundamental theorem. Now Theorem 5.5, which is the analogue of Nevanlinna's second fundamental theorem, tells us that it is the contribution of the islands (corresponding to N) and even the simple simply connected islands (corresponding to $\overline{N}$) which in general yields the more significant contribution to $S(r,D)$.

Ahlfors's theory, which is essentially metric rather than analytic in character, can be applied to much more general maps than merely meromorphic ones, such as, for instance, quasi-conformal mappings. Ahlfors also applied his theory to mappings of Riemann surfaces other than spheres into each other. For these and other generalizations as well as a purely analytic approach which yields a rather weaker version of Theorem 5.6 we refer the reader to Ahlfors [3].

Theorem 5.6 contains many of the qualitative conclusions from Nevanlinna's second fundamental theorem 2.4. For instance, if all the roots of the equation $f(z) = a_\nu$ have multiplicity μ_ν for $\nu = 1$ to q, then we can surround the a_ν by small mutually exclusive domains D_ν. It will follow that all the islands over the D_ν have multiplicity at least μ_ν and we get a contradiction unless

$$\sum \left(1-\frac{1}{\mu_\nu}\right) \leqslant 2.$$

As we saw in section 2.5.1 this inequality, which contains Picard's theorem, is best possible. However, Theorem 5.6 also contains a far-reaching generalization of Bloch's theorem, which does not seem to be obtainable by the methods of Chapter 2. As against this Ahlfors's theory is by its nature less sensitive to analytic relations between different functions $f(z)$ and so results such as Theorem 2.7 and the main results of Chapter 3 would not seem to be accessible by the methods of this chapter.

6

FUNCTIONS MEROMORPHIC IN THE UNIT DISK

6.0. Introduction

WE have seen that if $f(z)$ is meromorphic in $|z| < 1$ and satisfies certain geometric conditions, if for instance $f(z) \neq a$, b, c, or if $f(z)$ maps no subdomain of $|z| < 1$ (1, 1) conformally onto any of five simply connected domains Δ_ν ($\nu = 1$ to 5) whose closures are disjoint on the w-sphere, then we have, by Theorems 5.5 and 5.2,

$$S(r) < h_1 L(r) \quad (0 < r < 1), \tag{6.1}$$

and hence by (5.24)

$$S(r) \leqslant h_2/\log(1/r) \quad (0 < r < 1), \tag{6.2}$$

where h_1, h_2 are constants depending only on the geometrical nature of the conditions satisfied by $f(z)$. Also $\pi S(r)$, $L(r)$ are respectively the area of the image of $|z| < r$ and the length of the image of $|z| = r$ under the mapping by $f(z)$ into the Riemann sphere.

In section 5.6 we saw that the condition (6.2) restricts the growth of $f(z)$ in the unit circle. However, the methods used there gave only asymptotic inequalities for the characteristic $T(r,f)$. In this chapter we develop first a method due to Dufresnoy which leads from (6.1) to a refinement of (6.2) and hence to a numerical bound for $T_0(r,f)$ in $0 < r < 1$. This in turn will lead to a series of inequalities which contain as special cases classical theorems of Schottky, Landau and Bloch. We shall also see that functions of the type we consider form special kinds of normal families in the sense of Montel which we shall call uniformly normal families, and that the numerical bounds we obtain extend to uniformly normal families in general. We conclude the chapter with an analysis of functions having bounded characteristic in the unit disk.

We continue to use the notation and terminology of Chapter 5.

6.1. The theory of Dufresnoy

We suppose in this section that $f(z)$ is meromorphic in $|z| < 1$ and satisfies (6.1) there.

We recall from section 1.5 that the Ahlfors–Shimizu characteristic of $f(z)$ is given by

$$T_0(r,f) = \int_0^r \frac{S(t,f)\,dt}{t} \quad (0 < r < 1).$$

If in this equation we substitute (6.2) we obtain no bound for $T_0(r,f)$ since

$$\int_0^r \frac{dt}{t\log(1/t)}$$

diverges at the origin. It thus becomes imperative to obtain a stronger inequality than (6.2) for small values of r. This was done by Dufresnoy who proved†

THEOREM 6.1. *If $f(z)$ is meromorphic for $|z| \leqslant r_0$, and $S(r_0,f) < 1$, then we have for $S(r) = S(r,f)$ the inequality*

$$\frac{1}{r^2}\frac{S(r)}{1-S(r)} \leqslant \frac{1}{r_0^2}\frac{S(r_0)}{1-S(r_0)} \quad (0 < r < r_0), \tag{6.3}$$

and hence by making $r \to 0$,

$$\left(\frac{|f'(0)|}{1+|f(0)|^2}\right)^2 \leqslant \frac{1}{r_0^2}\frac{S(r_0)}{1-S(r_0)}. \tag{6.4}$$

6.1.1. We need the isoperimetric property for circles on spheres.

LEMMA 6.1. *If γ is a simple closed Jordan curve on the Riemann sphere having length L and dividing the sphere into two domains with area πS, $\pi(1-S)$ respectively then we have*

$$L^2 \geqslant 4\pi^2 S(1-S).$$

Equality holds when γ is a circle.

The following proof is the analogue of one given by Blaschke [2, pp. 7 et seq.] in the plane case. We may suppose without loss in generality that $L < \pi$, since otherwise there is nothing to prove. Then γ lies entirely in a hemisphere. In fact let P_1, P_2 be two points on γ, such that each of the arcs P_1P_2 of γ has length $\frac{1}{2}L$, and let P_0 be the midpoint of the shorter great circle arc P_1P_2. Then each point of γ lies inside the hemisphere of centre P_0, radius $\frac{1}{4}\pi$. For otherwise γ would contain at least one point P on the circumference of this hemisphere. Let P_1', P_0', P_2' be the points diametrically opposite to P_1, P_0, P_2. Then P lies on the great circle of centre P_0', radius $\frac{1}{4}\pi$, with respect to which the pairs of points P_2, P_1' and P_1, P_2' are symmetrical. Thus

$$P_1P + P_2P = P_1P + PP_1' \geqslant \tfrac{1}{2}\pi,$$

† Dufresnoy [1]; see also Valiron [3, p. 136].

since P_1, P_1' are diametrically opposite. Since the arc $P_1 P P_2$ has length $\frac{1}{2}L < \frac{1}{2}\pi$, and the length of an arc is not less than that of the corresponding chord, we obtain a contradiction.

The proof of Lemma 6.1 now runs quite analogously to the plane case. Straight lines in the plane correspond to arcs of great circles on a hemisphere and so the notion of a polygon and a convex figure makes sense in a hemisphere. We can prove just as in the plane case that if a Jordan domain D in a hemisphere is replaced by its convex cover† $\bar{D}$, then $\bar{D}$ has an area which is at least as great and a perimeter which is not greater than that of D.

Suppose that D is a convex domain and that $P_1 P_2$ are two points on the boundary of D, such that the arcs $P_1 P_2$ have equal length. Then the diagonal $P_1 P_2$ divides D into two subdomains D_1 and D_2 having areas A_1, A_2, say, and the same perimeter. Suppose that $A_1 \geqslant A_2$. Then we replace D_2 by the reflection D_1' of D_1 in the diagonal $P_1 P_2$. If

$$D^* = D_1 \cup D_1' \cup P_1 P_2,$$

then D^* has the same perimeter as D, and area which is not less than that of D, and D^* is symmetrical about a line. D^* may not be convex, but the convex cover D^{**} of D^* has area which is not less and perimeter which is not greater than that of D, and D^{**} has in addition a line of symmetry. Thus we may confine ourselves to such domains. We can now prove that such domains can be approximated by spherical polygons. Thus it is enough to prove our results for spherical convex polygons with a line of symmetry. We prove

LEMMA 6.2. *Let* $\pi(l_1,...,l_n)$ *be the class of convex polygons* p, $P_1 P_2 ... P_{2n}$ *having* $2n$ *sides at most, whose lengths satisfy*

$$P_r P_{r+1} \leqslant l_r \quad (r = 1 \text{ to } n),$$

and such that p *is symmetrical about the diagonal* $P_1 P_{n+1}$. *Then there exists* p_0 *having maximal area in the class* $\pi(l_1,...,l_n)$, *and* p_0 *has all its vertices on a circle.*

It is not difficult to see from Weierstrass's convergence theorem that the class is compact, so that the maximum is attained in the class. In case $n = 2$, the lemma reduces to showing that in a spherical triangle with given sides $P_1 P_2$ of length l_1, and $P_2 P_3$ of length l_2, the triangle $P_1 P_2 P_3$ has maximum area if the angle $P_1 P_2 P_3$ is equal to the sum of the angles $P_2 P_1 P_3$ and $P_2 P_3 P_1$. This is an elementary exercise in spherical trigonometry. We can also show that if the triangle $P_1 P_2 P_3$

† The convex cover of $\bar{D}$ is defined as the intersection of all convex sets containing D.

is not of maximum area, we can increase or decrease the angle $P_1 P_2 P_3$ slightly so as to increase the area $P_1 P_2 P_3$.

The method leads us to our general proof. We suppose that p_0, $P_1 P_2 \ldots P_{2n} P_1$ is our extremal polygon, and that one of the vertices P_r does not lie on the circle with $P_1 P_{n+1}$ as ends of a diameter. We may suppose that $1 < r < n+1$. Then we may form a new triangle $P_1 P'_{n+1} P'_r$ having bigger area than $P_1 P_{n+1} P_r$, and such that $P_1 P_r = P_1 P'_r$ and $P_r P_{n+1} = P'_r P'_{n+1}$. We then construct P'_s for $s \neq r$ in such a manner that the pairs of polygons $P_1 P'_2 \ldots P'_{r-1} P'_r$, $P_1 P_2 \ldots P_r$, and $P'_r P'_{r+1} \ldots P'_{n+1}$, $P_r P_{r+1} \ldots P_{n+1}$ are congruent and so have the same area. Since the triangle $P_1 P_{r+1} P_{n+1}$ has smaller area than $P_1 P'_{r+1} P'_{n+1}$ we see that the polygon $P_1 P'_2 \ldots P'_{n+1} P_1$ has greater area than $P_1 P_2 \ldots P_{n+1} P_1$ and by reflecting in $P_1 P_{n+1}$ and taking convex covers we obtain a new polygon p'_0 which belongs to our class and has greater area than p_0. This gives a contradiction.

It is clear that if we take $l_1 = l_2 = \ldots = l_n = \lambda/n$, where λ is fixed, the corresponding extremal polygon has area and circumference which approximate to those of the corresponding circle. Thus in this case we have for fixed λ,

$$\lambda^2 \geqslant 4\pi^2 S(1-S) - \epsilon, \quad \text{if } n \geqslant n_0(\epsilon), \quad \text{where } \pi S \text{ is the area of } p_0,$$

and so this inequality remains true for any polygon in our class.

Now if $l_1, \ldots, l_p$ are fixed finite numbers, the class $\pi(l_1, \ldots, l_p)$ is contained in $\pi(\lambda/n, \ldots, \lambda/n)$, provided that

$$r_1(\lambda/n) \geqslant l_1, \quad r_2(\lambda/n) \geqslant l_2, \ldots, \quad r_p(\lambda/n) \geqslant l_p,$$

$$\text{where } r_1 + r_2 + \ldots + r_p = n,$$

since a side of length l_1 can be considered as made up of r_1 sides of length not greater than λ/n. Thus we may take

$$r_\nu = \left[\frac{nl_\nu}{\lambda} \right] + 1,$$

and so

$$\frac{\lambda}{n}(r_\nu - 1) \leqslant l_\nu \quad (\nu = 1 \text{ to } p),$$

$$\lambda \leqslant \sum_{\nu=1}^{p} l_\nu + \frac{p}{n}.$$

Then if S is the area of our polygon we deduce that for large n

$$4\pi^2 S(1-S) \leqslant \left(\sum l_\nu + \frac{p}{n} \right)^2 + \epsilon,$$

and since l_1 to l_p are fixed and ϵ is arbitrary, we deduce Lemma 6.1

for any polygon and so for any rectifiable Jordan curve on the Riemann sphere.

6.1.2. We deduce

LEMMA 6.3. *If $f(z)$ is meromorphic in $|z| \leqslant R$, and $L(r)$, $S(r)$ are defined by (5.21), (5.22) for $0 < r < R$, then we have*

$$L(r)^2 \geqslant 4\pi^2 S(r)\{1 - S(r)\} \quad (0 < r < R).$$

The inequality is trivial unless $S(r) < 1$. As in section 5.3.2, we consider the nth sheet, consisting of all those points covered at least n times by the image of $w = f(z)$. Suppose that this nth sheet has area πS_n and length of circumference L_n.

Let D be a domain on the sphere bounded by curves γ_1 to γ_p, having lengths l_1 to l_p and suppose that the complement of D on the sphere consists of domains D_1 to D_p having areas $\pi\sigma_1$ to $\pi\sigma_p$. Then we have by Lemma 6.1

$$l_\nu^2 \geqslant 4\pi^2 \sigma_\nu (1 - \sigma_\nu).$$

Thus if $l = \sum l_\nu$, $1 - \sigma = \sum \sigma_\nu$, we deduce that

$$l^2 \geqslant \sum l_\nu^2 \geqslant 4\pi^2 \left\{ \sum \sigma_\nu - \sum \sigma_\nu^2 \right\} \geqslant 4\pi^2 \left\{ \sum \sigma_\nu - \left(\sum \sigma_\nu \right)^2 \right\}$$
$$= 4\pi^2 \{(1 - \sigma) - (1 - \sigma)^2\} = 4\pi^2 \sigma(1 - \sigma).$$

Thus if D is an arbitrary domain of circumference l, and area $\pi\sigma$, we deduce that $l^2 \geqslant 4\pi^2 \sigma(1 - \sigma)$. By addition this result remains true for a set consisting of the union of a finite number of domains and thus we deduce

$$L_n^2 \geqslant 4\pi^2 S_n(1 - S_n).$$

Also we have $S(r) = \sum S_n$, and $L(r) \geqslant \sum L_n$ by (5.4). Thus we have finally

$$L(r)^2 \geqslant \sum L_n^2 \geqslant 4\pi^2 \left(\sum S_n - \sum S_n^2 \right) \geqslant 4\pi^2 \{S(r) - S(r)^2\}.$$

This proves Lemma 6.3.

We now recall the inequality

$$L(r)^2 \leqslant 2\pi^2 r \frac{dS}{dr}$$

from section 5.6. On combining this with Lemma 6.3 we deduce

$$4\pi^2 S(r)\{1 - S(r)\} \leqslant 2\pi^2 r \frac{dS}{dr},$$

so that we have

$$\int_{r_1}^{r_0} \left(\frac{2dr}{r} - \frac{S'(r)\,dr}{S(r)\{1 - S(r)\}} \right) \leqslant 0 \quad (0 < r_1 < r_0)$$

and this yields Theorem 6.1, on changing r_1 to r.

6.2. Consequences of Theorem 6.1

We now deduce

THEOREM 6.2. *Suppose that $f(z)$ is meromorphic in $|z| < 1$ and satisfies there the inequality* (6.1). *Then we have the inequalities*

$$T_0(r,f) \leqslant \tfrac{1}{2}h_3 \log\frac{1}{1-r^2} \quad (0 < r < 1), \tag{6.5}$$

$$S(r,f) \leqslant h_3\frac{r^2}{1-r^2} \quad (0 < r < 1) \tag{6.6}$$

and

$$\left(\frac{|f'(0)|}{1+|f(0)|^2}\right)^2 \leqslant h_3, \tag{6.7}$$

where h_3 is a positive constant, depending only on h_1.

We start with (6.2) and choose r_0 so that

$$h_2/\log(1/r_0) = \tfrac{1}{2},$$

so that

$$r_0 = e^{-2h_2}.$$

Then (6.2) shows that (6.6) holds for $r \geqslant r_0$. For $r \leqslant r_0$ we now use (6.3) which shows that

$$\frac{S(r)}{r^2} \leqslant \frac{1}{r_0^2}\frac{S(r_0)}{1-S(r_0)} \leqslant \frac{1}{r_0^2} = e^{-4h_2} \quad (0 < r \leqslant r_0).$$

Thus (6.6) holds also for $r \leqslant r_0$. Making $r \to 0$ in (6.6) we obtain (6.7). Finally integrating (6.6) we deduce that

$$T_0(r,f) = \int_0^r \frac{S(t,f)\,dt}{t} \leqslant h_3 \int_0^r \frac{t}{1-t^2}\,dt = \frac{h_3}{2}\log\frac{1}{1-r^2},$$

as required.

COROLLARY 1. *The conclusion of Theorem 6.2 holds if $f(z)$ is meromorphic in $|z| < 1$ and fails to take there three complex values a, b, c, with h_3 depending on a, b, c only.*

COROLLARY 2. *The conclusion of Theorem 6.2 holds if $f(z)$ is meromorphic in $|z| < 1$ and fails to map any subdomain of $|z| < 1$ $(1,1)$ conformally onto any of five simply connected domains D_ν $(\nu = 1$ to $5)$ whose closures are disjoint.*

These corollaries are consequences of Ahlfors's Five Islands Theorem. Corollary 1 contains the theorems of Schottky and Landau, and Corollary 2 that of Bloch, at least in a qualitative form. We shall return to this point in section 6.6.

6.3. Normal families

Following Montel [1], a class F of functions $f(z)$ meromorphic in a domain D is called *normal* in D if, given any sequence $f_n(z)$ of functions in F, we can find a subsequence $f_{n_p}(z)$ which converges everywhere in D and uniformly on compact subsets of D with respect to the chordal metric on the Riemann sphere. We then say that $f_{n_p}(z)$ converges *locally uniformly* in D.

An equivalent statement is that for every z_0 in D there exists a neighbourhood $|z-z_0| < \delta$ in which either $f_{n_p}(z)$ or $f_{n_p}(z)^{-1}$ converges uniformly as $p \to \infty$. Suppose in fact that the second condition is satisfied. If w_1, w_2 are two points in the w-plane, their distance in the chordal metric of the Riemann sphere is†

$$k(w_1, w_2) = \frac{|w_1 - w_2|}{\sqrt{\{(1+|w_1|^2)(1+|w_2|^2)\}}} \leqslant |w_1 - w_2|.$$

Also

$$k(w_1, w_2) = \left| \frac{1}{w_1} - \frac{1}{w_2} \right| \frac{|w_1|}{\sqrt{(1+|w_1|^2)}} \frac{|w_2|}{\sqrt{(1+|w_2|^2)}} \leqslant \left| \frac{1}{w_1} - \frac{1}{w_2} \right|.$$

Thus if either $f_n(z) \to f(z)$ or $f_n(z)^{-1} \to f(z)^{-1}$ uniformly in a set E, then $k\{f_n(z), f(z)\} \to 0$, uniformly in E. Thus if one of these two conditions holds uniformly in some neighbourhood of every point of D,

$$k\{f_n(z), f(z)\} \to 0$$

uniformly in some neighbourhood of every point of D and hence by the Heine–Borel theorem uniformly on every compact subset of D.

Conversely, suppose that $k\{f_n(z), f(z)\} \to 0$, uniformly on every compact subset of D, where $f_n(z)$ is meromorphic. Let z_0 be a point of D such that $f(z_0) = \infty$. Then we can find a neighbourhood $|z-z_0| < \delta$, such that $|f(z)| > 2$, for $|z-z_0| \leqslant \delta$, and so

$$k\{f(z_0), f(z)\} = k\{\infty, f(z)\} = \frac{1}{\sqrt{(1+|f(z)|^2)}} < \frac{1}{\sqrt{5}}.$$

Choose n so large that for $|z-z_0| < \delta$, $n > n_0$, $k\{f(z), f_n(z)\} \leqslant \epsilon < \frac{1}{4}$. Then

$$k\{f_n(z), \infty\} \leqslant \frac{1}{4} + \frac{1}{\sqrt{5}} < \frac{3}{4},$$

$$\frac{1}{1+|f_n(z)|^2} \leqslant \frac{9}{16}, \quad |f_n(z)|^2 \geqslant \frac{7}{9}, \quad |f_n(z)| \geqslant \frac{2}{3}.$$

Thus $\dfrac{1}{f_n(z)}$ and $\dfrac{1}{f(z)}$ are regular in $|z-z_0| < \delta$ for large n and since

$$k(w_1, w_2) = \left| \frac{1}{w_1} - \frac{1}{w_2} \right| \frac{|w_1|}{\sqrt{(1+|w_1|^2)}} \frac{|w_2|}{\sqrt{(1+|w_2|^2)}} > \frac{1}{4} \left| \frac{1}{w_1} - \frac{1}{w_2} \right|,$$

† See section 1.5.

if $|w_1| \geqslant \frac{2}{3}$, $|w_2| \geqslant \frac{2}{3}$, we deduce that

$$\left| \frac{1}{f_n(z)} - \frac{1}{f(z)} \right| < 4\epsilon \qquad (|z-z_0| < \delta, \quad n > n_0).$$

Thus $f_n(z)^{-1} \to f(z)^{-1}$ uniformly in $|z-z_0| < \delta$.

We deduce similarly that if $f(z_0) \neq \infty$, so that $f(z)$ is regular and so bounded in some neighbourhood $|z-z_0| \leqslant \delta$, then if

$$k\{f_n(z), f(z)\} \to 0$$

as $n \to \infty$ uniformly in $|z-z_0| \leqslant \delta$, $f_n(z)$ is finally regular and uniformly bounded in $|z-z_0| \leqslant \delta$ and $f_n(z) \to f(z)$ uniformly in $|z-z_0| \leqslant \delta$.

6.3.1. We have next a criterion due to Marty [1].

THEOREM 6.3. *A class F of functions $f(z)$ meromorphic in a domain D of the complex plane is normal in D if and only if† $|f'(z)| / \{1 + |f(z)|^2\}$ is uniformly bounded on any compact subset of D for $f \in F$.*

Suppose that the condition is not satisfied. Then we can find a compact set E in D and a sequence of points z_n in E and of functions $f_n(z) \in F$, such that

$$\frac{|f_n'(z_n)|}{1 + |f_n(z_n)|^2} \to +\infty. \tag{6.8}$$

By changing z_n slightly we may assume that $f_m(z_n) \neq \infty$, for any pair m, n. By taking subsequences if necessary we may assume that $z_n \to z_0$, where z_0 is a point of E, and $f_n(z_n) \to w$, where w is a finite complex number or $w = \infty$.

We note that $|f'| / (1 + |f|^2)$ is continuous at all points where $f(z)$ is regular. At a pole z_0 of $f(z)$, we set $f(z) = 1/\phi(z)$, so that $\phi(z)$ remains regular at z_0. Also†

$$\frac{|f'|}{1 + |f|^2} = \frac{|\phi'|}{1 + |\phi|^2}$$

which remains continuous at z_0. Suppose now that a subsequence $f_{n_p}(z)$ converges to $f(z)$ in $|z-z_0| \leqslant \delta$, so that

$$f_{n_p}'(z) \to f'(z), \quad \text{uniformly in } |z-z_0| \leqslant \tfrac{1}{2}\delta.$$

Thus $$f_{n_p}'(z) = f'(z) + o(1), \qquad f_{n_p}(z) = f(z) + o(1)$$

and so

$$\frac{|f_{n_p}'(z)|}{1 + |f_{n_p}(z)|^2} = \frac{|f'(z)| + o(1)}{1 + \{|f(z)| + o(1)\}^2} = \frac{|f'(z)|}{1 + |f'(z)|^2} + o(1) = O(1)$$

uniformly as $p \to \infty$, for $|z-z_0| \leqslant \tfrac{1}{2}\delta$, and this contradicts (6.8).

---

† If f, ϕ are finite and $f = 1/\phi$, then $|f'|/(1+|f|^2) = |\phi'|/(1+|\phi|^2)$. At points where f is infinite we use this relation as a definition.

Similarly we obtain a contradiction if

$$\frac{1}{f_{n_p}(z)} \to \frac{1}{f(z)}$$

uniformly in $|z-z_0| \leqslant \delta$. Thus the condition of Theorem 6.3 is necessary for the family F to be normal.

The condition is also sufficient. Suppose in fact that

$$\frac{|f'(z)|}{1+|f(z)|^2} \leqslant M \tag{6.9}$$

for $f(z) \in F$, and $|z-z_0| \leqslant \delta$. Then we deduce for $z = z_0 + re^{i\theta}$, $0 \leqslant r \leqslant \delta$,

$$|\tan^{-1}|f(z)| - \tan^{-1}|f(z_0)|| \leqslant \int_0^r \frac{|f'(z_0+\rho e^{i\theta})|\, d\rho}{1+|f(z_0+\rho e^{i\theta})|^2} \leqslant M\delta.$$

Suppose first that $|f(z_0)| \leqslant 1$, and choose $\delta \leqslant \pi/12M$. Then

$$\tan^{-1}|f(z)| \leqslant \tfrac{1}{4}\pi + \tfrac{1}{12}\pi = \tfrac{1}{3}\pi, \quad |f(z)| \leqslant \sqrt{3}, \quad |z-z_0| \leqslant \delta.$$

Similarly if $|f(z_0)| \geqslant 1$,

$$\tan^{-1}|f(z)| \geqslant \tfrac{1}{6}\pi, \quad \text{so that} \quad |f(z)| \geqslant \frac{1}{\sqrt{3}}, \quad \text{for } |z-z_0| \leqslant \delta.$$

Thus if (6.9) holds in $|z-z_0| \leqslant \delta$, we have either $|f(z)| \leqslant \sqrt{3}$, or $|f(z)^{-1}| \leqslant \sqrt{3}$ in $|z-z_0| \leqslant \pi/(12M)$. Given a sequence $f_n(z)$ of functions $f(z) \in F$ satisfying (6.9) we can find an infinite subsequence which satisfies

$$|f_n(z)| \leqslant \sqrt{3} \tag{6.10}$$

or an infinite subsequence which satisfies

$$|f_n(z)^{-1}| \leqslant \sqrt{3}. \tag{6.11}$$

In the former case we use a diagonal process to find a subsequence $f_{n_p}(z)$ converging at each of the points z_m, of a sequence dense in $|z-z_0| \leqslant \delta$.

We now assert that $f_{n_p}(z) = g_p(z)$, say, converges uniformly in $|z-z_0| \leqslant \delta$. In fact we have

$$|g_p(z)| \leqslant \sqrt{3}, \qquad |z-z_0| \leqslant \delta,$$

and so

$$|g_p'(z)| \leqslant M(1+|g_p(z)|^2 \leqslant 4M,$$

so that for $|z_1-z_0| < \delta$, $|z_2-z_0| < \delta$,

$$|g_p(z_2)-g_p(z_1)| \leqslant 4M|z_2-z_1| \leqslant \tfrac{1}{3}\epsilon, \quad \text{if } |z_2-z_1| \leqslant \frac{\epsilon}{12M}.$$

Let $z_1,..., z_N$ be N points of the dense sequence in $|z-z_0| < \delta$ such that each point z in $|z-z_0| < \delta$ satisfies

$$|z-z_\nu| < \frac{\epsilon}{12M},$$

for at least one ν. Since $g_p(z)$ converges at each of z_1 to z_N, we can find p_0, such that

$$|g_p(z_\nu)-g_q(z_\nu)| < \tfrac{1}{3}\epsilon \quad (p > p_0, \ q > p_0, \ \nu = 1 \text{ to } N).$$

Then, for $|z-z_0| < \delta$, choose z_ν such that $|z-z_\nu| < \epsilon/12M$. We deduce that for $p > p_0, \ q > p_0$,

$$|g_p(z)-g_q(z)| \leqslant |g_p(z)-g_p(z_\nu)| + |g_p(z_\nu)-g_q(z_\nu)| + |g_q(z_\nu)-g_q(z)|$$
$$\leqslant \tfrac{1}{3}\epsilon+\tfrac{1}{3}\epsilon+\tfrac{1}{3}\epsilon = \epsilon.$$

Thus $g_p(z) = f_{n_p}(z)$ converges uniformly in $|z-z_0| \leqslant \delta$. Similarly if (6.11) holds we can find a subsequence $f_{n_p}(z)$ for which $f_{n_p}^{-1}(z)$ converges uniformly in $|z-z_0| \leqslant \delta$. Thus any point in D has a neighbourhood in which a subsequence $f_{n_p}(z)$ converges uniformly in the chordal metric. The argument shows in fact that if $f_{n_p}(z)$ is a subsequence of $f_n(z)$ which converges in the sense of the chordal metric at each point of a countable dense subset of D, then $f_{n_p}(z)$ converges in the same sense locally uniformly in D if (6.9) holds. Since such a subsequence can always be formed by a diagonal process, Theorem 6.3 is proved.

6.3.2. It follows from Theorem 6.3 that a bounded family of regular functions is always normal in any domain D. For if $|f(z)| < M$ in D, for $f \in F$, and E is a compact subset of D, then E is at a positive distance δ from the complement of D. If z_0 is any point of E then

$$|f(z)| \leqslant M \quad \text{for} \quad |z-z_0| \leqslant \delta, \quad z_0 \text{ in } E,$$

and so by the Cauchy inequality, $|f'(z_0)| \leqslant M/\delta$, and so

$$\frac{|f'(z_0)|}{1+|f(z_0)|^2} \leqslant |f'(z_0)| \leqslant \frac{M}{\delta}.$$

Thus the family F is normal in D. We shall show presently that the functions satisfying criteria of the kind considered in Corollaries 1 and 2 of Theorem 6.2 are also normal in $|z| < 1$. Functions satisfying the criterion (6.1) are not in general normal in the whole unit disk, though we shall see that they are normal in a neighbourhood of the origin. To see this we consider two examples.

Example 1. Let

$$f_n(z) = 2z-1+\frac{1}{8n(2z-1)} \quad (n = 1, 2,...).$$

Then for $|z| < \frac{1}{4}$,

$$|f_n(z)| < 1 + \tfrac{1}{2} + \frac{1}{4n} < 2,$$

$$|f_n'(z) - 2| \leqslant \frac{2}{8n|2z-1|^2} \leqslant 1.$$

Thus

$$\frac{1}{5} \leqslant \frac{|f_n'(z)|}{1 + |f_n(z)|^2} \leqslant 3,$$

and so, for $0 \leqslant r \leqslant \frac{1}{4}$, we have

$$\frac{r^2}{25} \leqslant S(r) \leqslant 9r^2,$$

$$\frac{2\pi r}{5} \leqslant L(r) \leqslant 6\pi r.$$

Thus we have

$$S(r) \leqslant \frac{45r}{2\pi} L(r) < 2L(r) \quad (0 < r < \tfrac{1}{4}) \tag{6.12}$$

for all the functions $f_n(z)$, so that (6.1) holds for $0 < r < \frac{1}{4}$. Again for $z = x + iy$ $(x < 0)$ and $|z| < 1$

$$|f_n'(z) - 2| = \left| \frac{2}{8n(2z-1)^2} \right| \leqslant \frac{2}{8n(2|x|+1)^2} < 1,$$

and

$$|f(z)| < 3 + \frac{1}{8n} < 4.$$

Thus

$$\frac{|f'(z)|}{1 + |f(z)|^2} > \frac{1}{17},$$

and

$$L(r) \geqslant \int_{\frac{1}{2}\pi}^{\frac{3}{2}\pi} \frac{|f'(re^{i\theta})| r \, d\theta}{1 + |f(re^{i\theta})|^2} > \frac{\pi r}{17} \geqslant \frac{\pi}{68} \quad (\tfrac{1}{4} \leqslant r < 1).$$

Again since $f(z)$ assumes no value more than twice in the whole plane

$$S(r) \leqslant 2 \quad (0 < r < \infty),$$

so that for $\frac{1}{4} \leqslant r < 1$ $\quad S(r) \leqslant \dfrac{136}{\pi} L(r).$

In view of (6.12) this inequality holds for $0 < r < 1$. On the other hand, $f_n(z)$ is not normal in any neighbourhood of $z = \frac{1}{2}$. For otherwise we could find a subsequence $f_{n_p}(z)$ such that either $f_{n_p}(z)$ or $f_{n_p}(z)^{-1}$ was uniformly convergent in some neighbourhood $|z - \frac{1}{2}| < \delta$. However, $f_n(z)$ has a pole at $z = \frac{1}{2}$, and a zero at $z = \frac{1}{2} + i/4\sqrt{(2n)}$, so that for all large n neither $f_n(z)$ nor $f_n^{-1}(z)$ is regular in $|z - \frac{1}{2}| < \delta$.

Example 2. Consider the functions

$$f_n(z) = nz.$$

They take no value more than once and so $S(r) < 1$ for these functions for $0 < r < \infty$. But they do not form a normal family. In fact

$$\frac{|f_n'(z)|}{1+|f_n(z)|^2} = n \quad \text{at } z = 0,$$

so that $f_n(z)$ is not normal at the origin. Against this we can prove

THEOREM 6.4. *If $0 < K < 1$ and $F(K)$ is the class of all functions meromorphic in $|z| < 1$ and satisfying $S(r,f) \leqslant K$ $(0 < r < 1)$ there, then we have for $f(z) \in F(K)$*

$$\frac{|f'(z)|}{1+|f(z)|^2} \leqslant \frac{1}{(1-|z|^2)} \sqrt{\left(\frac{K}{1-K}\right)}. \tag{6.13}$$

Thus $F(K)$ is a normal family in $|z| < 1$.

We deduce from Theorem 6.1 that

$$\frac{|f'(0)|}{1+|f(0)|^2} \leqslant \frac{1}{r} \sqrt{\left(\frac{K}{1-K}\right)} \quad (0 < r < 1)$$

and letting $r \to 1$, we deduce (6.13) with $z = 0$.

Next it is clear that if $f(z) \in F(K)$ and $|z_0| < 1$, then

$$g(z) = f\left(\frac{z_0+z}{1+\bar{z}_0 z}\right) \in F(K).$$

In fact the images of $|z| < 1$ by $g(z)$ and $f(z)$ are identical and have area at most K. Thus we deduce that

$$\frac{|g'(0)|}{1+|g(0)|^2} = \frac{(1-|z_0|^2)|f'(z_0)|}{1+|f(z_0)|^2} \leqslant \sqrt{\left(\frac{K}{1-K}\right)} \quad (|z_0| < 1),$$

and this proves (6.13). Thus $F(K)$ is a normal family by Theorem 6.3. On the other hand, Example 2 above shows that $F(1)$ is not a normal family.

6.4. Normal invariant families

We have seen that functions $f(z)$ which satisfy (6.1) do not form a normal family in $|z| < 1$ but only in some disk $|z| < r_0$, where r_0 depends on h_1. (This latter result follows from (6.6) and Theorem 6.4.)

The reason for this lies in the fact that we have confined our considerations to disks centred at the origin. However, in many cases (6.1) holds if $L(r)$ and $S(r)$ refer to any disk whose closure lies in $|z| < 1$, even if its centre is not necessarily at the origin. This remark leads to a significant extension of our theory.

Let $f(z)$ be meromorphic in $|z| < 1$. For any real λ and z_0, such that $|z_0| < 1$, we shall call

$$f(z, z_0, \lambda) = f\left(e^{i\lambda} \frac{z+z_0}{1+\bar{z}_0 z}\right)$$

a *translate* of $f(z)$. Thus the translates of $f(z)$ are the various mappings of $|z| < 1$ onto the Riemann surface of $f(z)$. A family F of functions $f(z)$ is said to be *invariant* (Hayman [2]) if whenever $f(z) \in F$ then all the translates $f(z, z_0, \lambda) \in F$. Many normal families turn out also to be invariant, and for these it is possible to obtain bounds of considerably greater precision than for general normal families.

Following Lehto and Virtanen [1] a function $f(z)$ is called *normal* if $f(z)$ together with its translates constitutes a normal family.† We have

THEOREM 6.5. *An invariant family F of functions $f(z)$ meromorphic in $|z| < 1$ is normal there if and only if there is a constant B, such that*

$$\frac{|f'(0)|}{1+|f(0)|^2} \leqslant B \tag{6.14}$$

for $f(z) \in F$. A function $f(z)$ meromorphic in $|z| < 1$ is normal if and only if

$$\frac{(1-|z|^2)|f'(z)|}{1+|f(z)|^2} \leqslant B \quad (|z| < 1), \tag{6.15}$$

where B is a constant.

Suppose that F is an invariant family. Then if F is normal we deduce from Theorem 6.3 that (6.14) holds for $f(z) \in F$. We apply this result to the translate

$$g(z) = f\left(\frac{z_0+z}{1+\bar{z}_0 z}\right) \in F$$

and obtain

$$\frac{(1-|z_0|^2)|f'(z_0)|}{1+|f(z_0)|^2} \leqslant B.$$

Thus (6.15) holds for $f(z) \in F$. In particular if $f(z)$ is a normal function $f(z)$ belongs to a normal invariant family and so (6.15) holds.

Conversely if F is an invariant family whose members satisfy (6.14) then they also satisfy (6.15) and so by Theorem 6.3 F is a normal family. Finally if $f(z)$ is a meromorphic function satisfying (6.15) then the translates

$$f(z, z_0, \lambda) = f\left(\frac{z+z_0}{1+\bar{z}_0 z} e^{i\lambda}\right)$$

† The authors obtain some very interesting boundary properties of such functions, showing that they have some properties similar to those of bounded functions.

all satisfy (6.14) and so form a normal invariant family by the first part. Thus $f(z)$ is a normal function. We deduce at once

THEOREM 6.6. *Let $f(z)$ give a meromorphic map of $|z| < 1$ into the Riemann sphere and let L be the length of the image of the circumference and πS the area of the image of some disk whose closure lies in $|z| < 1$. We define $\mathscr{L}(h)$ to be the class of functions such that*

$$S \leqslant hL \qquad (6.16)$$

for all such disks, where h is a positive constant. Then $\mathscr{L}(h)$ is a normal invariant family.

It is clear that $\mathscr{L}(h)$ is an invariant family. In fact if

$$Z = e^{i\lambda} \frac{z+z_0}{1+\bar{z}_0 z},$$

then disks C whose closures lie in $|z| < 1$ correspond to disks γ whose closures lie in $|Z| < 1$ in the Z-plane and the images of γ, C by

$$f(z) \text{ and } g(z) = f\!\left(\frac{e^{i\lambda}(z+z_0)}{1+\bar{z}_0 z}\right)$$

respectively are identical. Thus if $f(z)$ satisfies (6.16) then so does $g(z)$. Further, if (6.16) holds it follows from Theorem 6.2 that

$$\left(\frac{|f'(0)|}{1+|f(0)|^2}\right)^2 \leqslant h_3$$

for $f(z) \in \mathscr{L}(h)$, where h_3 depends only on h, and so by Theorem 6.5 $\mathscr{L}(h)$ is a normal family. We have seen, for instance, that the functions which do not satisfy the conclusions of the five-islands theorem for a set of five fixed domains belong to $\mathscr{L}(h)$ for a suitable constant h and so constitute an invariant normal family.

We have obtained in Theorem 6.2 some bounds for the functions of $\mathscr{L}(h)$. Similar bounds hold for arbitrary normal invariant families. We have in fact

THEOREM 6.7. *If F is a normal invariant family then (6.5), (6.6) and (6.7) hold with $h_3 = B^2$, where B is the constant in Theorem 6.5.*

In fact we have by Theorem 6.5 for $f(z) \in F$

$$\frac{|f'(0)|}{1+|f(0)|^2} \leqslant B,$$

where B is a suitable positive constant. By applying this to

$$f\!\left(\frac{z_0+z}{1+\bar{z}_0 z}\right) \quad \text{where } z_0 = re^{i\theta},$$

we obtain
$$\left\{\frac{|f'(z)|}{1+|f(z)|^2}\right\}^2 \leqslant \frac{B^2}{(1-r^2)^2} \quad (|z|=r).$$

We integrate this inequality and deduce

$$S(r,f) = \frac{1}{\pi}\int\limits_0^{2\pi} d\theta \int\limits_0^r \left(\frac{|f'(\rho e^{i\theta})|}{1+|f(\rho e^{i\theta})|^2}\right)^2 \rho\, d\rho \leqslant 2B^2 \int\limits_0^r \frac{\rho\, d\rho}{(1-\rho^2)^2} = \frac{B^2 r^2}{1-r^2},$$

$$T_0(r,f) = \int\limits_0^r \frac{S(t)\, dt}{t} \leqslant \frac{B^2}{2}\log\frac{1}{1-r^2}.$$

This proves Theorem 6.7.

6.5. Normal invariant families of regular functions†

If F is a normal invariant family of regular functions, such as, for instance, the sub-class of the regular functions in $\mathscr{L}(h)$, we can obtain bounds for the maximum modulus and the derivative at the origin which are essentially best possible even in the special case of functions $f(z) \neq 0, 1$. We thus obtain strong versions of the theorems of Schottky [1] and Landau [1].

THEOREM 6.8. *Suppose that F is a normal invariant family of functions regular in $|z| < 1$. Then there exists a constant C depending only on F such that for*
$$f(z) = a_0 + a_1 z + \ldots \in F,$$

we have
$$|a_1| \leqslant 2\mu(\log\mu + C) \tag{6.17}$$

and
$$M(r,f) \leqslant \mu^{(1+r)/(1-r)}\exp\frac{2Cr}{1-r}, \tag{6.18}$$

where $\mu = \max(1, |a_0|)$, and $M(r,f) = \sup\limits_{|z|=r}|f(z)|$.

For any real C and positive D the functions
$$f(z) = e^{-C+D(1+z)/(1-z)}$$

satisfy $|f(z)| > e^{-C}$ and so belong to a normal invariant family. On the other hand, for $D > C$,

$$f(0) = \mu = e^{D-C},$$

$$f'(0) = 2Df(0) = 2\mu(\log\mu + C),$$

and
$$M(r,f) = e^{(D-C)(1+r)/(1-r)+2Cr/(1-r)} = \mu^{(1+r)/(1-r)}e^{2Cr/(1-r)}.$$

Thus the general form of the bounds obtained in Theorem 6.8 cannot be sharpened even in this special case, though in other cases one may try to obtain good estimates for C.

† Hayman [2].

6.5.1. To prove Theorem 6.8 we shall need two lemmas.

LEMMA 6.4. *There exist positive constants B_1 and r_0, such that $f(z) \in F$, $|z_1| < 1$, $|z_2| < 1$, $|f(z_1)| \leqslant 1$, $|f(z_2)| \geqslant e^{B_1}$ imply*

$$\left| \frac{z_2 - z_1}{1 - \bar{z}_1 z_2} \right| \geqslant r_0.$$

Suppose that the lemma is false. Then we can find sequences z_n, z'_n, and functions $f_n(z) \in F$, such that

$$|f_n(z_n)| \leqslant 1, \qquad |f_n(z'_n)| \to +\infty, \quad \text{and} \quad \left| \frac{z_n - z'_n}{1 - \bar{z}_n z'_n} \right| \to 0.$$

We set

$$g_n(z) = f_n\left(\frac{z_n + z}{1 + \bar{z}_n z} \right)$$

so that $g_n(z) \in F$. Also

$$|g_n(0)| \leqslant 1, \qquad |g_n(\zeta'_n)| \to +\infty,$$

where

$$\frac{z_n + \zeta'_n}{1 + \bar{z}_n \zeta'_n} = z'_n,$$

so that

$$|\zeta'_n| = \left| \frac{z_n - z'_n}{1 - z'_n \bar{z}_n} \right| \to 0.$$

Thus no subsequence of $g_n(z)$ or $g_n^{-1}(z)$ can converge uniformly in any neighbourhood of $z = 0$, contradicting our hypothesis that $f_n(z)$ and hence $g_n(z)$ belongs to the normal invariant family F for all n.

We have next

LEMMA 6.5. *Suppose that $\phi(z) = b_0 + b_1 z + \dots$ is regular and satisfies $|\phi(z)| > 1$ in $|z| < 1$. Then we have $|b_1| \leqslant 2|b_0||\log|b_0||$ and if $|z_i| < 1$ $(i = 1, 2)$, we have*

$$|\phi(z_1)| \geqslant |\phi(z_2)|^{(1-t)/(1+t)},$$

where

$$t = \left| \frac{z_1 - z_2}{1 - \bar{z}_1 z_2} \right|.$$

Suppose that $b_0 = \rho e^{i\lambda}$, where $\rho > 1$, so that for a suitable branch of the logarithm

$$g(z) = \log\{e^{-i\lambda}\phi(z)\} = g_0 + g_1 z + \dots \quad (g_0 > 0).$$

Then $g(z)$ has positive real part and so if

$$g(z) = u + iv, \qquad \mu(z) = \frac{g(z) - g_0}{g(z) + g_0},$$

we have

$$|\mu(z)|^2 = \left| \frac{(u - g_0)^2 + v^2}{(u + g_0)^2 + v^2} \right| < 1 \quad (|z| < 1).$$

Also $\mu(0) = 0$, so that $\mu(z)$ satisfies the hypotheses of Schwarz's lemma. Thus

$$|\mu'(0)| = \left|\frac{g_1}{2g_0}\right| \leqslant 1,$$

which gives $|b_1| \leqslant 2|b_0||\log|b_0||$ as required. Further, for $|z| = t$, we deduce

$$|\mu(z)| \leqslant t,$$

$$|g(z)| - |g_0| \leqslant |g(z) - g_0| \leqslant t|g(z) + g_0| \leqslant t(|g(z)| + |g_0|),$$

so that

$$|g(z)| \leqslant |g_0|\frac{1+t}{1-t},$$

and hence

$$|\phi(z)| \leqslant e^{|g(z)|} \leqslant \exp\left(\frac{1+t}{1-t}\log|\phi(0)|\right) = |\phi(0)|^{(1+t)/(1-t)}.$$

We apply this inequality to

$$\psi(z) = \phi\left(\frac{z_1+z}{1+\bar{z}_1 z}\right),$$

which also satisfies $|\psi(z)| > 1$ for $|z| > 1$, and deduce for $|z_1| < 1$,

$$|\phi(z_2)| \leqslant |\phi(z_1)|^{(1+t)/(1-t)},$$

where $t = |z|$, and z is given by

$$\frac{z_1+z}{1+\bar{z}_1 z} = z_2, \quad \text{i.e. } z = \frac{z_2 - z_1}{1-\bar{z}_1 z_2}.$$

This completes the proof of Lemma 6.5.

6.5.2. *Proof of Theorem* 6.8. Suppose now that B_1, r_0 are the constants of Lemma 6.4. If $|a_0| \leqslant e^{B_1}$, we have by Theorem 6.5

$$|a_1| \leqslant B(1 + |a_0|^2) \leqslant 2Be^{B_1}\mu,$$

so that (6.17) holds with $C = Be^{B_1}$.

Suppose next that $|a_0| > e^{B_1}$. Let ρ be the largest positive number such that

$$|f(z)| > 1 \quad (|z| < \rho).$$

If $\rho \geqslant 1$, (6.17) follows from Lemma 6.5 with $C = 0$. If $\rho < 1$, let r be the largest positive number such that $|f(z)| > e^{B_1}$, for $|z| < r$. Then there exists θ, such that $|f(re^{i\theta})| = e^{B_1}$. Consider the function

$$\phi(z) = f(\rho z).$$

This satisfies the hypotheses of Lemma 6.5 and hence we have, taking $z_2 = 0$, $z_1 = (r/\rho)e^{i\theta}$, $t = r/\rho$,

$$e^{B_1} = |\phi(z_1)| \geqslant |a_0|^{(\rho-r)/(\rho+r)},$$

$$\frac{\rho-r}{\rho+r}\log|a_0| \leqslant B_1. \tag{6.19}$$

On the other hand, we have for a suitable θ_1, $|f(\rho e^{i\theta_1})| = 1$, whereas by hypothesis

$$|f(re^{i\theta_1})| \geqslant e^{B_1}.$$

In view of Lemma 6.4 this implies

$$\frac{\rho-r}{1-\rho r} \geqslant r_0. \tag{6.20}$$

Combining (6.19) and (6.20) we obtain

$$B_1 \geqslant \frac{\rho-r}{\rho+r}\log|a_0| \geqslant \frac{r_0}{2}(1-\rho r)\log|a_0|,$$

so that

$$1-\rho \leqslant 1-\rho r \leqslant \frac{2B_1}{r_0\log|a_0|}.$$

Also we have, by Lemma 6.5,

$$|\phi'(0)| = \rho|f'(0)| \leqslant 2|a_0||\log|a_0||.$$

Hence we find

$$|a_1| \leqslant \frac{2}{\rho}|a_0||\log|a_0|| = 2|a_0||\log|a_0|| + \frac{2(1-\rho)}{\rho}|a_0||\log|a_0||$$

$$\leqslant 2|a_0||\log|a_0|| + \frac{4B_1}{r_0\rho}|a_0|.$$

Since $\rho \geqslant r_0$, we have (6.17).

It remains to prove (6.18). We first apply (6.17) to the translate

$$g(z) = f\left(\frac{z_0+z}{1+\bar{z}_0 z}\right) = f(z_0)+(1-|z_0|^2)f'(z_0)z+\ldots$$

and deduce that if $|f(z_0)| > 1$, we have for $f(z) \in F$, $|z_0| < 1$,

$$(1-|z_0|^2)|f'(z_0)| \leqslant 2|f(z_0)|\{\log|f(z_0)|+C\}.$$

Suppose now that $\qquad M(r,f) = |f(re^{i\theta})| \geqslant 1,$

since otherwise (6.18) holds trivially. Let r_1 be the lower bound of all positive numbers such that

$$|f(te^{i\theta})| \geqslant 1 \quad (r_1 \leqslant t \leqslant r).$$

Then either $r_1 > 0$, and $|f(r_1 e^{i\theta})| = 1$, or $r_1 = 0$, so that in any case

$$|f(r_1 e^{i\theta})| \leqslant \mu = \max(1, |a_0|).$$

Also we have, for $r_1 \leqslant t \leqslant r$,

$$|f'(te^{i\theta})| \leqslant \frac{2}{1-t^2}|f(te^{i\theta})|\{\log|f(te^{i\theta})|+C\},$$

and hence

$$\frac{\partial}{\partial t}\log\{\log|f(te^{i\theta})|+C\} \leqslant \frac{2}{1-t^2}.$$

Integrating this from $t = r_1$ to r, we deduce

$$\frac{\log\{M(r,f)+C\}}{\log|f(r_1 e^{i\theta})|+C} \leqslant \frac{1+r}{1-r}\left(\frac{1-r_1}{1+r_1}\right)$$

and hence *a fortiori*

$$\log M(r,f)+C \leqslant (\log\mu+C)\frac{1+r}{1-r}.$$

This completes the proof of Theorem 6.8.

6.6. Theorems of Schottky, Landau, Bohr and Bloch

The theorem of *Schottky* [1] states that if $f(z)$ is regular and satisfies $f(z) \neq 0, 1$ in $|z| < 1$, then

$$M(r,f) \leqslant \Omega(a_0, r),$$

where $\Omega(a_0, r)$ depends only on a_0 and r. It follows from Ahlfors's Theorem 5.5, that since $f(z)$ has no islands over any domains containing $w = 0, 1, \infty$ we have in this case

$$S(r) \leqslant hL(r) \quad (0 < r < 1),$$

where h is an absolute constant. In view of Theorem 6.2, (6.7) we deduce that

$$\frac{|f'(0)|}{1+|f(0)|^2} \leqslant h_1$$

for such functions and since our class of functions is invariant it follows from Theorem 6.5 that it is normal. Thus we may apply Theorem 6.8 and have Schottky's theorem with

$$\Omega(a_0, r) < \exp\frac{1}{1-r}\{(1+r)\log\max(1, |a_0|)+2Cr\},$$

where C is an absolute constant.† At the same time we have for $|a_0| > 1$,

$$|a_1| \leqslant 2|a_0|(|\log|a_0||+C), \tag{6.21}$$

and by applying this result to $f(z)^{-1}$ we see that it is also true for $|a_0| < 1$. Thus we obtain a strong form of *Landau's* [1] *theorem*. This asserts that if

$$f(z) = a_0+a_1 z+\ldots \quad (a_1 \neq 0)$$

is regular in $|z| < R$, then for $R \geqslant \Omega_1(a_0, a_1)$, either $f(z)$ or $f(z)-1$ has a zero. By applying (6.21) to $f(Rz)$, we obtain

$$|a_1|R \leqslant 2|a_0|(|\log|a_0||+C),$$

if $f(z) \neq 0, 1$ in $|z| < R$ so that Landau's theorem holds with

$$\Omega_1(a_0, a_1) = \frac{2|a_0|(|\log|a_0||+C)}{|a_1|}.$$

† For the sharpest numerical bounds known see Jenkins [1].

These bounds are of the right order of magnitude in every way except for the unknown absolute constant C.†

As an application we prove Lemma 2.5, whose proof was left over from Chapter 2.

THEOREM 6.9 (Bohr [1]). *If $f(z) = a_1 z + a_2 z^2 + ...$ is regular in $|z| < 1$, and satisfies*

$$M(\tfrac{1}{2}, f) \geqslant 1,$$

then $f(z)$ assumes in $|z| < 1$ all values on a circle $|w| = r$, where $r \geqslant A$, and A is a positive absolute constant.

Suppose that for all $r \geqslant l$ we have a value w_r, such that $|w_r| = r$, and $f(z) \neq w_r$ in $|z| < 1$. We choose w_1, w_2 such that $|w_1| = l$, $|w_2| = 2l$ and $f(z) \neq w_1$ or w_2 in $|z| < 1$. Then

$$\phi(z) = \frac{f(z) - w_1}{w_2 - w_1}$$

satisfies the hypotheses of Schottky's theorem and

$$|\phi(0)| = \left| \frac{w_1}{w_2 - w_1} \right| \leqslant 1.$$

Thus Schottky's theorem gives for $|z| \leqslant \tfrac{1}{2}$

$$|\phi(z)| < A_1, \qquad |f(z)| \leqslant |w_1| + |w_2 - w_1|\,|\phi(z)| < l(1 + 3A_1).$$

This gives a contradiction if

$$l = (1 + 3A_1)^{-1},$$

and so $f(z)$ assumes all values on some circle $|w| = r$, with

$$r \geqslant (1 + 3A_1)^{-1}.$$

Actually our argument proves a little more, namely that for

$$r \leqslant (1 + 3A_1)^{-1},$$

either $f(z)$ assumes all values on $|w| = r$ or on $|w| = 2r$.

As another application of Theorem 6.7 we obtain

BLOCH'S THEOREM‡ 6.10. *Suppose that $w = f(z) = z + ...$ is regular in $|z| < 1$. Then $f(z)$ has a simple island over at least one disk of radius B in the w-plane, where B is an absolute constant* (called Bloch's constant).

Suppose that $f(z)$ has no simple island over any of the disks

$$|w - nd| < \tfrac{1}{4}d \quad (n = 0, \mp 1),$$

---

† The best result for C in Landau's theorem is due to Lai [1], who obtained $4.37 \leqslant C \leqslant 4.76$, sharpening an earlier result of Jenkins [2].

‡ Bloch [1], Théorème G, p. 9. The sharpest known bounds are $B \leqslant 0.472$, due to Ahlfors and Grunsky [1], and $B \geqslant 0.433$, due to Ahlfors [4].

where d is a positive constant. Then

$$\phi(z) = \frac{f(z)}{d} = \frac{z}{d} + \dots$$

has no simple islands over any of the disks $|w-n| < \frac{1}{4}$ ($n = 0, \mp 1$).
Also $\phi(z)$ is regular and so has no islands at all over the region $|w| > 2$.
Such functions $\phi(z)$ again form a normal invariant family by Theorems
5.5 and 6.2, and so we deduce from Theorem 6.7 that

$$|\phi'(0)| = \frac{1}{d} \leqslant 2C, \qquad d \geqslant (2C)^{-1},$$

where C is an absolute constant. Thus $f(z)$ has a simple island over at
least one of the three disks $|w-nd| < \frac{1}{4}d$ ($n = 0, \mp 1$), and $d = (3C)^{-1}$,
where C is an absolute constant. This proves Theorem 6.9 with
$B = (3C)^{-1}$, and in fact rather more. A similar argument shows that
if D_1, D_2, D_3 are any three mutually exclusive simply connected domains
in the plane and λD_ν denotes the domain obtained from D_ν by a magni-
fication in the ratio 1 to λ about the origin, then the function $f(z) = z + \dots$
regular in $|z| < 1$ has a simple island over at least one of the domains
λD_ν, if λ is less than a constant depending on D_1, D_2, D_3 only. The
corresponding result for two domains D_ν is false. In fact for any
positive λ

$$f(z) = \lambda \sin \frac{z}{\lambda} = z + \dots$$

contains no simple island over any domain containing either of the
points $\mp \lambda$, since $f(z) = \mp \lambda$ implies $f'(z) = 0$.

For some further applications of normal invariant families see Hayman [2].

Example 1. If $r \geqslant \frac{1}{2}$, $|z_0| < 1-r$, and $f(z) \in F$, where F is a normal
invariant family, show by using a suitable translate of $f(z)$ that

$$S(r, f(z_0+z)) \leqslant \frac{B_1}{\sqrt{\{(1-r)^2 - |z_0|^2\}}}$$

and hence that $\qquad T(r, f(z_0+z)) \leqslant B_2 \log \frac{1}{1-r},$

where B_1, B_2 depend on F only.

Hence by using this result with $r = \frac{3}{4}$, and suitable z_0, show again that

$$\log M(r, f(z)) = \frac{O(1)}{1-r}, \quad \text{as } r \to 1.$$

Example 2. If $f(z) = a_0 + a_1 z + \dots$ has no simple island over any disk of radius 1, show that

$$|a_1| \leqslant \frac{1}{B}, \qquad |f'(re^{i\theta})| \leqslant \frac{1}{B(1-r^2)} \quad (0 < r < 1),$$

and hence by applying Cauchy's inequality to $f'(z)$ prove that

$$|a_n| \leqslant \frac{2e}{B\sqrt{3}} \quad (n = 1, 2, \dots),$$

where B is Bloch's constant.

Example 3. If F is a family of functions $w = f(z)$ regular in $|z| < 1$ whose images contain no simple island over any disk having its centre over the imaginary axis and radius greater than B in the w-plane, prove that the functions e^f constitute a normal invariant family. By considering the functions $z = f^{-1}(w)$ and applying Schwarz's lemma, prove also a converse result.

6.7. Functions of bounded characteristic

If $f(z)$ is meromorphic in $|z| < 1$ we know that $T(r,f)$ is an increasing function of r for $0 < r < 1$. It follows that

$$T(1,f) = \lim_{r \to 1} T(r,f)$$

exists as a finite or infinite limit. If $T(1,f)$ is finite we say that $f(z)$ has bounded characteristic in $|z| < 1$. If f, g have bounded characteristic in $|z| < 1$ then so has f/g, unless $g(z) \equiv 0$, since

$$T\left(r, \frac{f}{g}\right) \leqslant T(r,f) + T\left(r, \frac{1}{g}\right) \leqslant T(r,f) + T(r,g) + O(1).$$

Thus in particular if $f(z)$ and $g(z)$ are bounded in $|z| < 1$ and $g(z) \not\equiv 0$, then $f(z)/g(z)$ has bounded characteristic in $|z| < 1$. We shall see that the converse is also true. Functions of bounded characteristic are necessarily ratios of bounded functions. We shall proceed to prove this result, due to R. Nevanlinna [1, 3], but the proof is fairly involved and will have to be carried out in a number of steps.

We have first the following result due to Blaschke [1].

LEMMA 6.6. *If a_n is a finite or infinite sequence of numbers, such that $0 < |a_n| < 1$, $\sum (1 - |a_n|) < +\infty$, then the product*

$$\prod \left(\frac{a_n - z}{1 - \bar{a}_n z}\right) \frac{\bar{a}_n}{|a_n|} \tag{6.22}$$

converges to a function $\pi(z)$ regular in $|z| < 1$, satisfying $|\pi(z)| < 1$ there, and vanishing only at the points $z = a_n$.

A product such as (6.22) is called a *Blaschke product*. If the number of factors is finite the product is called a *finite Blaschke product*, otherwise an *infinite Blaschke product*.

We note that if

$$p_n = p_n(z) = \frac{a_n - z}{1 - \bar{a}_n z} \frac{\bar{a}_n}{|a_n|},$$

then

$$1 - p_n = \frac{(z\bar{a}_n + |a_n|)(1 - |a_n|)}{(1 - \bar{a}_n z)|a_n|}.$$

Thus for $|z| \leqslant r < 1$, we have

$$|1 - p_n| \leqslant \frac{2(1 - |a_n|)}{(1 - r)|a_n|}.$$

Since $\sum (1 - |a_n|)$ converges, $|a_n| \to 1$ as $n \to \infty$. Thus the sum $\sum (1 - p_n(z))$ and hence the product $\prod p_n(z)$ converges uniformly and absolutely in $|z| \leqslant r$, for every fixed $r < 1$, to a regular function $\pi(z)$. Also $\pi(z) = 0$ if and only if $p_n(z) = 0$ for some n, i.e. at the points $z = a_n$. Finally $|p_n(z)| < 1$ for each n, and so $|\pi(z)| < 1$, for $|z| < 1$. This proves Lemma 6.6.

6.7.1. Suppose now that $f(z)$ is meromorphic in $|z| < 1$, that $f(z)$ has bounded characteristic and $f(0) \neq 0, \infty$. Let a_μ be the zeros and b_ν the poles of $f(z)$ in $|z| < 1$, each counted according to multiplicity. Then

$$\sum (1 - |b_\nu|) = \int_0^1 (1 - t) \, dn(t, \infty) = \int_0^1 n(t, \infty) \, dt \leqslant \lim_{r \to 1} N(r, \infty) \leqslant T(1, f).$$

Hence, by Lemma 6.6, we may form the convergent Blaschke product

$$\pi_1(z) = \prod_{\nu=1}^N \left(\frac{b_\nu - z}{1 - \bar{b}_\nu z} \frac{\bar{b}_\nu}{|b_\nu|} \right) \quad (0 \leqslant N \leqslant \infty).$$

Similarly we may form the convergent Blaschke product

$$\pi_2(z) = \prod_{\mu=1}^M \frac{a_\mu - z}{1 - \bar{a}_\mu z} \frac{\bar{a}_\mu}{|a_\mu|}.$$

Since $\pi_1(z)$, $\pi_2(z)$ are bounded,

$$g(z) = \frac{\pi_1(z)}{\pi_2(z)} f(z)$$

still has bounded characteristic in $|z| < 1$, and $g(z) \neq 0, \infty$ there. If $f(0) = 0$ or ∞, so that

$$f(z) \sim cz^p, \quad \text{as } z \to 0,$$

where $c \neq 0$, we apply the above procedure to $f(z)z^{-p}$. We deduce

LEMMA 6.7. *If $f(z)$ is meromorphic and of bounded characteristic in $|z| < 1$, then*

$$f(z) = z^p \frac{\pi_1(z)}{\pi_2(z)} e^{h(z)},$$

where p is an integer, $\pi_1(z)$, $\pi_2(z)$ are Blaschke products, and $h(z) = u+iv$ is regular in $|z| < 1$ and such that

$$I_1(r, u) = \frac{1}{2\pi} \int_0^{2\pi} |u(re^{i\theta})| \, d\theta$$

remains bounded as $r \to 1$.

In fact we have seen that

$$g(z) = z^{-p} \frac{\pi_1(z)}{\pi_2(z)} f(z)$$

remains regular in $|z| < 1$, and $g(z) \neq 0$, ∞ there. Thus $g(z) = e^{h(z)}$. Also since $f(z)$, $\pi_1(z)$, $\pi_2(z)$ have bounded characteristic so has $g(z)$. Thus

$$\frac{1}{2\pi} \int_0^{2\pi} |u(re^{i\theta})| \, d\theta = m(r, g) + m\left(r, \frac{1}{g}\right) = O(1), \quad \text{as } r \to 1.$$

6.7.2. We prove next

LEMMA 6.8. *If $u(z)$ is harmonic in $|z| < 1$, and satisfies there*

$$I_1(r, u) = O(1), \quad \text{as } r \to 1,$$

then $u(z) = u_1(z) - u_2(z)$, where $u_1(z)$, $u_2(z)$ are positive harmonic functions in $|z| < 1$.

The converse is obvious. In fact if the $u_j(z)$ are positive and harmonic in $|z| < 1$, then

$$I_1(r, u_j(z)) = \frac{1}{2\pi} \int_0^{2\pi} |u_j(re^{i\theta})| \, d\theta = \frac{1}{2\pi} \int_0^{2\pi} u_j(re^{i\theta}) \, d\theta = u_j(0).$$

Thus

$$I_1(r, u_1 - u_2) \leqslant I_1(r, u_1) + I_1(r, u_2) = u_1(0) + u_2(0) \quad (0 < r < 1).$$

We suppose now that the hypotheses of Lemma 6.8 are satisfied and set

$$u^+(z) = \max\{u(z), 0\},$$

and for $0 < \rho < 1$, $z = re^{i\theta}$, where $0 < r < \rho$, we form the function

$$u_\rho(z) = \frac{1}{2\pi} \int_0^{2\pi} u^+(\rho e^{i\phi}) \frac{(\rho^2 - r^2) \, d\phi}{\rho^2 + r^2 - 2\rho r \cos(\theta - \phi)}. \tag{6.23}$$

Evidently $u_\rho(z)$ is positive and harmonic in $|z| < \rho$. Also by the

Poisson–Jensen formula applied to $f(z) = e^{u(z)+iv(z)}$, where $v(z)$ is the conjugate function of $u(z)$, we have

$$u(z) = \frac{1}{2\pi} \int_0^{2\pi} u(\rho e^{i\phi}) \frac{(\rho^2 - r^2)\, d\phi}{\rho^2 + r^2 - 2\rho r \cos(\theta - \phi)}.$$

Thus $u_\rho(z) \geqslant u(z)$,   and hence $u_\rho(z) \geqslant u^+(z)$ $(|z| < \rho)$.

Suppose now that $\rho_1 < \rho_2 < 1$. Then for $|z| = \rho_1$

$$u_{\rho_2}(z) \geqslant u^+(z).$$

Also for $r = |z| < \rho_1$

$$u_{\rho_1}(re^{i\theta}) = \frac{1}{2\pi} \int_0^{2\pi} u^+(\rho_1 e^{i\theta}) \frac{(\rho_1^2 - r^2)\, d\phi}{\rho_1^2 + r^2 - 2r\rho_1 \cos(\theta - \phi)},$$

$$u_{\rho_2}(re^{i\theta}) = \frac{1}{2\pi} \int_0^{2\pi} u_{\rho_2}(\rho_1 e^{i\theta}) \frac{(\rho_1^2 - r^2)\, d\phi}{\rho_1^2 + r^2 - 2r\rho_1 \cos(\theta - \phi)}, \tag{6.24}$$

since $u_{\rho_2}(z)$ is harmonic for $|z| < \rho_2$. Thus we deduce that

$$u_{\rho_1}(re^{i\theta}) \leqslant u_{\rho_2}(re^{i\theta}).$$

Thus the function $u_\rho(z)$ is harmonic and positive in $|z| < \rho$, and increases steadily with ρ for fixed z in the range $|z| < \rho < 1$. We now set

$$u_1(z) = \lim_{\rho \to 1} u_\rho(z).$$

Evidently $u_1(z)$ exists as a finite or infinite limit throughout $|z| < 1$. Also for $|z| = r < \rho_1 < 1$, (6.23) gives

$$u_{\rho_1}(z) \leqslant \frac{\rho_1 + r}{\rho_1 - r} \frac{1}{2\pi} \int_0^{2\pi} u^+(\rho_1 e^{i\theta})\, d\theta \leqslant \frac{\rho_1 + r}{\rho_1 - r} I(\rho_1, u) = O(1)$$

as $\rho_1 \to 1$, by hypothesis. Thus $u_1(z)$ is finite in $|z| < 1$. We now set $\rho_2 = 1 - 1/n$, and make $n \to \infty$ in the relation (6.24). By Fatou's theorem,[†] since the integrand is an increasing function of n, the integral of the limit is the limit of the integral. We deduce that

$$u_1(re^{i\theta}) = \frac{1}{2\pi} \int_0^{2\pi} u_1(\rho_1 e^{i\phi}) \frac{(\rho_1^2 - r^2)\, d\phi}{\rho_1^2 + r^2 - 2r\rho_1 \cos(\theta - \phi)}.$$

We deduce that $u_1(z)$ is continuous in $|z| < \rho_1$, and so in $|z| < 1$, and hence that $u_1(z)$ is harmonic in $|z| < 1$. Also for $|z| < \rho < 1$,

$$u^+(z) \leqslant u_\rho(z) \leqslant u_1(z),$$

† Fatou [1], see also Titchmarsh [1, p. 346].

so that $u_1(z)$ is positive and $u_1(z) \geqslant u(z)$. Thus $u_2(z) = u_1(z) - u(z)$ is also positive and harmonic in $|z| < 1$, so that Lemma 6.8 is proved.

6.7.3. We can now prove our first representation theorem.

THEOREM 6.11. *If $f(z)$ is meromorphic and of bounded characteristic in $|z| < 1$, then*

$$f(z) = \frac{g_1(z)}{g_2(z)},$$

where $g_j(z)$ is regular and $|g_j(z)| < 1$, for $|z| < 1$ ($j = 1, 2$).

In fact by Lemma 6.7, we have

$$f(z) = z^p \frac{\pi_1(z)}{\pi_2(z)} e^{h(z)},$$

where $h(z) = u + iv$, and $I_1(r, u) = O(1)$ as $r \to 1$. By Lemma 6.8 it follows that $u(z) = u_1(z) - u_2(z)$, where $u_1(z)$, $u_2(z)$ are positive harmonic in $|z| < 1$. Hence we can find functions $h_j(z)$ regular in $|z| < 1$, and such that

$$h_j(z) = u_j(z) + iv_j(z).$$

We now set

$$g_1(z) = e^{i\lambda} z^{\rho_1} \pi_1(z) e^{-h_2(z)}, \qquad g_2(z) = z^{\rho_2} \pi_2(z) e^{-h_1(z)},$$

and choose $\rho_1 = p$, $\rho_2 = 0$ if $p \geqslant 0$, $\rho_1 = 0$, $\rho_2 = -p$, if $p < 0$. Then $g_1(z)$, $g_2(z)$ are regular and satisfy $|g_j(z)| < 1$ for $|z| < 1$, and

$$\left| \frac{g_1(z)}{g_2(z)} \right| = |z|^{\rho_1 - \rho_2} \left| \frac{\pi_1(z)}{\pi_2(z)} \right| e^{u_1 - u_2} = |z|^p \left| \frac{\pi_1(z)}{\pi_2(z)} \right| e^{u(z)} = |f(z)|.$$

Thus by properly choosing λ we can ensure that

$$f(z) = \frac{g_1(z)}{g_2(z)}$$

as required.

6.7.4. Our next result is due to Fatou [1].

LEMMA 6.9. *If $f(z)$ is bounded in $|z| < 1$, then the radial limit*

$$f(e^{i\theta}) = \lim_{r \to 1-0} f(re^{i\theta})$$

exists p.p. in θ. More generally p.p. in θ, $f(z) \to f(e^{i\theta})$ as $z \to e^{i\theta}$ from inside $|z| < 1$, so that $|e^{i\theta} - z|/(1 - |z|)$ remains bounded.

This is easily proved from the theory of Fourier series. Let

$$f(z) = \sum_0^\infty a_n z^n.$$

Then $$\frac{1}{2\pi} \int_0^{2\pi} |f(re^{i\theta})|^2 \, d\theta = \sum_0^\infty |a_n|^2 r^{2n} = O(1) \quad (r \to 1).$$

Thus
$$\sum_0^\infty |a_n|^2 = \lim_{r\to 1} \sum_0^\infty |a_n|^2 r^{2n} < +\infty.$$

Hence, by the Riesz–Fischer theorem, the Fourier series

$$\sum_0^\infty a_n e^{in\theta}$$

belongs to a function $f(e^{i\theta})$ in L^2, and is $(C,1)$ summable p.p. in θ to $f(e^{i\theta})$ (Titchmarsh [1, p. 423]). Thus if

$$s_n(\theta) = \sum_{k=0}^n a_k e^{ik\theta},$$

$$\sigma_n(\theta) = \frac{1}{(n+1)} \sum_{k=0}^n s_k(\theta) = \sum_{k=0}^n \left(1 - \frac{k}{n+1}\right) a_k e^{ik\theta},$$

then $\sigma_n(\theta)$ converges to $f(e^{i\theta})$ as $n \to \infty$, p.p. in θ. Let θ be a value for which this conclusion holds. It then follows from a classical theorem, that the series

$$\sum_0^\infty a_k e^{ik\theta}$$

is *a fortiori* Abel summable to $f(e^{i\theta})$ so that $f(re^{i\theta}) \to f(e^{i\theta})$, as $r \to 1-0$. We can prove this directly as follows.

A simple rearrangement shows that we have for $0 < r < 1$,

$$f(re^{i\theta}) = \sum_0^\infty a_n e^{in\theta} r^n = \sum_0^\infty \{s_n(\theta) - s_{n-1}(\theta)\} r^n = \sum_0^\infty s_n(\theta) r^n (1-r)$$

$$= (1-r) \sum_0^\infty \{(n+1)\sigma_n(\theta) - n\sigma_{n-1}(\theta)\} r^n$$

$$= (1-r)^2 \sum_0^\infty (n+1)\sigma_n(\theta) r^n$$

$$= (1-r)^2 \sum_0^\infty (n+1)\{f(e^{i\theta}) + \epsilon_n\} r^n = f(e^{i\theta}) + (1-r)^2 \sum_1^\infty (n+1)\epsilon_n r^n,$$

where $\epsilon_n \to 0$ as $n \to \infty$. Thus if $|\epsilon_n| < \epsilon$, for $n > N$, we have

$$|f(re^{i\theta}) - f(e^{i\theta})| \leqslant (1-r)^2 \Big\{ \sum_1^N |\epsilon_n| r^n + \epsilon \sum_1^\infty (n+1) r^n \Big\} \leqslant \epsilon + O(1-r)^2.$$

Thus $f(re^{i\theta}) \to f(e^{i\theta})$, as $r \to 1$, wherever

$$\sum_0^\infty a_n e^{in\theta}$$

is $(C,1)$ summable, i.e. p.p. in θ. Moreover, we have for all such values of θ,

$$f(re^{i\phi}) = (1 - re^{i(\phi-\theta)})^2 \sum_0^\infty (n+1)\{f(e^{i\theta}) + \epsilon_n\} (re^{i(\phi-\theta)})^n$$

$$= f(e^{i\theta}) + o\,(1 - re^{i(\phi-\theta)})^2 \sum_0^\infty (n+1) r^n$$

$$= f(e^{i\theta}) + o\,(1)$$

provided that $re^{i\phi} \to e^{i\theta}$, in such a manner that $|1-re^{i(\phi-\theta)}| = O(1-r)$. This completes the proof of Lemma 6.9.

6.7.5. We next need a result of F. Riesz and M. Riesz [1].

LEMMA 6.10. *If $f(z)$ is bounded and not constant in $|z| < 1$ and a is a fixed complex number then the set of θ for which $f(e^{i\theta}) = a$ has measure zero, where $f(e^{i\theta}) = \lim\limits_{r \to 1} f(re^{i\theta})$.*

We may suppose without loss in generality that $a = 0$, and that

$$f(re^{i\theta}) \to 0,$$

as $r \to 1$, for a set of θ of positive measure. We set

$$f_n(\theta) = f\left\{\left(1 - \frac{1}{n}\right)e^{i\theta}\right\},$$

and deduce by Egoroff's theorem† that $f_n(\theta) \to 0$ uniformly as $n \to \infty$ on a set E of positive measure δ. We also suppose that $|f(z)| < 1$ in $|z| < 1$, and that $f(0) \neq 0$, since we may achieve this by considering $f(z)/(Mz^p)$ if necessary, where M is a positive constant and p a positive integer. Then Jensen's formula gives for $r = 1-1/n$ ($n = 2, 3, ...$),

$$\log|f(0)| \leqslant \frac{1}{2\pi} \int_0^{2\pi} \log|f(re^{i\theta})| \, d\theta \leqslant \frac{1}{2\pi} \int_E \log|f(re^{i\theta})| \, d\theta$$

$$= \frac{1}{2\pi} \int_E \log|f_n(\theta)| \, d\theta \to -\infty, \quad \text{as } n \to \infty.$$

This gives a contradiction which proves Lemma 6.10.

We deduce at once‡

THEOREM 6.12. *If $f(z)$ is meromorphic, non-constant and of bounded characteristic in $|z| < 1$, then p.p. in θ the limit*

$$f(e^{i\theta}) = \lim f(z)$$

exists uniformly as $z \to e^{i\theta}$ so that $|e^{i\theta} - z| / (1-|z|)$ remains bounded. Further, for any fixed a, finite or infinite, the set of θ in $(0, 2\pi)$ for which $f(e^{i\theta}) = a$ has measure zero.

By Theorem 6.11 $f(z) = g_1(z)/g_2(z)$, where $g_1(z)$, $g_2(z)$ are bounded in $|z| < 1$. By Lemma 6.9 we have p.p. in θ

$$g_1(z) \to \phi_1(\theta), \qquad g_2(z) \to \phi_2(\theta)$$

---

† Egoroff [1], see also Titchmarsh [1, p. 339].
‡ Theorems 6.12 and 6.13 are due to F. Riesz and M. Riesz [1] for bounded functions, and to R. Nevanlinna [1, 3] in the general case.

as $z \to e^{i\theta}$ in $|z| < 1$ so that $|e^{i\theta}-z|\,/\,(1-|z|)$ remains bounded. For all such θ we deduce that

$$f(z) = \frac{g_1(z)}{g_2(z)} \to \frac{\phi_1(\theta)}{\phi_2(\theta)} = f(e^{i\theta}), \quad \text{unless } \phi_1(\theta) = \phi_2(\theta) = 0.$$

Let $E(a)$ be the set of θ in $(0, 2\pi)$ such that $f(e^{i\theta}) = a$. Then if $\theta \in E(\infty)$ we deduce that $\phi_2(\theta) = 0$. Thus by Lemma 6.10 $f(e^{i\theta})$ exists and is finite except on a set of measure zero, so that $E(\infty)$ has measure zero. By considering $\{f(z)-a\}^{-1}$ instead of $f(z)$, we deduce that $E(a)$ has measure zero also for every finite a.

6.7.6. *The integral representation formula.* We conclude by proving

THEOREM 6.13. *If $f(z)$ is meromorphic of bounded characteristic in $|z| < 1$, then*

$$f(z) = z^p\{\pi_1(z)/\pi_2(z)\}\exp\left\{\frac{1}{2\pi}\int_0^{2\pi} \frac{e^{i\phi}+z}{e^{i\phi}-z}\,d\mu(\theta)+iC\right\}, \qquad (6.25)$$

where p is an integer, $\pi_1(z)$, $\pi_2(z)$ are the Blaschke products formed with the zeros and poles of $f(z)$, C is a real constant, and $\mu(\theta)$ is of bounded variation in $[0, 1]$. If $|f(z)| < 1$ in $|z| < 1$, then $p \geqslant 0$, $\pi_2(z) \equiv 1$, and $\mu(\theta)$ is monotonic decreasing.

The converse is obvious. If $\mu_1(\theta)$ is decreasing then

$$h_1(z) = \frac{1}{2\pi}\int_0^{2\pi} \frac{e^{i\phi}+z}{e^{i\phi}-z}\,d\mu_1(\theta) \qquad (6.26)$$

is regular in $|z| < 1$ and has negative real part, so that if p is a non-negative integer

$$f_1(z) = z^p\pi_1(z)h_1(z)$$

is regular and satisfies $|f_1(z)| < 1$ in $|z| < 1$. If $\mu(\theta)$ has bounded variation, then $\mu(\theta) = \mu_1(\theta)-\mu_2(\theta)$, where $\mu_1(\theta)$, $\mu_2(\theta)$ are decreasing functions and if $h_1(z)$, $h_2(z)$ correspond to $\mu_1(\theta)$, $\mu_2(\theta)$ by (6.26) then

$$f_1(z) = e^{iC}z^{p_1}\pi_1(z)h_1(z), \qquad f_2(z) = z^{p_2}\pi_2(z)h_2(z)\,.$$

are regular and bounded in $|z| < 1$, and

$$f(z) = \frac{f_1(z)}{f_2(z)},$$

provided that $p_1 = \max(p, 0)$, $p_2 = \min(-p, 0)$. Thus $f(z)$ has bounded characteristic.

To prove Theorem 6.13, suppose first that $|f(z)| < 1$, $f(z) \neq 0$ in

$|z| < 1$. Then by the Poisson–Jensen formula, we have for $r < \rho < 1$

$$\log|f(re^{i\theta})| = \frac{1}{2\pi} \int_0^{2\pi} \log|f(\rho e^{i\phi})| \frac{(\rho^2 - r^2)\,d\phi}{\rho^2 - 2r\rho\cos(\theta - \phi) + r^2},$$

and adding the harmonic conjugate of both sides, we deduce that

$$\log f(z) = \frac{1}{2\pi} \int_0^{2\pi} \log|f(\rho e^{i\phi})| \left(\frac{\rho e^{i\phi} + z}{\rho e^{i\phi} - z}\right) d\phi + iC.$$

We write

$$\mu_n(\phi) = \frac{1}{2\pi} \int_0^{\phi} \log\left|f\left\{\left(1 - \frac{1}{n}\right)e^{i\phi}\right\}\right| d\phi \quad (0 \leqslant \phi \leqslant 2\pi).$$

Then $\log|f(re^{i\phi})|$ is non-positive and so $\mu_n(\phi)$ is a decreasing function of ϕ for each n. Also

$$\mu_n(2\pi) = \log|f(0)| \leqslant \mu_n(\phi) \leqslant 0 \quad (0 \leqslant \phi \leqslant 2\pi).$$

Thus we can extract a subsequence $\mu_{n_p}(\phi)$ by Cantor's diagonal process which converges, as $p \to \infty$, to a decreasing function $\mu(\phi)$ for each ϕ belonging to a sequence $\phi = \phi_m$, dense in $(0, 2\pi)$. For $\phi \neq \phi_m$, we define

$$\mu(\phi) = \inf_{\phi_m < \phi} \mu(\phi_m).$$

Then $\mu(\phi)$ is decreasing in $(0, 2\pi)$ and so continuous except on a countable set $\phi = \phi'_m$ of ϕ. Suppose that $0 < \phi < 2\pi$ and that ϕ is not equal to any of the points ϕ'_m. Then given $\epsilon > 0$, we can choose ϕ_m, ϕ_k, such that

$$\phi_m < \phi < \phi_k,$$

and

$$\mu(\phi) - \epsilon \leqslant \mu(\phi_k) \leqslant \mu(\phi) \leqslant \mu(\phi_m) \leqslant \mu(\phi) + \epsilon.$$

Since the functions $\mu_{n_p}(\phi)$ are decreasing functions of ϕ, which converge at $\phi = \phi_m$, ϕ_k, we deduce that

$$\mu(\phi) - \epsilon \leqslant \mu(\phi_k) = \lim_{p \to \infty} \mu_{n_p}(\phi_k) \leqslant \varliminf_{p \to \infty} \mu_{n_p}(\phi)$$

$$\leqslant \varlimsup_{p \to \infty} \mu_{n_p}(\phi) \leqslant \lim_{p \to \infty} \mu_{n_p}(\phi_m) = \mu(\phi_m) \leqslant \mu(\phi) + \epsilon.$$

Since ϵ is arbitrary we deduce that $\mu_{n_p}(\phi) \to \mu(\phi)$, as $p \to \infty$, and that this holds outside a countable set of ϕ, consisting of the points of discontinuity of the decreasing function $\mu(\phi)$. Setting $\rho_p = (1 - 1/n_p)$ we have

$$\log f(z) = \frac{1}{2\pi} \int_0^{2\pi} \frac{(\rho_p e^{i\phi} + z)}{(\rho_p e^{i\phi} - z)} d\mu_{n_p}(\phi) + iC$$

$$= \mu_{n_p}(2\pi)\{(\rho_p + z)/(\rho_p - z)\} + iC + \frac{iz}{2\pi} \int_0^{2\pi} \mu_{n_p}(\phi) \frac{2\rho_p e^{i\phi}\,d\phi}{(\rho_p e^{i\phi} - z)^2}.$$

For fixed z the integrand $\mu_{n_p}(\phi)2\rho_p e^{i\phi}/(\rho_p e^{i\phi}-z)^2$ is uniformly bounded, provided that $\rho_p > \frac{1}{2}(1+|z|)$, and tends to the limit

$$\mu(\phi)2e^{i\phi}/(e^{i\phi}-z)^2$$

as $p \to \infty$, p.p. in ϕ.

Also $\mu_{n_p}(2\pi) = -\log|f(0)| = \text{constant} = \mu(2\pi)$. Thus by Lebesgue's convergence theorem (Titchmarsh [1, p. 345]) we deduce that

$$\log f(z) = \mu(2\pi)\{(1+z)/(1-z)\}+iC+\frac{iz}{2\pi}\int_0^{2\pi} \mu(\phi)\frac{2e^{i\phi}}{(e^{i\phi}-z)^2}\,d\phi$$

$$= \frac{1}{2\pi}\int_0^{2\pi} \frac{e^{i\phi}+z}{e^{i\phi}-z}\,d\mu(\phi)+iC,$$

where the right-hand side is a Riemann–Stieltjes integral and the integration by parts is justified since $\mu(\phi)$ is decreasing and $(e^{i\phi}+z)/(e^{i\phi}-z)$ continuous. This yields our theorem when $|f(z)| < 1$, $f(z) \neq 0$.

In the general case we use Lemma 6.7 and Theorem 6.10. They show that

$$f(z) = z^p \frac{\pi_1(z)}{\pi_2(z)} \frac{h_1(z)}{h_2(z)},$$

where $h_1(z)$, $h_2(z)$ are bounded and not zero. Thus by what we have just shown

$$h_j(z) = \exp\left\{\frac{1}{2\pi}\int_0^{2\pi} \frac{e^{i\phi}+z}{e^{i\phi}-z}\,d\mu_j(\phi)\right\} (j = 1, 2),$$

where $\mu_j(\phi)$ is a decreasing function of ϕ, and we deduce (6.25). If $|f(z) < 1$, $f(z)$ has no poles in $|z| < 1$, so that $\pi_2(z) \equiv 1$. Further,

$$\pi_1(z) = \prod_{n=1}^{K} \frac{z_n-z}{1-\bar{z}_n z} \frac{\bar{z}_n}{|z_n|} = \prod_{n=1}^{K} p_n(z),   \text{say.}$$

Here K may be finite or infinite. If N is finite and $N \leqslant K$ we see that

$$f_N(z) = f(z)/z^p \prod_{n=1}^{N} p_n(z)$$

is regular in $|z| < 1$, and if r is sufficiently near 1 we have

$$|f_N(z)| < 1+\epsilon   (|z| = r).$$

Thus by the maximum-modulus theorem

$$|f_N(z)| < 1+\epsilon   (|z| \leqslant r),$$

and hence we deduce that

$$|f_N(z)| \leqslant 1   (|z| < 1).$$

Since this is true for every finite $N \leqslant K$, we deduce that

$$|h(z)| = \left| f(z)/z^p \prod_{n=1}^{K} p_n(z) \right| \leqslant 1,$$

and $h(z) \neq 0$ in $|z| < 1$. Thus we may apply the above analysis to $h(z)$ and deduce (6.26) with a decreasing function $\mu(\theta)$. This completes the proof of Theorem 6.13.

We note as a special case the representation (6.26) for any function $h_1(z)$ having negative real part in terms of a decreasing function $\mu_1(\theta)$. To obtain this we apply Theorem 6.13 to $f(z) = e^{h_1(z)}$.

Example (i). If $\Pi(z)$ is a Blaschke product, prove that

$$\int_0^{2\pi} \log|\Pi(re^{i\theta})|\, d\theta \to 0, \quad \text{as } r \to 1.$$

(Use Jensen's formula.) Deduce that $|\Pi(e^{i\theta})| = 1$, p.p. in θ.

Example (ii). If $h_1(z)$ is given by (6.26), where $\mu_1(\theta)$ has bounded variation, then

$$\mathscr{R}h_1(e^{i\theta}) = \mu_1'(\theta)$$

whenever both sides exist. Deduce that in Theorem 6.12 $|f(e^{i\theta})| = 1$ p.p. in θ if and only if $\mu'(\theta) = 0$ p.p. in θ in (6.25) (Seidel [1]).

BIBLIOGRAPHY

AHLFORS, L. V.
[1] 'Beiträge zur Theorie der meromorphen Funktionen', *C.R. 7ᵉ Congr. Math. Scand.* Oslo (1929), 84–88.
[2] 'Ein Satz von Henri Cartan und seine Anwendung auf die Theorie der meromorphen Funktionen', *Soc. sci. Fenn. Comment. Phys. Math.* 5, nr. 16 (1931).
[3] 'Zur Theorie der Überlagerungsflächen', *Acta Math.* 65 (1935), 157–94.
[4] 'An extension of Schwarz's lemma', *Trans. Amer. Math. Soc.* 43 (1938), 359–64.

AHLFORS, L. V. and GRUNSKY, H.
[1] 'Über die Blochsche Konstante', *Math. Zeit.* 42 (1937), 671–3.

AHLFORS, L. V. and SARIO, L.
[1] *Riemann Surfaces.* Princeton University Press (1960).

ARAKELJAN, N. U.
[1] 'Entire functions of finite order with an infinite set of deficient values' (Russian), *Dokl. Akad Nauk SSSR* 170 (1966), 999–1002.

BAKER, I. N.
[1] 'The existence of fixpoints of entire functions', *Math. Zeit.* 73 (1960), 280–4.

BLASCHKE, W.
[1] 'Eine Erweiterung des Satzes von Vitali über Folgen analytischer Funktionen', *S.B. Leipziger Akad. Wiss.* 67 (1915), 194–200.
[2] *Kreis und Kugel*, 2nd edition. Berlin (1956).

BLOCH, A.
[1] 'Les théorèmes de M. Valiron sur les fonctions entières et la théorie de l'uniformisation', *Ann. Fac. Sci. Univ. Toulouse* (3), 17 (1926), 1–22.

BOHR, H.
[1] 'Über einen Satz von Edmund Landau', *Scripta Univ. Hierosolymitanarum*, 1 (1923), nr. 2, 5 pp.

BOREL, E.
[1] 'Sur les zéros des fonctions entières', *Acta Math.* 20 (1897), 357–96.

CARTWRIGHT, M. L.
[1] *Integal functions.* Cambridge University Press (1956).

CARTAN, H.
[1] 'Sur la fonction de croissance attachée à une fonction méromorphe de deux variables, et ses applications aux fonctions méromorphes d'une variable', *C.R. Acad. Sci. Paris*, 189 (1929), 521–3.

CHUANG, C. T.
[1] 'Une généralisation d'une inégalité de Nevanlinna', *Sci. Sinica*, 13 (1964), 887–95.

CLUNIE, J.
[1] 'On integral and meromorphic functions', *J. London Math. Soc.* 37 (1962), 17–27.
[2] Oral communication.

184   BIBLIOGRAPHY

CSILLAG, P.
    [1] 'Über ganze Funktionen, welche drei nicht verschwindende Ableitungen
        besitzen', *Math. Ann.* **110** (1935), 745–52.
DUFRESNOY, J.
    [1] 'Sur les domaines couvertes par les valeurs d'une fonction méromorphe ou
        algébroïde', *Ann. Sci. École Norm. Sup.* (3), **58** (1941), 179–259.
EDREI, A. and FUCHS, W. H. J.
    [1] 'On the growth of meromorphic functions with several deficient values',
        Trans. Amer. Math. Soc. **93** (1959), 292–328.
    [2] 'Valeurs déficientes et valeurs asymptotiques des fonctions méromorphes',
        Comment. Math. Helv. **33** (1959), 258–95.
    [3] 'The deficiencies of meromorphic functions of order less than one', *Duke
        Math. J.* **27** (1960), 233–49.
    [4] 'Bounds for the number of deficient values of certain classes of mero-
        morphic functions', *Proc. London Math. Soc.* **12** (1962), 315–44.
EDREI, A., FUCHS, W. H. J. and HELLERSTEIN, S.
    [1] 'Radial distribution and deficiencies of the values of a meromorphic
        function', *Pacific J. Math.* **11** (1961), 135–51.
EGOROFF, D. T.
    [1] 'Sur les suites de fonctions mesurables', *C.R. Acad. Sci. Paris,* **152** (1911),
        244–6.
FATOU, P.
    [1] 'Séries trigonométriques et séries de Taylor', *Acta Math.* **30** (1906), 335–400.
FLETT, T. M.
    [1] 'Note on a function-theoretic identity', *J. London Math. Soc.* **29** (1954),
        115–18.
FROSTMAN, C.
    [1] 'Über die defekten Werte einer meromorphen Funktion', *C.R. 8ᵉ Congr.
        Math. Scand.* Stockholm (1934), 392–6.
FUCHS, W. H. J.
    [1] 'A theorem on the Nevanlinna deficiencies of meromorphic functions of
        finite order', *Ann. of Math.* (2) **68** (1958), 203–9.
FUCHS, W. H. J. and HAYMAN, W. K.
    [1] 'An entire function with assigned deficiencies', *Studies in mathematical
        analysis and related topics,* essays in honor of George Pólya. Stanford
        University Press (1962).
GOL'DBERG, A. A.
    [1] 'On the inverse problem of the theory of the distribution of values of
        meromorphic functions' (Russian), *Ukrain. Mat. Zh.* **6** (1954), 385–97.
    [2] 'On the deficiencies of meromorphic functions' (Russian), *Dokl. Akad.
        Nauk S.S.S.R.* (N.S.) **98** (1954), 893–5.
    [3] 'On an inequality for logarithmically convex functions' (Ukrainian),
        Dopovidi Akad. Nauk Ukrain. R.S.R. (1957), nr. 3, 227–30.
    [4] 'On the set of deficient values of meromorphic functions of finite order'
        (Russian), *Ukrain. Mat. Zh.* **11** (1959), 438–43.
HADAMARD, J.
    [1] 'Essai sur l'étude des fonctions données par leur développement de Taylor',
        J. de Math. (4) **8** (1892), 101–86.

HAYMAN, W. K.
 [1] 'Some applications of the transfinite diameter to the theory of functions',
   J. Analyse Math. **1** (1951), 155–79.
 [2] 'Uniformly normal families', *Lectures on functions of a complex variable*,
   University of Michigan Press (1955), 199–212.
 [3] 'On Nevanlinna's second theorem and extensions', *Rend. Circ. Mat.
   Palermo (2), 2* (1954), 346–92.
 [4] *Multivalent Functions.* Cambridge University Press (1958).
 [5] 'Picard values of meromorphic functions and their derivatives', *Ann. of
   Math.* **70** (1959), 9–42.

HAYMAN, W. K. and STEWART, F. M.
 [1] 'Real inequalities with applications to function theory', *Proc. Camb. Phil.
   Soc.* **50** (1954), 250–60.

JENKINS, J. A.
 [1] 'On explicit bounds in Schottky's theorem', *Canad. J. Math.* **7** (1955),
   76–82.
 [2] 'On explicit bounds in Landau's theorem', ibid. **8** (1956), 423–5.

JENSEN, J. L. W. V.
 [1] 'Sur un nouvel et important théorème de la théorie des fonctions', *Acta
   Math.* **22** (1899), 359–64.

LAI, W. T.
 [1] 'Über den Satz von Landau', *Sci. Record*, N.S. **4** (1960), 339–42.

LANDAU, E.
 [1] 'Über eine Verallgemeinerung des Picardschen Satzes', *S.B. Preuss. Akad.
   Wiss.* (1904), 1118–33.

LEHTO, O. and VIRTANEN, K. I.
 [1] 'Boundary behaviour and normal meromorphic functions', *Acta Math.* **97**
   (1957), 47–65.

LE-VAN THIEM
 [1] 'Über das Umkehrproblem der Wertverteilungslehre', *Comment. Math.
   Helv.* **23** (1949), 26–49.

MARTY, F.
 [1] 'Recherches sur la répartition des valeurs d'une fonction méromorphe',
   Ann. Fac. Sci. Univ. Toulouse (3), **23** (1931), 183–261.

MILLOUX, H.
 [1] *Les fonctions méromorphes et leurs dérivées.* Paris (1940).

MONTEL, P.
 [1] *Leçons sur les familles normales de fonctions analytiques et leurs applications.*
   Paris (1927).

NEVANLINNA, F.
 [1] 'Über eine Klasse meromorpher Funktionen', *C.R. 7ᵉ Congr. Math. Scand.*
   Oslo (1929), 81–83.

NEVANLINNA, R.
 [1] *Le théorème de Picard–Borel et la théorie des fonctions méromorphes.* Paris
   (1929).
 [2] 'Über Riemannsche Flächen mit endlich vielen Windungspunkten', *Acta
   Math.* **58** (1932), 295–373.
 [3] *Eindeutige analytische Funktionen.* Berlin (1936).

PFLUGER, A.
[1] 'Zur Defektrelation ganzer Funktionen endlicher Ordnung', *Comment. Math. Helv.* **19** (1946), 91–104.

POISSON, S. D.
[1] 'Mémoire sur le calcul numérique des intégrales définies', *Mémoires de l'Académie Royale des Sciences de l'Institut de France*, vi (1823, published 1827), 571–602, particularly p. 575.

PÓLYA, G.
[1] 'Über die Nullstellen sukzessiver Derivierten', *Math. Zeit.* **12** (1922), 36–60.
[2] 'On an integral function of an integral function, *J. London Math. Soc.* **1** (1926), 12–15.

PÓLYA, G. and SZEGÖ, G.
[1] *Aufgaben und Lehrsätze aus der Analysis.* Band 1. Berlin (1925).

RIESZ, F. and RIESZ, M.
[1] 'Über die Randwerte einer analytischen Funktion', *C.R. 4ᵉ Congr. Math. Scand.* Stockholm (1916), 27–44.

ROSENBLOOM, P. C.
[1] 'The fix-points of entire functions', *Medd. Lunds Univ. Mat. Sem. Tome Suppl. M. Riesz* (1952), 186–92.

SAXER, W.
[1] 'Sur les valeurs exceptionnelles des dérivées successives des fonctions méromorphes', *C.R. Acad. Sci. Paris*, **182** (1926), 831–3.

SCHOTTKY, F.
[1] 'Über den Picardschen Satz und die Borelschen Ungleichungen', *S.B. Preuss. Akad. Wiss.* (1904), 1244–63.

SEIDEL, W.
[1] 'On the distribution of values of bounded analytic functions', *Trans. Amer. Math. Soc.* **36** (1934), 201–26.

SHAH, S. M.
[1] 'A theorem on integral functions of integral order', *J. London Math. Soc.* **15** (1940), 23–31.
[2] 'A theorem on integral functions of integral order. II', *J. Indian Math. Soc.* N.S. **5** (1941), 179–88.
[3] 'A note on meromorphic functions', *Math. Student*, **12** (194), 67–70.

SHIMIZU, T.
[1] 'On the theory of meromorphic functions', *Jap. J. of Math.* **6** (1929), 119–71.

SPENCER, D. C.
[1] 'Note on some function-theoretic identities', *J. London Math. Soc.* **15** (1940), 84–86.

TEICHMÜLLER, O.
[1] 'Vermutungen und Sätze über die Wertverteilung gebrochener Funktionen endlicher Ordnung', *Deutsch. Math.* **4** (1939), 163–90.

TITCHMARSH, E. C.
[1] *The theory of functions*, 2nd edition. Oxford (1939).

TUMURA, Y.
[1] 'On the extensions of Borel's theorem and Saxer–Csillag's theorem', *Proc. Phys. Math. Soc. Japan* (3), **19** (1937), 29–35.

VALIRON, G.

[1] 'Sur la distribution des valeurs des fonctions méromorphes', *Acta Math.* **47** (1925), 117–42.

[2] 'Sur les valeurs déficientes des fonctions méromorphes d'ordre nul', *C.R. Acad. Sci. Paris*, **230** (1950), 40–42.

[3] *Fonctions entières d'ordre fini et fonctions méromorphes.* Geneva (1960).

WAHLUND, A.

[1] Über einen Zusammenhang zwischen dem Maximalbetrage der ganzen Funktion und seiner unteren Grenze nach dem Jensen'schen Theoreme. *Arkiv för Math.* **21** A, Nr. 23 (1929), 34 pp.

WEIERSTRASS, K.

[1] *Zur Theorie der eindeutigen analytischen Funktionen. Werke*, Band II. Berlin (1895), 77–124; reprinted from *Abhandlungen Königl. Akad. Wiss.* (1876), 11–60.

WHITTAKER, J. M.

[1] 'The order of the derivative of a meromorphic function', *J. London Math. Soc.* **11** (1936), 82–87.

WIMAN, A.

[1] 'Sur une extension d'un théorème de M. Hadamard', *Arkiv Math. Astr. och Fys.* **2**, no. 14 (1905) 5 pp.

WITTICH, H.

[1] *Neuere Untersuchungen über eindeutige analytische Funktionen.* Berlin (1955).

AUTHOR INDEX

INDEX OF TERMINOLOGY